SCHOLASTIC

READ 180®

Crime Lab Science

Going Global

Eyes on the Graduation Prize

Wired for Trouble

Facing the Elements

rBook™ FLEX

read • write • react

ENTERPRISE EDITION

rBook™ FLEX

Acknowledgments and credits appear on pages 285–286, which constitute an extension of this copyright page.

 Published by Scholastic Inc. Printed in the U.S.A.
ISBN-13: 978-0-439-90241-0
ISBN-10: 0-439-90241-X

11 12 13 14 15 16 14 15 14 13 12 11

Table of Contents

WORKSHOP 3

Literature

Long Journey to Justice 56

WORKSHOP 4

Science Nonfiction

Crime Lab Science 88

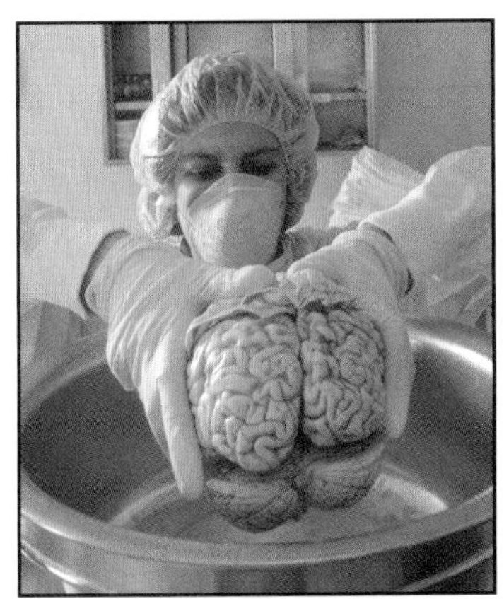

WORKSHOP 5

Life Issues Nonfiction

Wired for Trouble 112

WORKSHOP

Literature

Facing the Elements 136

WORKSHOP

Science Nonfiction

Creatures of the Deep 166

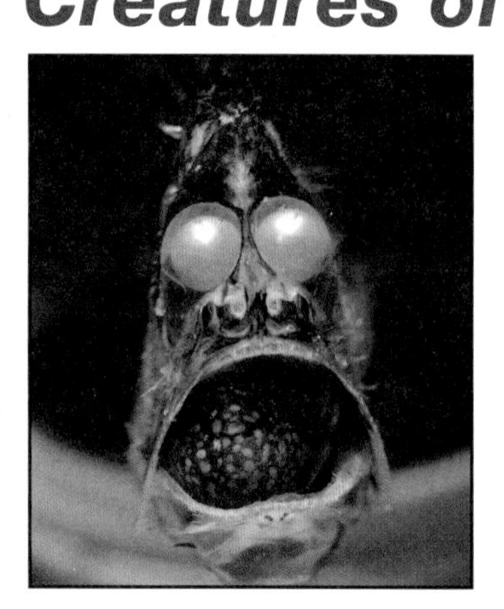

WORKSHOP

8

Social Studies Nonfiction

Going Global 190

Nonfiction and Literature

The Art of the Memoir

Student Log

Welcome to rBook Flex

Get ready for rBook Flex by taking this quiz. After you finish each Workshop, check back to see if your ideas or opinions have changed.

1 Eyes on the Graduation Prize

Read each statement below. Write ***A*** if you agree. Write ***D*** if you disagree.

____ Dropping out of high school is no big deal.

____ A high school diploma is a prize worth pursuing.

____ Getting a job is easy if you don't have a high school diploma.

____ People respect you if you have a high school diploma.

2 Tsunami: Disaster of the Century

A tsunami struck South Asia in 2004. Read the following statements. Circle the one you think is correct.

1. Most areas hit by the tsunami have recovered.

2. It will take years for the towns and villages to be rebuilt.

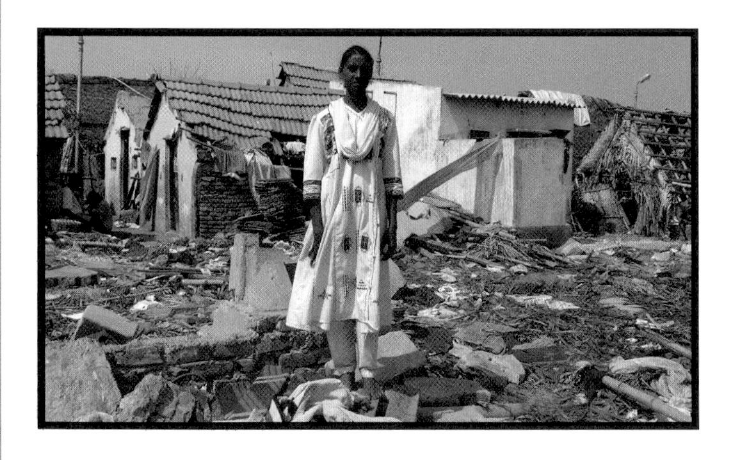

3 Long Journey to Justice

Think about the following statements. Write ***T*** if you think it is true. Write ***F*** if you think it is false.

____ Digging for diamonds is an easy job.

____ People who dig for diamonds make lots of money.

____ Workers are searched before leaving diamond mines.

____ Many diamonds are found in South Africa.

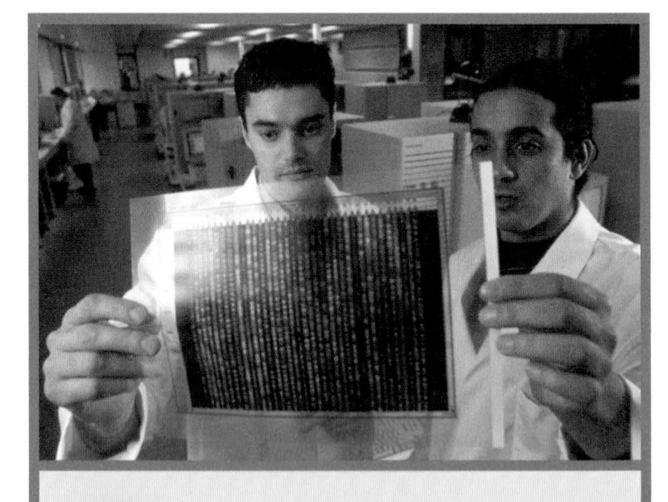

4 Crime Lab Science

What do you think happens in a crime lab? Check the ones you think are correct.

- ❑ Criminals talk about crimes.
- ❑ Fingerprints are analyzed.
- ❑ Dead bodies are examined.
- ❑ Historians write about crimes.

5 Wired for Trouble

Do teens use too much technology? Check the three types of technology you think teens use the most. Circle the one you use the most.

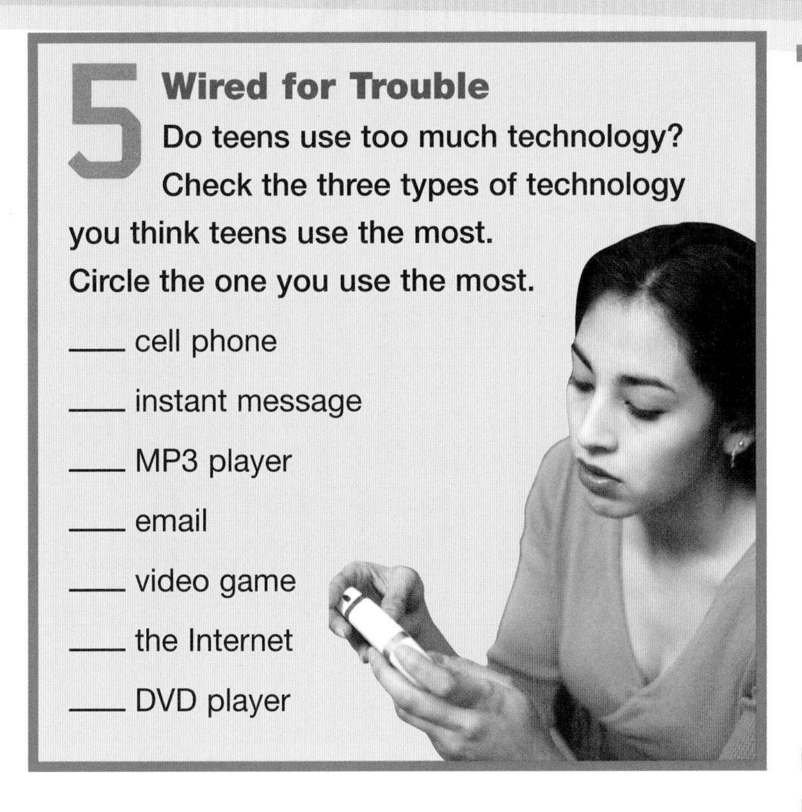

___ cell phone

___ instant message

___ MP3 player

___ email

___ video game

___ the Internet

___ DVD player

6 Facing the Elements

Jack London wrote many adventure stories, including "To Build a Fire." What would you do if you were stuck outside in the cold? Check one.

❑ Stop and build a fire.

❑ Keep walking and look for a warm building.

❑ Other: ______________________________

____

7 Creatures of the Deep

What would be the coolest thing about exploring the ocean? Circle one.

1. riding in an underwater machine

2. swimming next to strange creatures

3. walking on the ocean floor

8 Going Global

Read the following statements. Write ***A*** if you agree. Write ***D*** if you disagree.

___ It's important to be able to communicate with people in other countries.

___ All goods should be made in America.

___ It costs more to make goods in other countries.

9 The Art of the Memoir

Author Francisco Jiménez writes about his fears as a migrant worker from Mexico. Write about one thing that scares you.

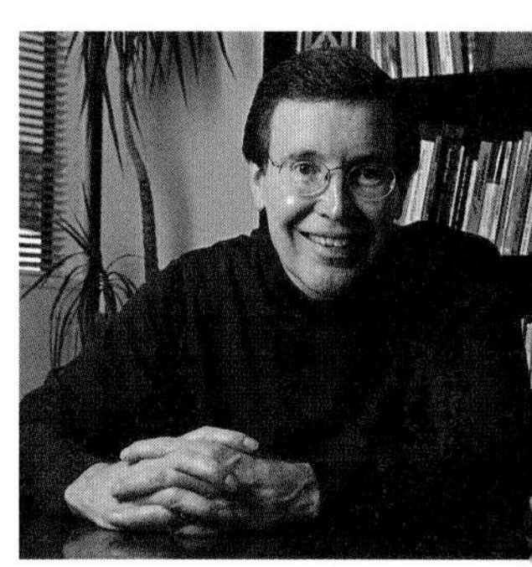

____

____

____

Comprehension Focus
Main Idea and Details

READINGS

Eyes on the Graduation Prize

It's graduation day. Students are throwing their caps in the air. Everyone's excited. Everyone who's here, that is.

Four years ago there were more students in this class—about 33 percent more, according to national statistics. So what happened to them? Like millions of high school students across the country, they dropped out without earning a diploma. This choice limits their options and compromises their futures.

What about your future?

Where will you be on graduation day?

VOCABULARY BUILDER

Target Word ▶ Read the Target Words. Rate each one using the scale below.*	Meaning ▶ Read the Target Word meanings. Write in the missing ones.	Example ▶ Finish the Target Word examples below. Write in the missing ones.
accomplish *ac•com•plish* *(verb)* ① ② ③		A big thing I want to accomplish is . . .
capable *ca•pa•ble* *(adjective)* ① ② ③	able to do something	
dedicate *ded•i•cate* *(verb)* ① ② ③		I **dedicate** myself to becoming a deejay.
individual *in•di•vid•u•al* *(noun)* ① ② ③	a person	
pursue *pur•sue* *(verb)* ① ② ③		I will pursue a career in . . .

*Rating Scale

① = I don't know it at all.
② = I've seen it before.
③ = I know it and use it.

The Big Idea

Write What is this article mainly about?

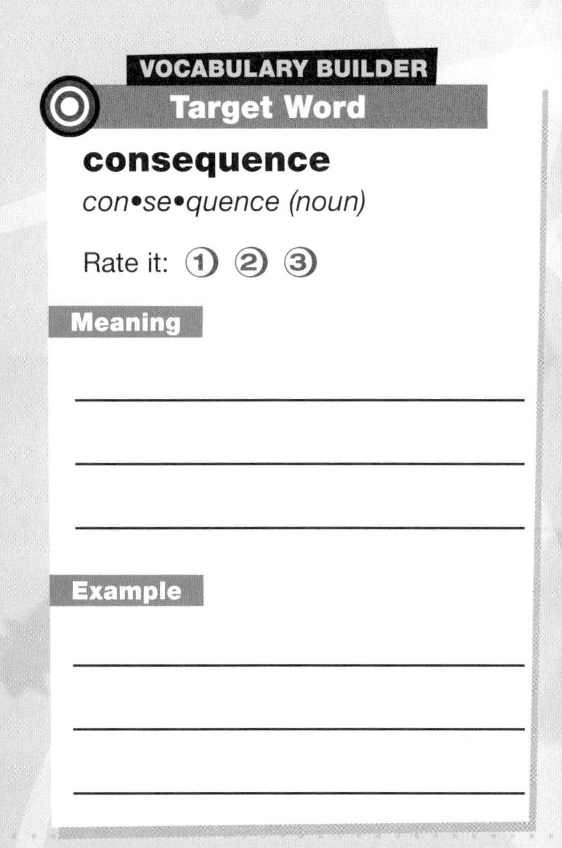

VOCABULARY BUILDER

Target Word

consequence

con•se•quence (noun)

Rate it: ① ② ③

Meaning

Example

React

Why do you think some students drop out? What's one possible solution to the dropout problem?

America's Dropout Crisis

America is facing an education crisis: about one in three students drops out of school. In cities, the statistics are even worse. Up to two-thirds of students quit before graduating. Some drop out because they're caught in a cycle of failure. Others drop out because they'd rather be working and earning money. Still others choose to join their friends on the street.

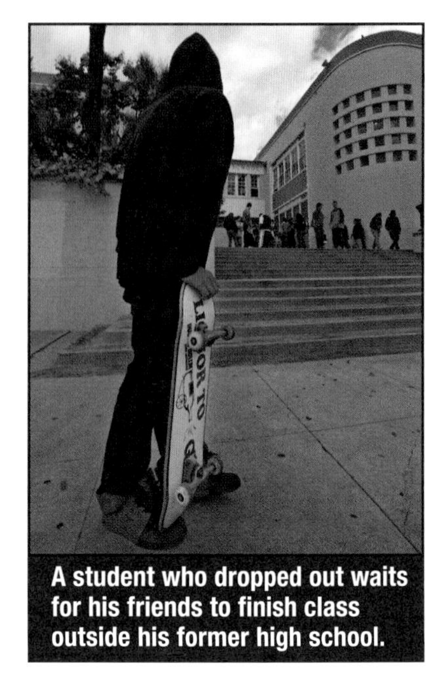

A student who dropped out waits for his friends to finish class outside his former high school.

The **consequences** of dropping out are serious—and they last a lifetime! Dropouts are more likely to have low-paying jobs or be unemployed. Employers see dropouts as less skilled and less capable. One study shows that non-graduates make about $9,200 less a year than graduates. Over a lifetime, that can add up to more than $200,000 in lost income.

Another disturbing statistic is that non-graduates are 3.5 times more likely to be jailed than graduates. In fact, approximately 75 percent of individuals in the state prison system are high school dropouts.

Giving up on a diploma can also mean giving up on dreams. Although students may think that leaving school offers greater freedom, it actually restricts future options. Graduating provides real freedom: the freedom to accomplish goals and make career choices. The reality is, a high school diploma is a prize worth pursuing. END

Words to Know! **restricts** *(v.)* keeps within limits

Comprehension Focus

Main Idea and Details

The **main idea** is the most important point about a topic. **Details** are the facts that support the main idea. To find the main idea and details:

- Decide what the topic is. Find the main idea about the topic.
- Look for details that support the main idea.

▶ **Fill in this chart with the main idea and details of "America's Dropout Crisis."**

Detail

About one in three students drops out of school.

Detail

Main Idea

Detail

Detail

Living in the Success Zone

Two former *READ 180* students talk about turning their lives around.

More than six million high school and middle school students read below their grade level. Tabitha Trujillo and Jorvorskie Lane, both graduates of Lufkin High School in Texas, were once part of this group. Today, they're strong readers on the path to accomplishing their goals. These teens overcame their limitations and became reading success stories.

Reading Struggles

Neither Tabitha nor Jorvorskie can remember a time when reading came easily. In high school, Tabitha struggled with her grades. When asked to **undertake** a simple assignment like reading aloud, she felt nervous and embarrassed. She knew she'd have to wrestle with the words in front of everyone. "It killed my confidence," Tabitha says.

Jorvorskie, a high school football star, was equally frustrated. At 6'1" and 240 pounds, he was unstoppable on the field. But just lifting the cover of a book knocked him out. "I'd doze off," he says. "My mind wandered. I'd want to be anywhere except in front of that book."

Tabitha Trujillo is in college and plans to pursue a law degree.

The Big Idea

Write ▷ What is this article mainly about?

____

____

____

VOCABULARY BUILDER

Target Word

undertake

un•der•take (verb)

Rate it: ① ② ③

Meaning

____

____

____

Example

____

____

____

React

Both Tabitha and Jorvorskie struggled with reading. How did that affect their self-esteem? And their futures?

Because he raised his SAT scores, Jorvorskie Lane is now a student and football player at Texas A&M.

At 16, Jorvorskie did poorly on the reading section of his SATs. The stakes were high because colleges were recruiting him for football scholarships. He knew that if he didn't dedicate himself to improving his scores, he had no chance. Betty Lewing, the school's reading teacher, urged him to imagine a future beyond football. "She told me it didn't matter how much talent I had," he says. "If I couldn't read, I didn't have anything."

Solving the Problem

Both Tabitha and Jorvorskie enrolled in Betty Lewing's *READ 180* class. Lewing says both wanted to quit at first; however, they each found something positive to focus on.

Tabitha focused on slow, steady progress. At first, just being in the class was embarrassing. But one day, another student praised her reading ability. This encouragement changed her attitude about the class.

Things changed for Jorvorskie when he discovered books that really interested him, like a paperback about Muhammad Ali. For the first time in his life, a book grabbed his attention and kept him reading. ➔

Words to Know! **limitations** *(n.)* things that block one from success

Main Idea and Details

1. **Write** Find the main idea in "Reading Struggles."

____
____
____
____
____
____

2. **Write** Find the main idea in "Solving the Problem."

____
____
____
____
____
____

3. **Underline** Find two important details to support the main idea in "Solving the Problem."

Active Reading

Underline What happened one year after Tabitha and Jorvorskie resolved to improve their reading?

VOCABULARY BUILDER

Target Word

resolve

re•solve (verb)

Rate it: ① ② ③

Meaning

___

___

___

Example

___

___

___

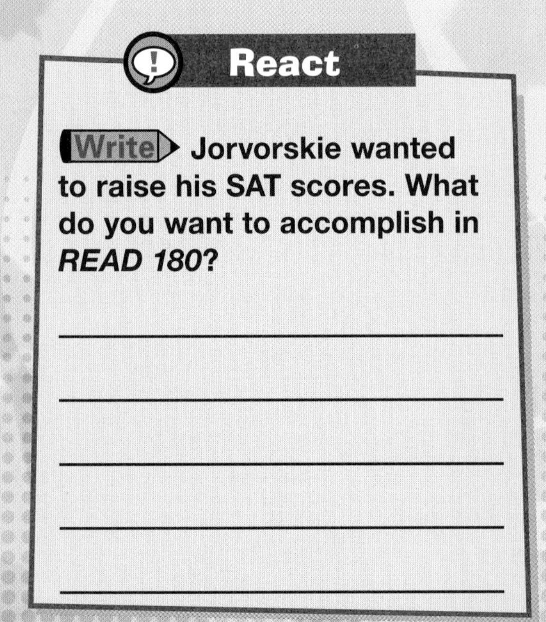

React

Write **Jorvorskie wanted to raise his SAT scores. What do you want to accomplish in *READ 180*?**

___

___

___

___

___

Making Progress

"In most cases, kids walk into my class feeling like failures," says Lewing. "Having zero self-esteem is a huge limitation." As Tabitha and Jorvorskie learned, their confidence grew. And the more confident they became, the more their reading progress accelerated.

Lewing thinks that Tabitha and Jorvorskie are perfect examples of the power of self-confidence. One year after they **resolved** to improve their reading, Jorvorskie raised his SAT scores by 400 points. And Tabitha was taking advanced placement classes. "For the first time, I was proud to show my report card to my parents," Tabitha says.

Success Stories

Today, both teens are capable readers who are pursuing their own goals: in other words, they are success stories. Tabitha studies at the City College of New York and wants to pursue a law degree. Jorvorskie plays football for Texas A&M. Both are the first in their families to go to college.

Reading is now one of Tabitha's hobbies. Five years ago, she didn't have a favorite book because she had never completed one. Today, she loves *To Kill a Mockingbird.* But the best thing Tabitha has ever read is her name on her high school diploma. "I didn't give up," she says, "and I made it."

As Ty would say, "Congratulations! You're in the Success Zone!" END

Some say Betty Lewing is teaching reading. Others say she's saving lives.

Words to Know! **accelerated** *(v.)* sped up

Comprehension Focus

Main Idea and Details

▶ Fill in this chart with the main idea and details in "Living in the Success Zone."

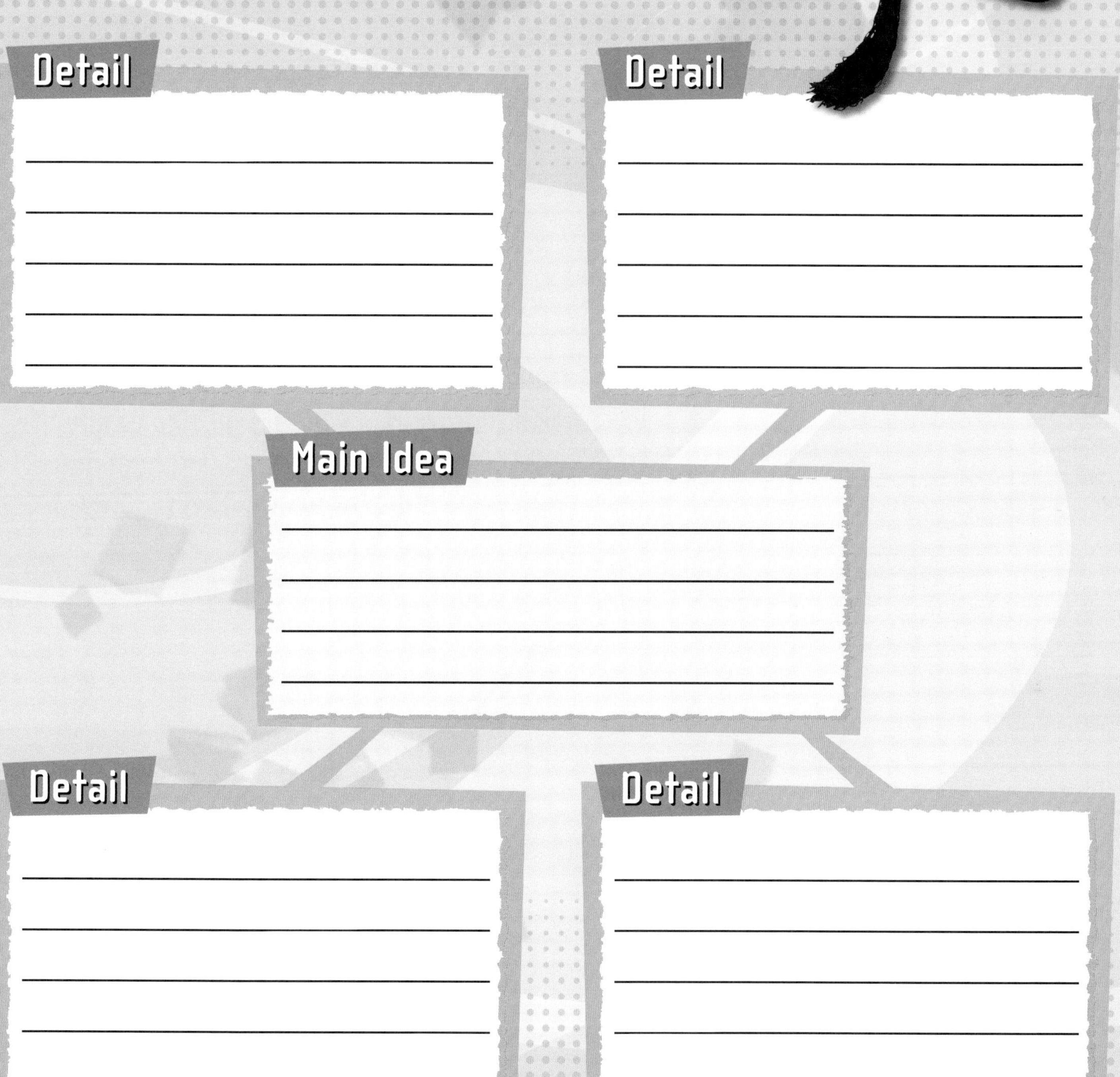

THE PACT

Three friends grew up on the streets of Newark, New Jersey, surrounded by the pitfalls of city life. They made a pact to go to medical school and, against all odds, they accomplished their goal.

How did they do it? They had a secret weapon: each other.

Drs. Rameck Hunt, George Jenkins, and Sampson Davis, authors of *The Pact*, after graduating from medical school

The Big Idea

Write What is this article mainly about?

___

___

___

VOCABULARY BUILDER

Target Word

define

de•fine (verb)

Rate it: ① ② ③

Meaning

___

___

___

Example

___

___

___

React

Why might making a pact with friends be a powerful thing? What could be one positive consequence of making a pact?

In this excerpt from their book, the doctors talk about their dedication to the pact and offer advice on pursuing a goal.

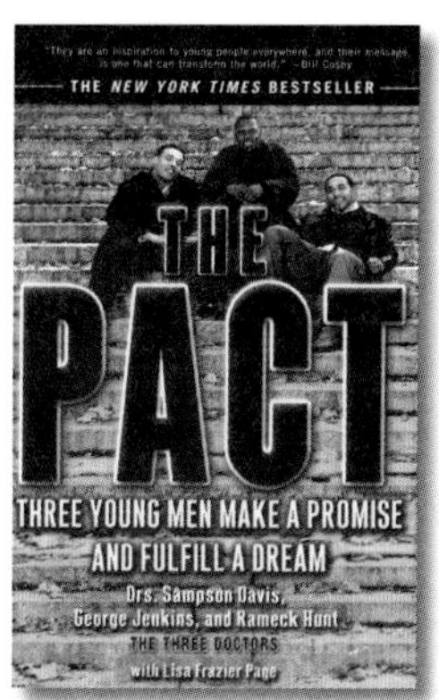

The Thin Line

We treat them in our hospitals every day. They are young brothers, often drug dealers, gang members, or small-time criminals, who show up shot, stabbed, or beaten after a hustle gone bad. To some of our medical colleagues, they are just nameless thugs, perpetuating crime and death in neighborhoods that have seen far too much of those things. But when we look into their faces, we see what we easily could have become as young adults. And we're reminded of the thin line that separates us—three twenty-nine-year-old doctors (an emergency-room physician, an internist, and a dentist)—from these patients whose lives are filled with danger and desperation.

Making the Pact

We grew up in poor, broken homes in Newark, New Jersey, neighborhoods that were riddled with crime, drugs, and death. We came of age in the 1980s at the height of a crack epidemic that ravaged communities like ours throughout the nation. There were no doctors or lawyers walking the streets of our communities. Where we lived, hustlers reigned, and it was easy to follow their example. Two of us landed in juvenile-detention centers before our eighteenth birthdays.

But one of us, early in childhood, **defined** his goal of becoming a dentist. He steered clear of trouble, and in his senior year of high school persuaded his two best friends to apply to a college program for minority students interested in becoming doctors. We knew we'd never survive if we went after it alone. So we made a pact: we'd help each other through, no matter what. ➔

Words to Know! **perpetuating** *(v.)* making something last

Main Idea and Details

1. **Write** Find the main idea in the section "The Thin Line."

____

____

____

____

____

____

2. **Underline** Find two important details in the section "The Thin Line."

3. **Write** Find the main idea in "Making the Pact."

____

____

____

____

____

____

Review: Read for Detail

Circle Find one detail that tells how the friends helped each other.

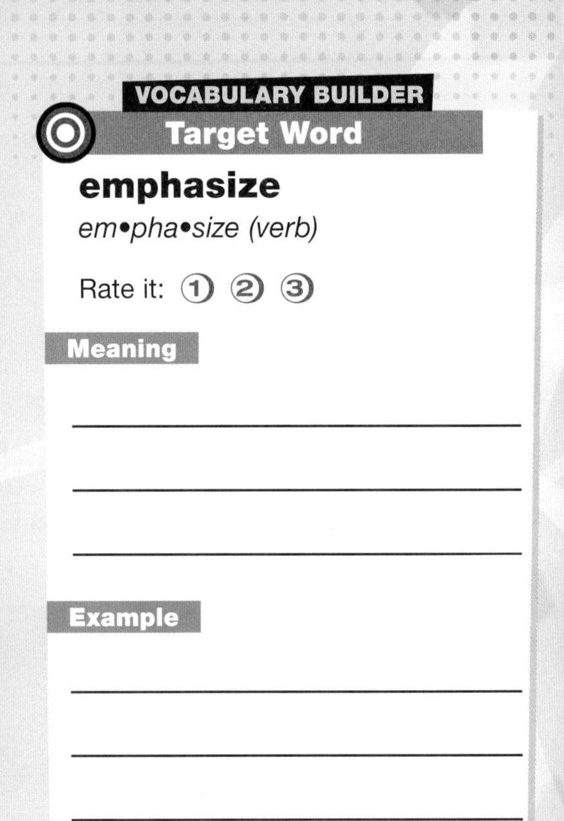

The Power of Friendship

The lives of most impressionable young people are defined by their friends, whether they are black, white, Hispanic, or Asian; whether they are rich, poor, or middle-class; whether they live in the city, the suburbs, or the country. Among boys, particularly, there seems to be some macho code that says to gain respect, you have to prove that you're bad. We know firsthand that the wrong friends can lead you to trouble. But even more, they can tear down hopes, dreams, and possibilities.

We know, too, that the right friends inspire you, pull you through, rise with you. In college, we stuck together to survive and thrive in a world that was different from anything we had ever known. We provided one another with a kind of positive peer pressure. And we are doctors today because of the positive influences that we had on one another.

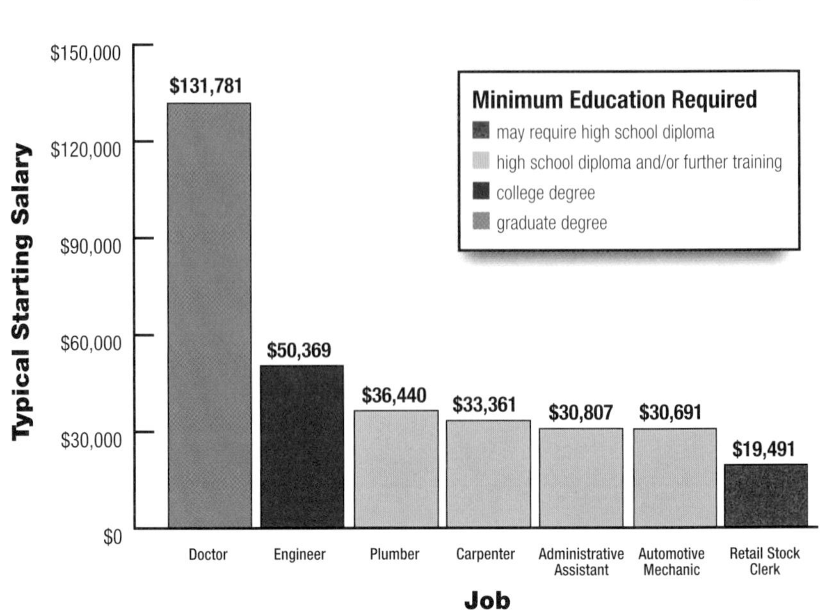

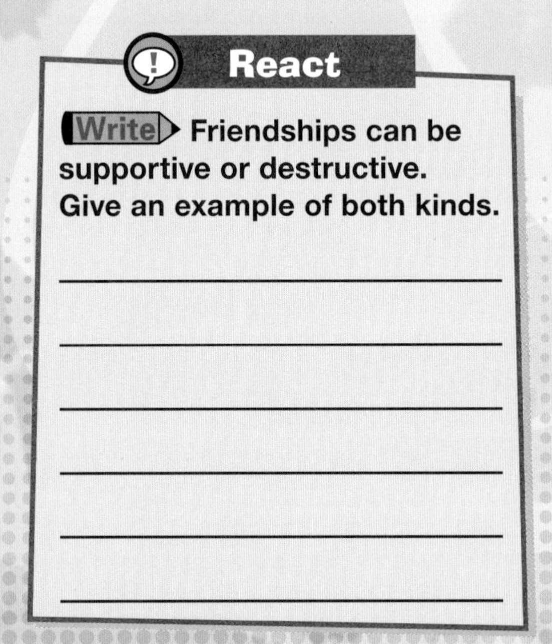

We were lucky. We found in each other a friendship that helped three vulnerable boys grow into successful, capable men—a friendship that helped save our lives.

Sharing Wisdom

We often speak at schools, churches, and community centers, telling kids that our pact filled us with motivation and purpose. The pact gave us a reason to keep pushing when it would have been easier to just give up.

It really makes us feel good when we finish a speech and kids tell us that they're going to form their own pact. We tell them to pick trustworthy friends who have the same goal. We remind them to communicate openly, honestly, and often with each other. And we **emphasize** that they must lean on their friends and allow their friends to lean on them. The power of friendship is a power greater than any one of us could have individually. This power can transform lives and fulfill dreams.

Make a pact. It may change your life. 

Words to Know! **impressionable** *(adj.)* easily influenced

A bar graph shows how different pieces of information relate to each other.

1. What's the minimum level of education required to be an automotive mechanic?

Ⓐ college degree
Ⓑ high school diploma
Ⓒ graduate degree
Ⓓ no degree

2. Which job on the graph pays the least?

Ⓐ plumber
Ⓑ engineer
Ⓒ retail stock clerk
Ⓓ lawyer

3. The job that pays the most requires what kind of degree?

____

Main Idea and Details

1. **Write** Find the main idea of "The Power of Friendship."

____
____
____
____
____
____
____

2. **Underline** Find two important details in this section.

Skills Check

1. **Write** Find the main idea of "Sharing Wisdom."

____
____
____
____
____
____

2. **Underline** Find three important details in "Sharing Wisdom."

VOCABULARY

TAKE THE WORD CHALLENGE

Start

1 **Check.** Which of the following would you consider major accomplishments?

- ❑ building an award-winning sports car
- ❑ getting great grades
- ❑ winning an Oscar
- ❑ graduating from high school

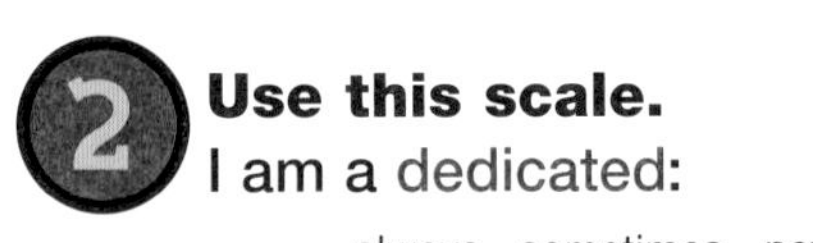

2 **Use this scale.** I am a dedicated:

	always	sometimes	never
athlete	❑	❑	❑
student	❑	❑	❑
musician	❑	❑	❑
friend	❑	❑	❑

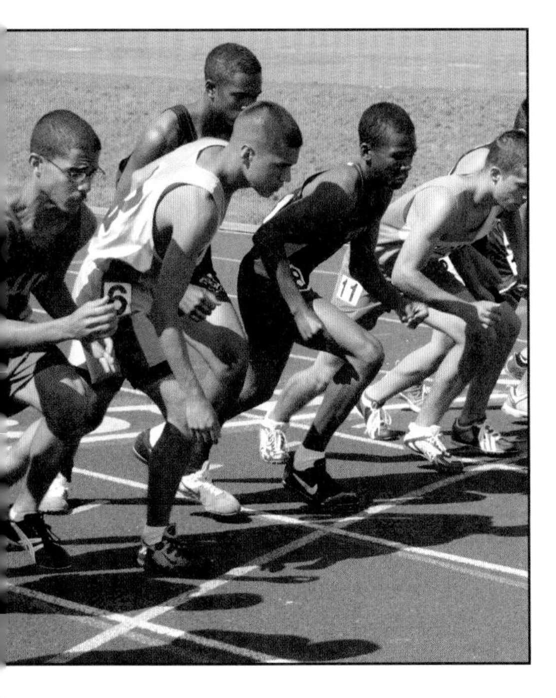

3 Synonyms

Synonyms are words that have similar meanings. Examples are *accomplish* and *achieve* or *goal* and *objective*.

Match each word to its synonym below:

capable **person** **undertake**

individual: ______________________

take on: ______________________

competent: ______________________

My **objective** is to play guitar. It's a **goal** I really want to attain.

4 **Word families.** A word family is a group of words that share the same base word and have related meanings, such as *act* and *action*.

Which sentences use words that come from the same word family as pursue?

- ❑ The police officer ran for blocks in pursuit of the mugger.
- ❑ Linda carries practically everything she owns in her purse.
- ❑ I am thinking of pursuing a career as a dental assistant.

5 **Check.** Which of these best defines you?

❑ shy	❑ interesting	❑ smart
❑ happy	❑ outgoing	❑ popular
❑ athletic	❑ energetic	❑ unable to sit still

Add another two words to define yourself:

______________________ ______________________

6 **Fill in.** Name an individual who has the following effect on you:

inspires you

____

makes you happy

____

gives you a headache

____

7 **Respond.** What can you do to emphasize your best quality?

____

____

____

____

How can you **emphasize** your best quality?

8 Antonyms

Antonyms are words that have opposite meanings. Examples are *quiet* and *noisy* or *meek* and *bold*.

Match each word to its antonym below:

oblivious **create** **capable**

destroy: _______________

unable: _______________

aware: _______________

Joy

Sorrow

9 **Respond.** List two consequences of dropping out.

1. _______________

____

2. _______________

____

10 **Complete the sentences.** Fill in each blank with the correct form of resolve from below.

resolve **resolution** **unresolved**

My New Year's __________ is to graduate from high school. Therefore, I __________ to work hard this year and to deal with any __________ issues from last year.

Finish

Writing Focus

Expository Paragraph

An **expository paragraph** provides information and explains it.

▶ **Read Devon's expository paragraph about his most important goal in life.**

Student Model

My Goal: To Save Lives

by Devon Williams

My most important goal in life is to become an EMT, or emergency medical technician. There are three things that I'm doing to accomplish this goal. First of all, I dedicate time as a volunteer at the emergency response center in my town. I've learned to take 911 calls and keep our emergency vehicles supplied. In addition, I've taken classes at the Red Cross to learn life-saving techniques. The most important thing I'm doing to meet my goal is getting good enough grades to graduate and be accepted in an EMT training program. To sum up, I am doing all I can to pursue my goal of saving lives as an EMT.

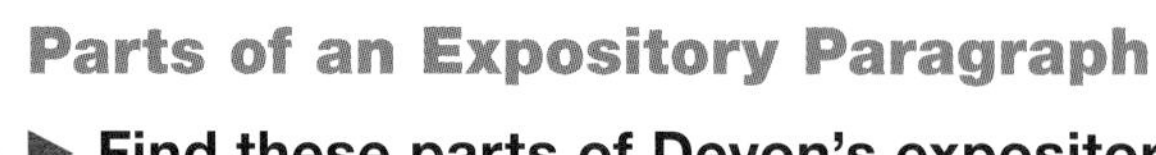

Parts of an Expository Paragraph

▶ **Find these parts of Devon's expository paragraph.**

1. Underline the sentence that states the **topic**.
2. Check three important **details** that support or explain the topic.
3. Notice the **order** of the details.
4. Circle the **linking words** that connect the ideas.
5. Put a star before the sentence that **sums up** or restates the topic.

Brainstorm

▶ **Read the writing prompt in the middle of the idea web. Then use the boxes to help you brainstorm your ideas.**

Education

Job

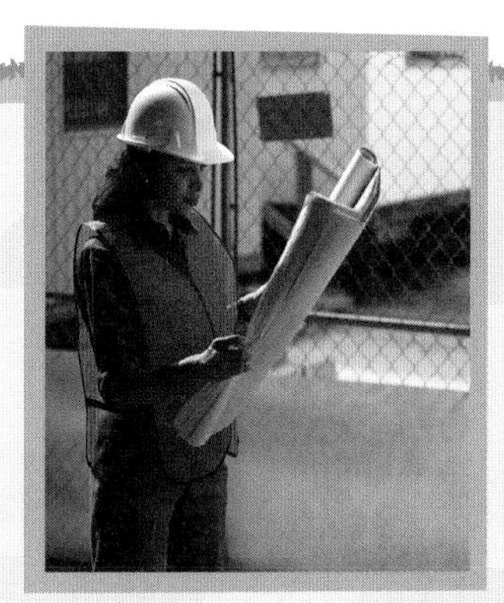

Writing Prompt:

Tell about an important goal in your life. Explain how you plan to reach it.

Personal

Social

Plan Your Paragraph

Writing Prompt: Tell about an important goal in your life. Explain how you plan to reach it.

▶ **Use this chart to plan and organize your paragraph.**

Word Choices

____

____

____

____

____

Topic Sentence

- *My most important goal . . .*
- *I have always wanted to . . .*
- *As I think about my future, . . .*

Detail 1

- *First of all, . . .*
- *To start with, . . .*
- *The first thing . . .*

Detail 2

- *In addition, . . .*
- *Also, . . .*
- *Another way that I . . .*

Detail 3

- *The most important thing . . .*
- *A third thing . . .*
- *Lastly, . . .*

Ending

- *To sum up, . . .*
- *In conclusion, . . .*
- *Overall, . . .*

Write Your Paragraph

▶ **Use this writing frame to write a first draft of your paragraph.**

____
(title)

My most important goal ____________________________
____
____
____

First of all, ______________________________________
____
____
____

In addition, ______________________________________
____
____
____

The most important thing ___________________________
____
____
____

To sum up, _______________________________________
____
____
____
____

Revise

▶ **Rate your paragraph. Then have a writing partner rate it.**

Scoring Guide			
weak	okay	good	strong
1	2	3	4

1. Does the first sentence state the **topic**?

Self	1	2	3	4
Partner	1	2	3	4

2. Do the **details** support or explain the topic?

Self	1	2	3	4
Partner	1	2	3	4

3. Are the supporting details in a **logical order**?

Self	1	2	3	4
Partner	1	2	3	4

4. Do **linking words** connect the details?

Self	1	2	3	4
Partner	1	2	3	4

5. Does the ending **sum up** or restate the topic?

Self	1	2	3	4
Partner	1	2	3	4

▶ Now revise your paragraph to make it stronger.

Grammar IDENTIFYING SENTENCES AND FRAGMENTS

A sentence is a group of words that tells a complete idea.

- The subject tells who or what the sentence is about.
- The predicate tells what someone or something does.

Example

Subject	Predicate
Tabitha	plans to pursue a law degree.
The doctors	work in their old neighborhood.

▶ **Identify the underlined part of each sentence below. Write subject or predicate on the line beside it.**

1. Three friends made a pact to become doctors. ___predicate___
2. They grew up in a rough neighborhood. ______
3. Obstacles could not stop the boys. ______
4. After several years, all three graduated. ______
5. Today the men inspire others. ______
6. Young boys and girls look at them as role models. ______

A **sentence fragment** is an incomplete sentence that can't stand by itself. Often, a fragment is missing either a subject or a predicate.

▶ **Rewrite the sentence fragments below as complete sentences.**

7. drop out of school before graduation

______

8. people without diplomas

______

9. The class full of students

______

10. began to love reading

______

Take a close look at each of the sentences in your draft on page 25. Do they all express complete ideas? Fix the ones that don't.

Mechanics USING END PUNCTUATION

Different kinds of sentences use different **end punctuation marks**.

- A statement always ends with a period.
- A question always ends with a question mark.

Example

Statement	Question
My sister wants to be a musician.	What career would you enjoy?
Tim's goal is to be a scientist.	How will you reach your goal?

▶ **Find and correct five errors in this paragraph.**

Student Model

My goal is to help others by being a nurse. To accomplish my goal, I dedicate volunteer time to our local hospital. I read stories to sick children? Another thing I do is study biology. The sciance of life. I know that a nurse needs to know all about the human body. Also, I ask my Aunt Ella questions about her job as a nurse? She tells me about her patients' illnesses. In conclusion, I am persuing my goal of being a nurse.

Check and Correct

- ❑ Circle two spelling errors and correct them.
- ❑ Underline two end punctuation errors and correct them.
- ❑ Correct one sentence fragment.

Edit *Look at the sentences in your own draft on page 25. Do they all have the correct end punctuation? Fix the ones that don't.*

Final Draft/Present

▶ **Write a final draft of your paragraph on paper or the computer. Check it again and correct any errors before you present it.**

Careers

Career Development Counselor

Job Corps is a government program that helps young people earn their diplomas, get job training, and launch careers. As a counselor with Job Corps, Alejandro Zuccaro helps individuals find rewarding careers. To succeed, he has to be a good listener and give advice on everything from work issues to personal problems. "I love my job because I get to help people realize their goals," says Alejandro.

Name: Alejandro Zuccaro

Hometown: Miami, Florida

Job: Career Development Counselor

Duties:
- guides students in finding jobs
- counsels students about personal issues
- motivates students to pursue their goals

Skills:
- listening and communicating
- problem-solving

Similar Jobs:
- high-school counselor
- therapist

Pay: $30,000 to $40,000 per year

Education: Bachelor's Degree in Psychology

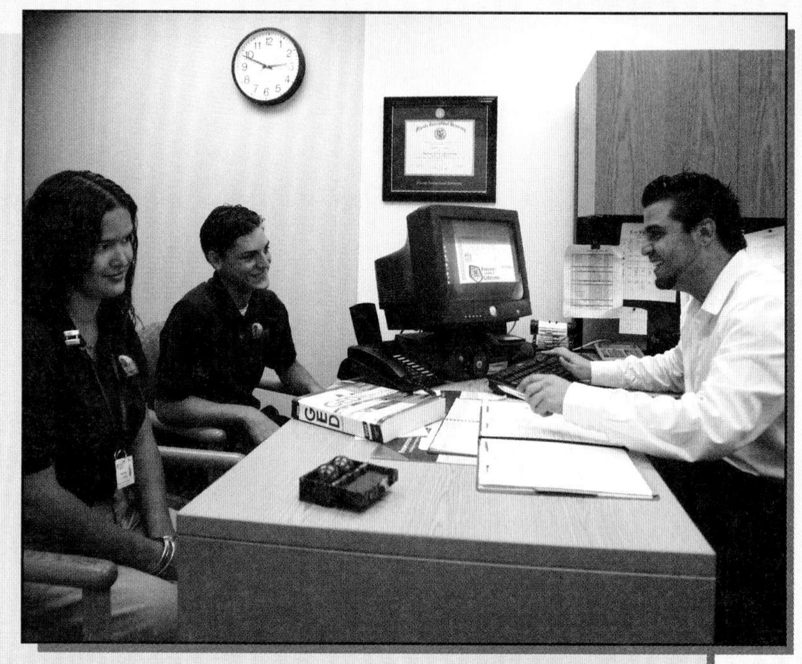

Alejandro Zuccaro talks to Job Corps students in his office.

Ask Yourself

1. **Underline** Find the section that lists similar jobs. Mark which one interests you most.
2. **Circle** In the "Skills" list, mark the skill you think you would be strongest at.
3. How much do you want this job?
   - ☐ I don't want it.
   - ☐ I might want it.
   - ☐ I really want it.

Reading a Brochure

Alejandro Zuccaro uses brochures like this one to help prospective Job Corps members decide whether Job Corps is right for them.

▶ **Read the brochure. Then answer each question below.**

1. What does Job Corps help students do?
Ⓐ find great jobs
Ⓑ find transportation
Ⓒ find health care
Ⓓ all of the above

2. Who can join Job Corps?
Ⓐ U.S. citizens or legal residents age 18 and over
Ⓑ high school graduates
Ⓒ college graduates
Ⓓ U.S. citizens or legal residents age 16–24

3. How much does Job Corps cost to join?
Ⓐ $62,000 per year
Ⓑ $6,200 per year
Ⓒ It's free.
Ⓓ $122 per month

4. Who runs Job Corps?
Ⓐ Alejandro Zuccaro
Ⓑ the U.S. Department of Labor
Ⓒ the U.S. Department of Education
Ⓓ private businesses

5. Where do Job Corps members usually live?
Ⓐ with their families
Ⓑ on a Job Corps campus
Ⓒ in a hotel
Ⓓ on a job site

6. How can you learn more about Job Corps?
Ⓐ by visiting their Web site
Ⓑ by calling their phone number
Ⓒ both of the above
Ⓓ none of the above

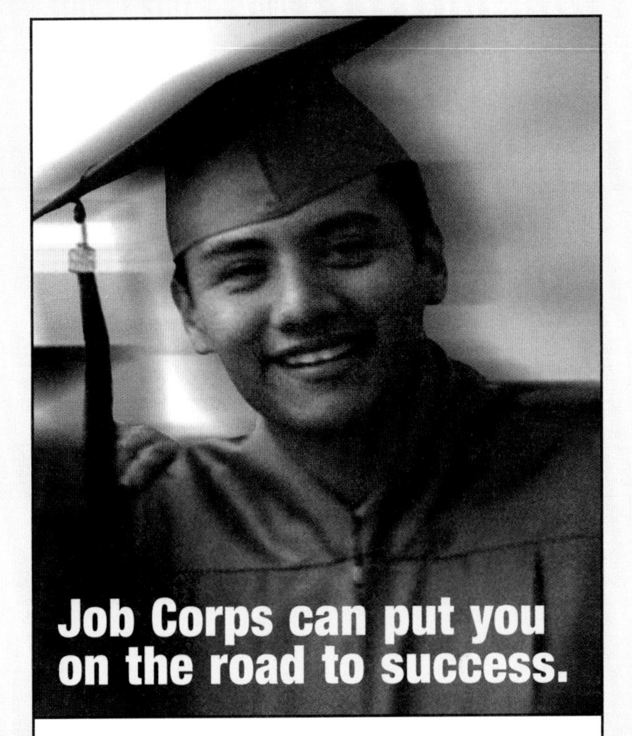

Who you are:
- Age 16 through 24
- A U.S. citizen or legal resident
- Meet the program's income requirements
- Ready to learn, work, and become a leader

Who we are:
- A free education and job training program, administered by the U.S. Department of Labor
- A residential program—most students live on campus, learning at one of 122 Job Corps centers across the country
- A successful program that helps 62,000 students find promising careers each year
- A support network that helps students find great jobs, transportation, housing, health care, and other necessities after graduation

For more information, call 1-800-733-JOBS, or visit http://jobcorps.doleta.gov

Comprehension

▶ **Fill in the circle next to the correct answer.**

1. How many students in city schools drop out before graduating?
Ⓐ one in three
Ⓑ up to two-thirds
Ⓒ 75 percent
Ⓓ less than in rural schools

Here's a tip.
Read all the answer choices before answering a question.

2. What is the main idea of "America's Dropout Crisis"?
Ⓐ School dropouts often become involved in crime.
Ⓑ It's difficult to get a high school diploma.
Ⓒ Dropping out of school has many serious consequences.
Ⓓ Graduation day is the best day of a student's life.

3. What is "Living in the Success Zone" mostly about?
Ⓐ two *READ 180* students who turned their lives around
Ⓑ the importance of learning to read
Ⓒ how to be successful as a college football player
Ⓓ Lufkin High School in Texas

4. The three doctors believe that teens can reach their goals by ________________.
Ⓐ going to dentistry school
Ⓑ staying off the streets and away from bad influences
Ⓒ forming close friendships
Ⓓ making a pact with friends to help each other reach goals

5. All three articles in the workshop agree that success comes from ________________.
Ⓐ friendship
Ⓑ education
Ⓒ reading books
Ⓓ earning more money

Vocabulary

▶ **Fill in the circle next to the correct definition of the underlined word.**

1. The musician wanted to <u>dedicate</u> herself to practicing her trumpet.
   Ⓐ put forth an effort
   Ⓑ criticize
   Ⓒ start a project
   Ⓓ commit to a goal

2. Each <u>individual</u> should think through his or her goals in life.
   Ⓐ person
   Ⓑ separate
   Ⓒ graduate
   Ⓓ friend

3. To <u>pursue</u> my goal of playing college football, I'm improving my reading.
   Ⓐ destroy
   Ⓑ celebrate
   Ⓒ try to achieve
   Ⓓ try to change

▶ **Choose the synonym for the underlined word.**

4. Getting a diploma is a goal I want to <u>accomplish</u>.
   Ⓐ dedicate
   Ⓑ achieve
   Ⓒ create
   Ⓓ consider

▶ **Choose the antonym for the underlined word.**

5. He became such a <u>capable</u> reader that he went to college.
   Ⓐ fast
   Ⓑ famous
   Ⓒ unskilled
   Ⓓ excellent

Short Answer

▶ **Use what you've read in this Workshop to answer the question below. Check your spelling and grammar.**

Why is it important to graduate from high school?

____

____

____

____

____

Comprehension Focus
Sequence of Events

READINGS
1 ***Waves of Destruction*** >> Online News Article
2 ***Terror and Tragedy*** >> Personal Narrative
3 ***Relief and Recovery*** >> Social Studies Text

TSUNAMI
DISASTER OF THE CENTURY

What happens when an earthquake strikes deep under the ocean floor? In just hours, a beautiful day at the beach can turn into a deadly disaster! That's what happened in the Indian Ocean on December 26, 2004.

That day, an earthquake struck under the sea—unleashing a giant tsunami! There was no warning before the waves hit land. For hundreds of thousands of people, there was no escape.

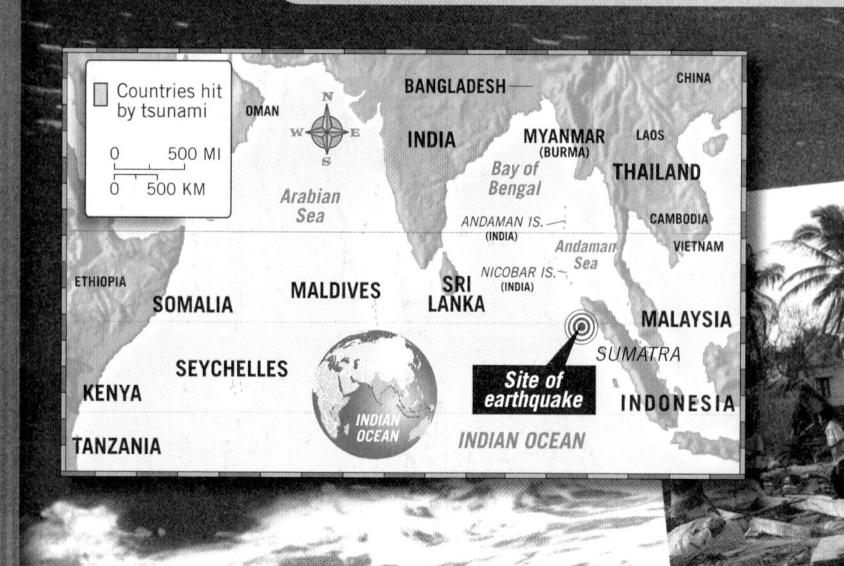

VOCABULARY BUILDER

Target Word ▶ Read the Target Words. Rate each one using the scale below.*	Meaning ▶ Read the Target Word meaning. Write in the missing ones.	Example ▶ Finish the Target Word examples below. Write in the missing ones.
complicate *com•pli•cate* *(verb)* ① ② ③		A problem that would complicate my life at school is . . .
crisis *cri•sis* *(noun)* ① ② ③	a big problem or an emergency	
hemisphere *hem•i•sphere* *(noun)* ① ② ③		Two countries in the Western Hemisphere are ______ and ______
phase *(noun)* ① ② ③	one part or stage of something	
process *pro•cess* *(noun)* ① ② ③		Rebuilding after the tsunami is a difficult **process**!

*Rating Scale

①=I don't know it at all.
②=I've seen it before.
③=I know it and use it.

The Big Idea

Write What is this article mainly about?

VOCABULARY BUILDER

Target Word

magnitude

mag•ni•tude (noun)

Rate it: ① ② ③

Meaning

Example

In late 2004, a killer tsunami struck South Asia. Here's how a news Web site covered the crisis.

Waves of Destruction

December 28, 2004—A deadly disaster shook the Eastern Hemisphere two days ago. It began with an earthquake of immense **magnitude**. The quake struck deep below the floor of the Indian Ocean. It was the most devastating earthquake in 40 years.

During the quake, a large chunk of the earth's crust shifted upward—displacing a huge volume of water in the process. Next, the water formed a giant wave called a tsunami. The deadly tsunami rushed through the ocean.

Then, the tsunami hit shore. Waves as tall as three-story buildings swept away everything in their path. Seven hours later, the waves had traveled 3,000 miles to the coast of East Africa!

Today, the world is struggling to grasp the magnitude of the crisis. Hundreds of thousands are dead. Millions of homes and businesses have been washed away. In some places, entire villages have been swept into the ocean.

Help for survivors is on the way. But it's clear that recovery will take years to accomplish. END

React

Many people think the tsunami is the biggest news story of the century so far. Do you agree? Explain your answer.

How a Tsunami Forms

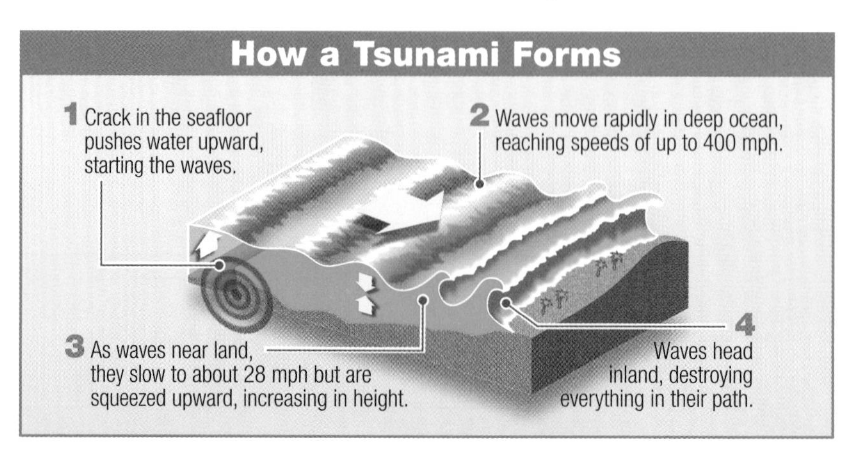

Words to Know! **immense** *(adj.)* extremely large

Comprehension Focus

Sequence of Events

Sequence is the order in which events happen. To find the sequence of events:

- Try to remember the order in which events take place.
- Look for times, dates, and signal words, such as *first, then, next, soon, before, after,* and *later.*
- When you know the order, check it again. Make sure it makes sense.

▶ **Fill in this chart with the sequence of events that happened before and during the tsunami.**

It began

with an earthquake of immense magnitude. During the quake, a large chunk of the earth's crust shifted upward–displacing a huge volume of water in the process.

Next,

Then,

Seven hours later,

The Big Idea

Write What is this article mainly about?

______

______

______

VOCABULARY BUILDER

Target Word

exert

ex•ert (verb)

Rate it: ① ② ③

Meaning

______

______

______

Example

______

______

______

React

The tsunami caught Latha off guard. She'd never seen anything like it. How can you prepare for a disaster where you live?

TERROR AND TRAGEDY

Latha Veerappan
as told to
Anuradha Raghunathan

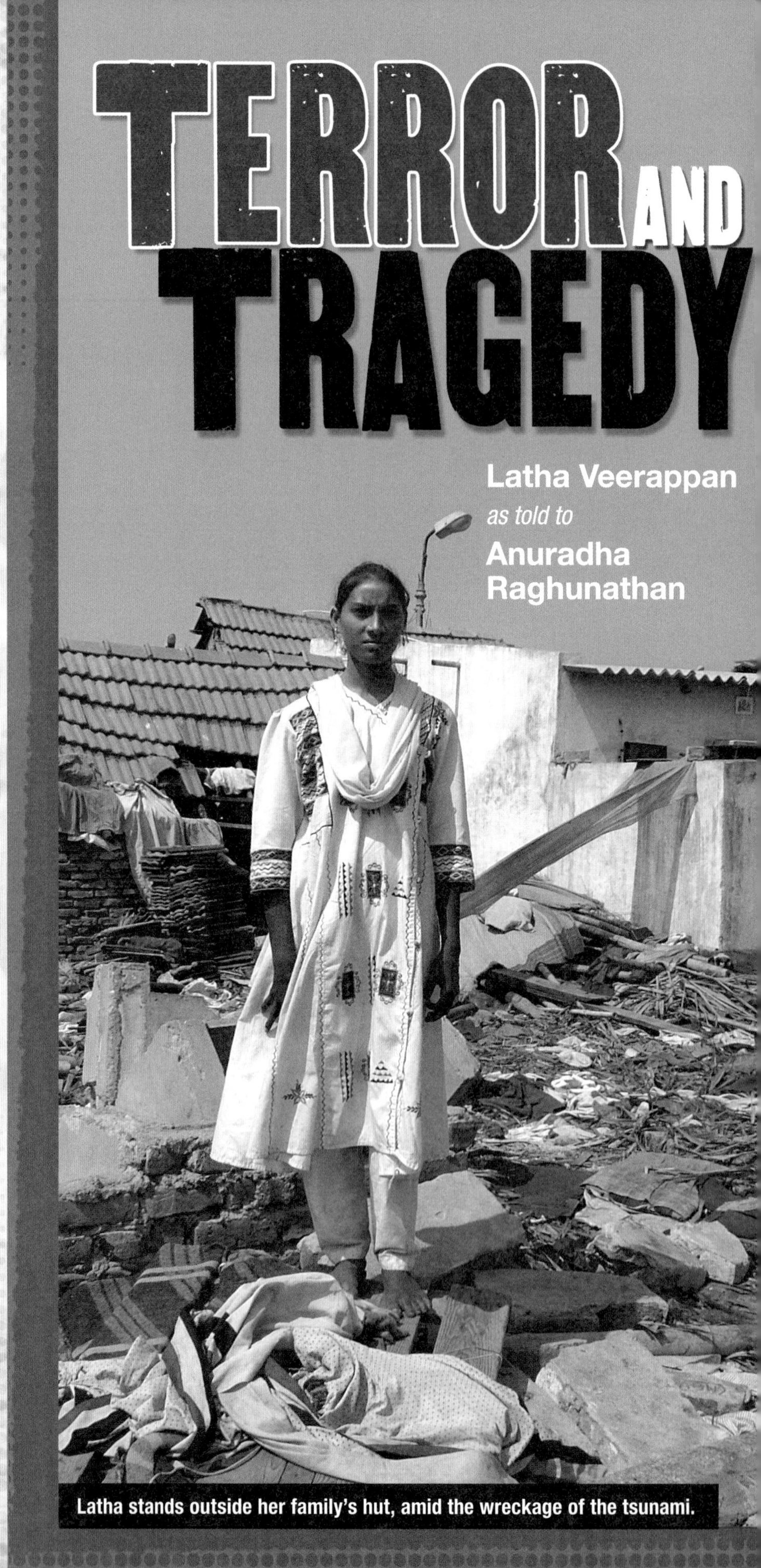

Latha stands outside her family's hut, amid the wreckage of the tsunami.

For Latha, 16, life changed forever the day the tsunami struck her village.

I live in southern India, a few minutes from the Indian Ocean. Like many men here, my father is a fisherman. My mother used to take the fish and sell them at a market.

I'm the oldest of four kids. Because we are poor, I left school after eighth grade to help out.

Terrifying Waves

The morning of December 26, 2004, I was home alone. My family was fishing at the beach.

At about 8:45 A.M., I heard my neighbor scream. When I ran out to see what the crisis was, all I could see were ocean waves rolling down our street. The waves lifted up a neighbor's hut and sent it flying through the air. I had never seen anything like it!

As I watched, another wave came and hit me. I was lucky—the water only reached my waist and didn't suck me under. But the wave **exerted** such force that our door flew open and water rushed in.

Where Is My Family?

Now I knew I had to escape the ocean. I began to run. Then I realized my whole family was missing.

Next, I decided to go to the police station. When I got there, it was swarming with terrified villagers. But the police couldn't help us look for our relatives. The beach was too dangerous to search.

After the second wave receded, I ran home. Our hut was a wreck. The water had swept away almost all our belongings. My family was not there, and I was so worried that I couldn't stop crying. →

Words to Know! **receded** *(v.)* moved back

Sequence of Events

1. **Write** Find four events in "Terrifying Waves."

- The morning of December 26, ____________________
- At about 8:45 A.M., ____________________
- When I ran out to see what the crisis was, ____________________
- As I watched, ____________________

2. **Underline** Find five signal words or phrases that help you know the sequence of events in "Where Is My Family?"

Active Reading

Underline ▶ Why did Latha's father let go of his family?

VOCABULARY BUILDER

Target Word

accurate

ac•cu•rate (adjective)

Rate it: ① ② ③

Meaning

___

___

___

Example

___

___

___

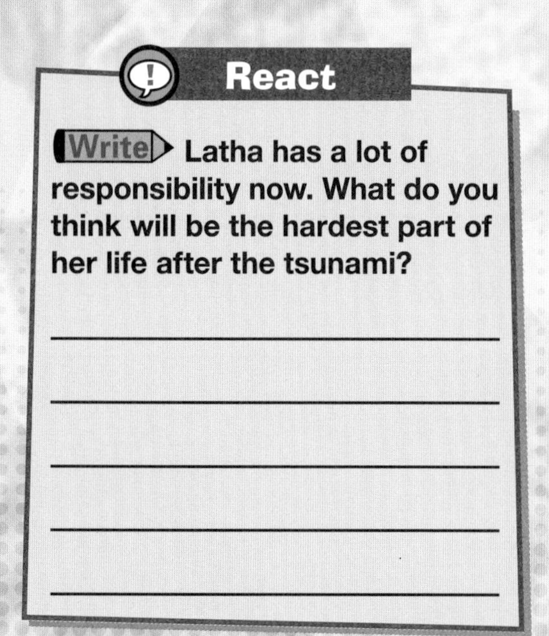

React

Write ▶ **Latha has a lot of responsibility now. What do you think will be the hardest part of her life after the tsunami?**

___

___

___

___

___

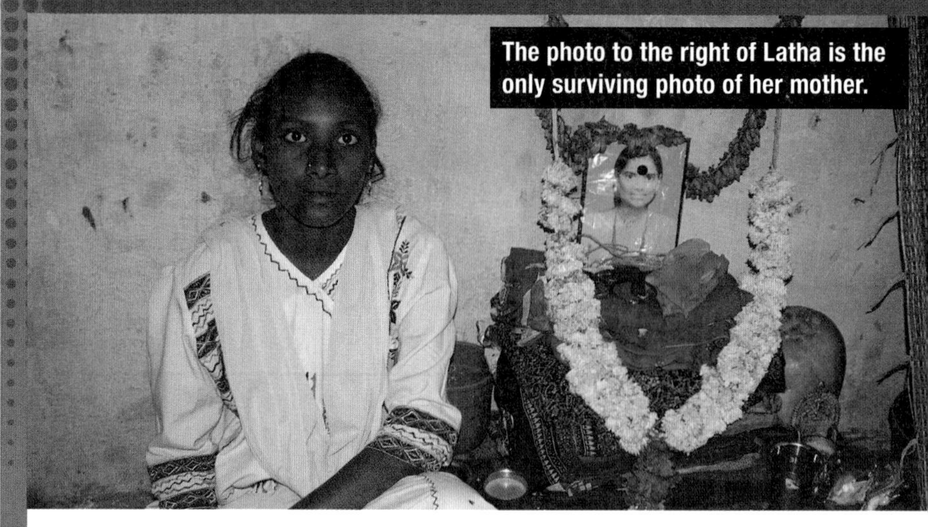

The photo to the right of Latha is the only surviving photo of her mother.

Sad Reunion

About 30 minutes later, the door banged open. In walked my father—alone. Where was everyone else?

"I grabbed onto them when the waves hit," he said. "But my shirt caught on something. I had to let go for fear I'd drag them under. In the process, I lost them."

I just stood there in shock. Had they all drowned? Suddenly, my brother appeared. He was scratched and bloody—but alive. He had washed ashore on a board.

Half an hour passed. At last, my other siblings came home. They had been stranded in the waves until fishermen rescued them. But where was my mother?

Grim Discovery

At 11 A.M., a neighbor came by with devastating news. My mother was at the hospital, but doctors had been incapable of saving her. She was dead.

Soon, we had a more **accurate** picture of the catastrophe. Hundreds in our village were dead. To complicate our grief, waves had destroyed many homes.

In minutes, the tsunami took everything we had. Now, I have resolved to care for my siblings and find a job. My father's fishing nets were destroyed, so we are poorer than ever. It's a lot of responsibility at this phase in my life, but with Mom gone, my family needs me. END

Words to Know! **catastrophe** *(n.)* disaster

Comprehension Focus

Sequence of Events

▶ **Fill in this chart with the events that tell how Latha learned what had happened to her family members, from "Sad Reunion" through the first paragraph of "Grim Discovery."**

About 30 minutes later,

____

____

____

Suddenly,

____

____

____

At last,

____

____

____

At 11 A.M.,

____

____

____

Relief + Recovery

The tsunami took just hours to cross the Indian Ocean. Rebuilding in its wake will take years.

MASSIVE DEVASTATION

In the days following the tsunami of December 2004, death tolls mounted. Home video footage hit the airwaves, revealing entire towns and villages reduced to piles of wood and broken glass. As the news and images poured in, people around the world struggled to comprehend the scope of the crisis.

The tsunami had battered coastal communities in twelve countries in the Eastern Hemisphere. Indonesia's Aceh province is located at ground zero—very near the epicenter of the earthquake that triggered the tsunami. In Aceh alone, more than 170,000 people died. An additional 50,000 were killed in areas farther away. Some 17,000 children lost a parent. Another 14,000 were orphaned.

The disaster's economic impact was as vast as its toll in human lives. Much of South Asia had struggled with poverty and unemployment even before the tsunami hit. Now, thousands of beach

Words to Know! **spurred** *(v.)* encouraged or prompted

The Big Idea

Write What is this article mainly about?

______

______

______

VOCABULARY BUILDER

Target Word

invest

in•vest (verb)

Rate it:   ③

Meaning

______

______

______

Example

______

______

______

React

People around the world responded to the tsunami. What could you do to help out after a disaster?

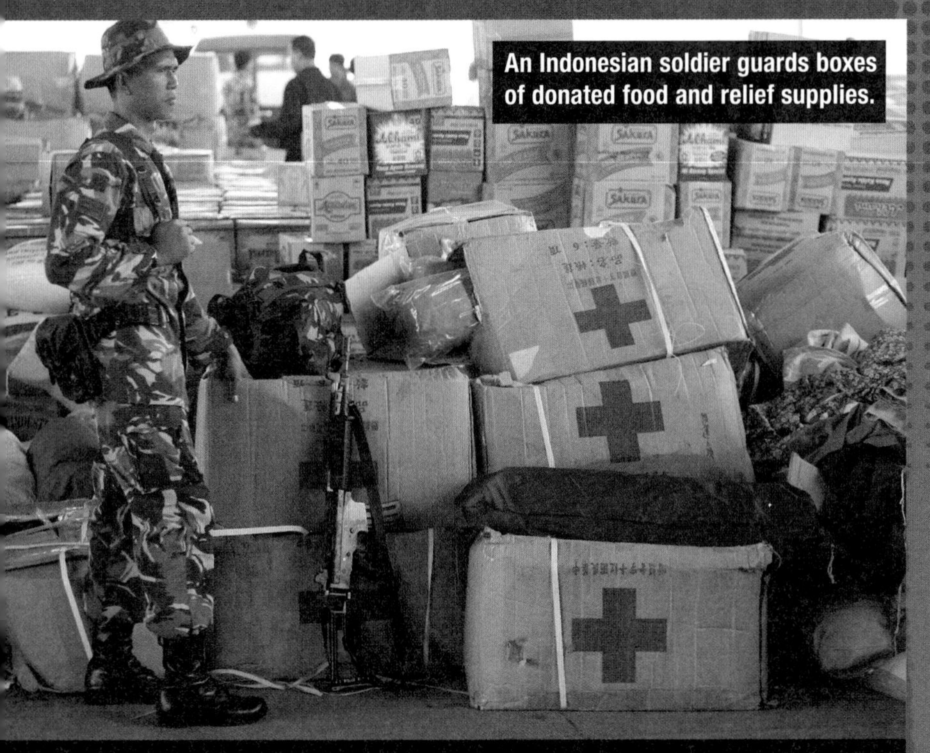

An Indonesian soldier guards boxes of donated food and relief supplies.

resorts and other businesses had been leveled. Fishing boats and equipment had been destroyed. Hundreds of thousands of survivors had lost their livelihoods. About 5 million had been left homeless.

THE WORLD RESPONDS

The relief effort began within 24 hours. As the global community absorbed the tsunami's horror, world leaders began pledging their help. One month later, countries had **invested** over $4 billion. One year later, that figure had increased to $13.6 billion.

The United States government made an initial pledge of $350 million. Eight days after the tsunami, President George W. Bush asked his father, George H.W. Bush, to join forces with Bill Clinton. The two former presidents had been election rivals in 1992. Now, they set aside their differences and hit the road to pursue a massive fund-raising campaign. By mid-February, their efforts had spurred U.S. corporations and private individuals to dedicate a staggering $7 billion to tsunami relief. ➔

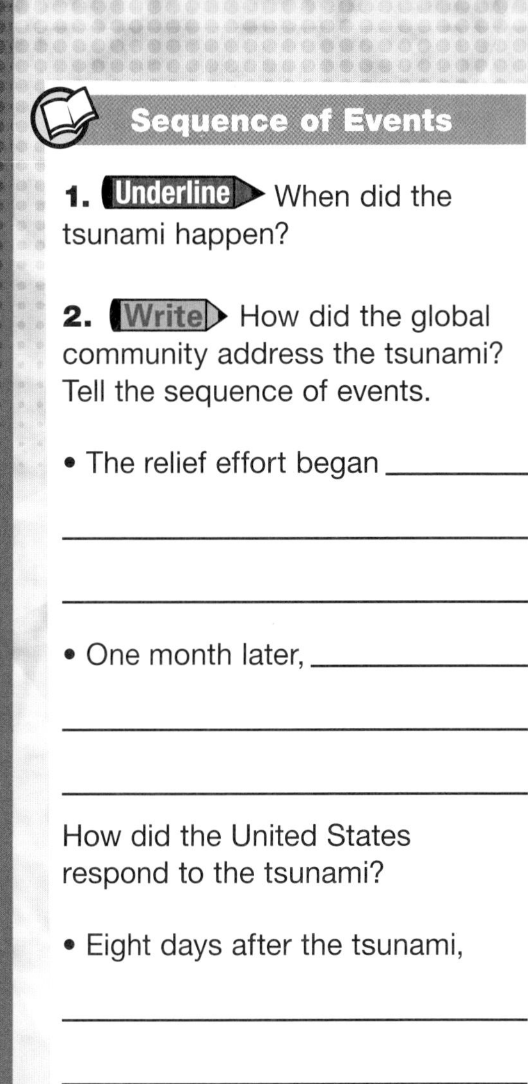

Sequence of Events

1. **Underline** When did the tsunami happen?

2. **Write** How did the global community address the tsunami? Tell the sequence of events.

- The relief effort began ________________________________
- One month later, ________________________________

How did the United States respond to the tsunami?

- Eight days after the tsunami, ________________________________
- By mid-February, ________________________________

Review: Main Idea and Details

Circle Find the main idea in the section "The World Responds."

Active Reading

 **Circle** How soon did the Red Cross begin helping after the tsunami?

VOCABULARY BUILDER

Target Word

distribute

dis•trib•ute (verb)

Rate it: ① ② ③

Meaning

____

____

____

Example

____

____

____

React

Write **Do you think Americans have a responsibility to help disaster victims in our country? In other countries? Why or why not?**

____

____

____

____

____

RECOVERY BEGINS

What happened to the billions donated for relief and recovery? The money was **distributed** among a wide variety of capable organizations.

With branches in 181 nations, the Red Cross is the largest such group. Red Cross workers were activated within hours after the tsunami struck. During the first phase of the relief process, volunteers searched for the missing. They gave first aid, distributed food and water, and set up shelters for the homeless.

By June 2005, the Red Cross had refocused its efforts, emphasizing long-term needs, such as employment and public health.

Habitat for Humanity is a group that builds homes for the homeless. Following the tsunami, the group concentrated its efforts in four countries: India, Indonesia, Sri Lanka, and Thailand. As a consequence of their proximity to the earthquake's epicenter, communities in these countries were especially hard hit by the disaster.

Habitat volunteers were in the region by January 2005. By the end of the year, they had built or repaired 4,000 homes and undertaken work on 2,000 more.

Words to Know! **proximity** *(n.)* nearness

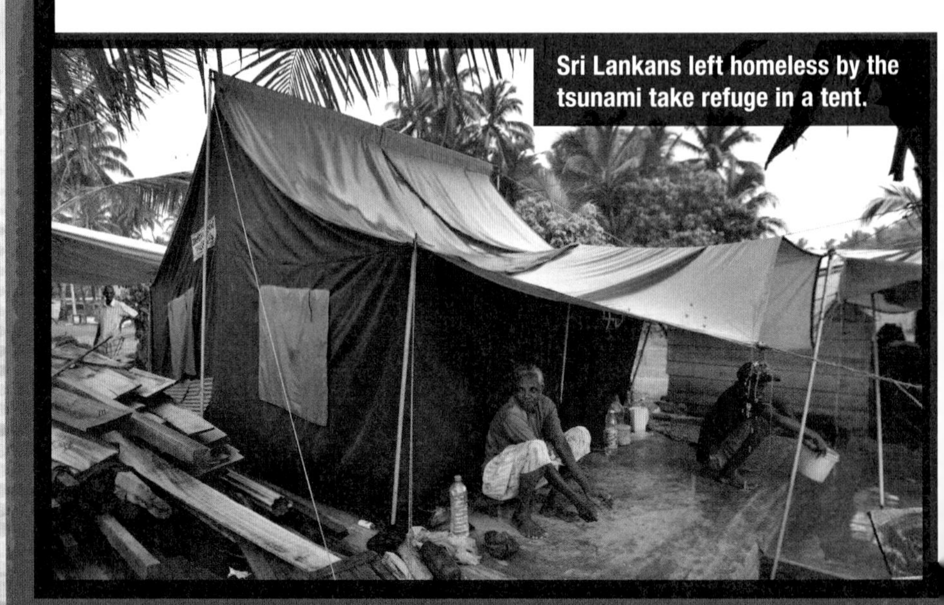

Sri Lankans left homeless by the tsunami take refuge in a tent.

LOOKING TO THE FUTURE

The scale of the tragedy has prompted the question: Why was there no warning? For years, experts have known that a tsunami could strike in this area. In the past, plans to develop a warning system were complicated by concerns about cost and maintenance. Now, a system is finally underway. But experts advise that warnings are not enough. Residents must be told what to do in the event of the unthinkable—another major tsunami. END

THE TSUNAMI'S PATH

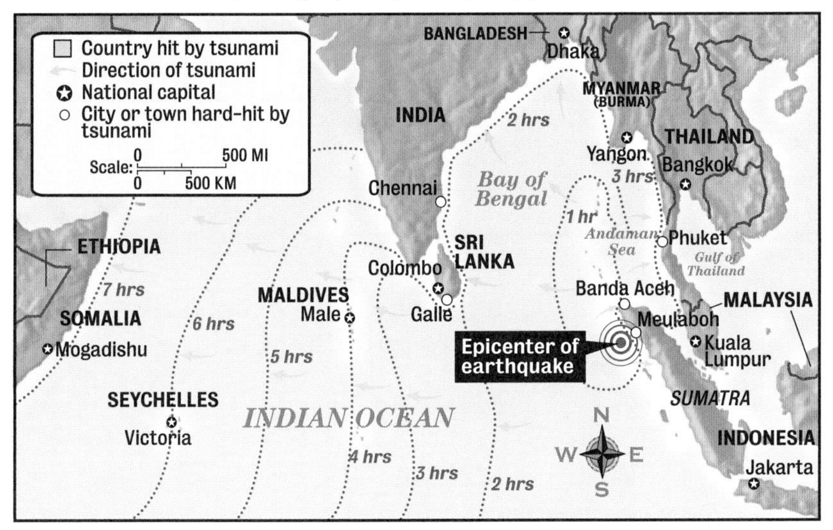

The dotted lines on the map tell how many hours it took for the tsunami to travel outward from the epicenter—the area directly above the earthquake.

1. Which country is farthest from the epicenter?

Ⓐ Sri Lanka Ⓒ Somalia
Ⓑ Thailand Ⓓ Indonesia

2. Which country did the tsunami reach in six hours?

Ⓐ Myanmar Ⓒ Maldives
Ⓑ Seychelles Ⓓ Thailand

3. Which countries did the waves reach in two hours?

____

Sequence of Events

1. **Underline** Find the signal words and phrases in the section "Recovery Begins."

2. **Write** Number these steps in the correct sequence from 1 to 4.

___ Red Cross volunteers were activated.

___ Habitat for Humanity had built or repaired 4,000 homes.

___ Habitat workers were in the region.

___ The Red Cross refocused its efforts.

Skills Check

1. **Underline** Find three signal words or phrases that tell the sequence of events in the section "Looking to the Future."

2. **Write** What system is now underway?

____

____

____

____

____

____

TAKE THE WORD CHALLENGE

Start

1

Choose one. Which of these things would most complicate your life?

_____ changing schools

_____ moving to a new house

_____ getting a new best friend

_____ winning the lottery

2

Rate them. Which of these is the biggest crisis? Rate them.
1 = smallest
4 = biggest

_____ losing your wallet

_____ experiencing an earthquake

_____ running out of gas on the highway

_____ fighting with a friend

3

Prefixes

A **prefix** is a letter or a group of letters added to the beginning of a word. A prefix changes the meaning of a word. The prefix *in-* can mean "not." So, *incomplete* means "not complete."

Define. All of these words use the prefix *in-*. Guess what the words mean, using your knowledge of the prefix.

❑ insane | not sane

❑ inaccurate | __________

❑ incorrect | __________

❑ incapable | __________

4

Check. Which country in each pair of countries is in the Northern Hemisphere? Check one.

❑ Canada	vs.	❑ Australia
❑ Argentina	vs.	❑ Russia
❑ Japan	vs.	❑ South Africa

5

Describe. Little kids go through lot of phases—for example, some kids eat the same food, wear the same shirt, or play the same video game all the time! Describe two phases you went through when you were little.

- When I was in my __________ phase, I __________
____

- When I was in my __________ phase, I __________
____

6 Describe.

Describe. Describe the process of making a sandwich.

1. First, ______________________________

____

2. Next, ______________________________

____

3. Then, ______________________________

____

4. Finally, ______________________________

____

7 Think.

Think. Answer these questions about distributing things.

List two things that should be distributed in school—for free!

____

____

How long would it take you to distribute the newspaper to all your neighbors?

____

8 Suffixes

A **suffix** is a letter or group of letters added to the end of a word. A suffix changes the meaning or part of speech of a word. The suffix *-ment* turns a verb into a noun. *Manage* is a verb. *Management* is a noun.

Fill in. Turn these verbs into nouns by adding the suffix *-ment*

state: ______________________

invest: ______________________

pave: ______________________

develop: ______________________

When I became part of **management**, I suddenly had to **manage** a lot of employees.

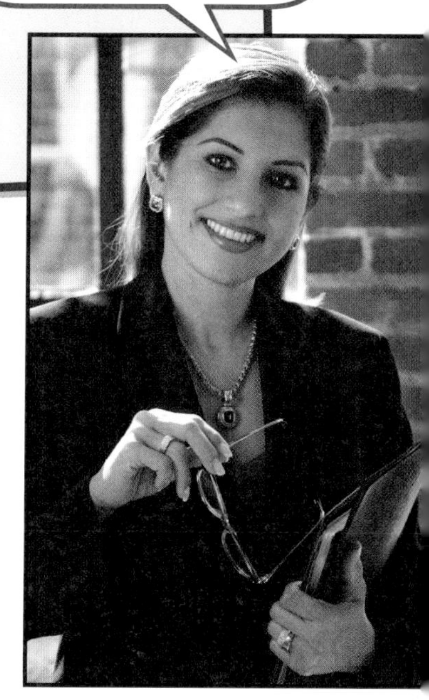

9 Evaluate.

Evaluate. For which activity would you need to exert the most effort?

- ❑ taking a nap
- ❑ running a mile
- ❑ lifting one hundred pounds
- ❑ eating a really big meal

10 Fill in.

Fill in. Complete these sentences with magnitude or invest.

A very powerful earthquake shook the small country. An earthquake of that ______________________ causes a lot of damage. The country can't rebuild on its own. It needs other countries to ______________________ money and resources in rebuilding.

Finish

Writing Focus

Narrative Paragraph

A **narrative paragraph** tells a story about an event.

▶ **Read Rosa's narrative paragraph about how she came to the rescue.**

Student Model

To the Rescue!

by Rosa Vargas

Last year, a terrible thunderstorm hit my town. I was babysitting for my two brothers, and things became complicated fast! First, our electricity went out. Then, my brothers started to cry. When I had calmed them down, I searched our house for flashlights. I gave one to my brothers and took the other to find my cell phone. Then I called my parents and told them to come home right away. Next, I tried to make my brothers feel safe. I gave them snacks and told them a story. Finally, my parents walked in. At the same time, the lights flickered on! I had survived the crisis, and I felt proud of myself.

Parts of a Narrative Paragraph

▶ **Find these parts of Rosa's narrative paragraph.**

1. Underline the sentence that tells about the **event**.
2. Check three **details** about the event.
3. Number these details in the **time order** they happened.
4. Circle the **linking words** that connect the details.
5. Put a star before the sentences that **sum up** the event and tell the writer's feelings about it.

Brainstorm

▶ **Read the writing prompt in the middle of the idea web. Then, use the boxes to help you brainstorm your ideas.**

At Home

At School

Writing Prompt:

Tell about a time when you came to the rescue or gave a helping hand.

In the Neighborhood

On a Trip

Plan Your Paragraph

Writing Prompt: Tell about a time when you came to the rescue or gave a helping hand.

▶ **Use this chart to plan and organize your paragraph.**

Word Choices

____

____

____

____

____

Event

- *Last year, . . .*
- *The crisis happened . . .*
- *It started when . . .*

Detail 1

- *First, . . .*
- *The first thing that happened . . .*
- *In the beginning, . . .*

Detail 2

- *Then, . . .*
- *The next thing I knew, . . .*
- *Before long, . . .*

Detail 3

- *Next, . . .*
- *After that, . . .*
- *At that moment, . . .*

Ending

- *Finally, . . .*
- *In the end, . . .*
- *Once it was over, . . .*

Write Your Paragraph

▶ **Use this writing frame to write a first draft of your paragraph.**

____
(title)

Last year, ______________________________

____

____

First, ______________________________

____

____

Then, ______________________________

____

____

Next, ______________________________

____

____

Finally, ______________________________

____

____

____

Revise

▶ **Rate your paragraph. Then have a writing partner rate it.**

Scoring Guide			
weak	okay	good	strong
1	2	3	4

1. Does the beginning clearly state the **event**?

Self 1 2 3 4

Partner 1 2 3 4

2. Are there **details** that tell about the event?

Self 1 2 3 4

Partner 1 2 3 4

3. Are the details arranged in the **time order** they happened?

Self 1 2 3 4

Partner 1 2 3 4

4. Do **linking words** connect the details?

Self 1 2 3 4

Partner 1 2 3 4

5. Does the ending **sum up** the event and tell the writer's feelings about it?

Self 1 2 3 4

Partner 1 2 3 4

▶ **Now revise your paragraph to make it stronger.**

Grammar Correcting Sentence Fragments

A sentence fragment is an incomplete sentence. Often, sentence fragments are missing a subject or a verb. To fix some fragments, add a subject or verb to make a complete sentence.

Example

Sentence Fragment	Complete Sentence
The tsunami many people. [missing verb]	The tsunami killed many people.
Caused major damage. [missing subject]	The waves caused major damage.

▶ **Write whether each fragment below is missing a subject or a verb.**

1. A gigantic wall of water. verb
2. Held onto a nearby tree. ______
3. Finally, the father and daughters. ______
4. Rescued by fishers. ______
5. Pieces of the house. ______

To correct some sentence fragments, you can connect the fragment to a complete sentence by adding a comma and any missing words.

Example

Sentence and Fragment	Complete Sentence
Many people lost their homes. Lost family members as well.	Many people lost their homes, and some lost their family members as well.

▶ **Rewrite each sentence and fragment as one complete sentence.**

6. A tsunami struck in the Indian Ocean. After an earthquake.

______

7. The tsunami destroyed many homes. Businesses, too.

______

8. Volunteers came from around the world. With food and supplies.

______

9. Many damaged houses have been rebuilt. But not all of them.

______

Take a close look at each of the sentences in your draft on page 49. Do they all express complete thoughts? Fix the ones that don't.

Mechanics Using Capitals

Some words begin with a **capital letter**.

- The first word in a sentence begins with a capital letter.
- A proper noun begins with a capital letter.

Example

Correct	Incorrect
The waves were huge.	the waves were huge.
They hit Indonesia.	They hit indonesia.

▶ **Find and correct five errors in this paragraph.**

Student Model

I helped my family when we had a car acident last year. First, we heard the screech of tires. Followed by the sound of a car hitting us. Luckily, our seat belts were on. Next I checked that Mom and maria were not hurt. then, I picked up the sell phone and called 911. I told the police what had happened. Finally, the police arrived. They said I had helped during the crisis, and I felt proud.

Check and Correct

- ❑ Circle two spelling errors and correct them.
- ❑ Underline two capitalization errors and correct them.
- ❑ Correct one sentence fragment.

Look at the sentences in your own draft on page 49. Do they all use capitals correctly? Fix the ones that don't.

Final Draft/Present

▶ **Write a final draft of your paragraph on paper or the computer. Check it again and correct any errors before you present it.**

Careers

Volunteer Coordinator

Desiree Adaway works for Habitat for Humanity International, an organization that builds homes for people in need. By 2008, HFH plans to have built or repaired 20,000 homes for victims of the 2004 tsunami. As director of HFH Youth Programs, Desiree organizes and supervises programs for youth volunteers. The teens and college students in her programs help build homes for homeless families in the United States and around the world.

Desiree helps out a volunteer at an HFH construction site.

Name: Desiree Adaway

Hometown: Americus, Georgia

Job: Director of Youth Programs

Duties:
- organizes and runs various HFH youth programs
- manages a staff of 20 people
- raises funds for new HFH programs

Skills:
- planning budgets
- writing grants
- strategic planning—thinking up new ways to engage youth volunteers

Pay: about $70,000 per year, depending on experience

Education: Bachelor's degree

Ask Yourself

1. **Underline** How much money does a volunteer coordinator make?
2. **Circle** Which duty do you think you'd be best at if you were a volunteer coordinator?
3. What would you like most about this job?

   ____

4. What would you dislike about this job?

   ____

Real-World Skills

Presenting a Budget

Part of Desiree Adaway's job is to present budgets that show how and where she'll spend the funds that she raises. Creating a pie chart is one way to present budget information. In 2005, Habitat for Humanity spent $14 million on tsunami recovery. The pie chart below shows how much of that money HFH allocated to each country where it rebuilt homes.

▶ **Fill in the circle next to each correct answer.**

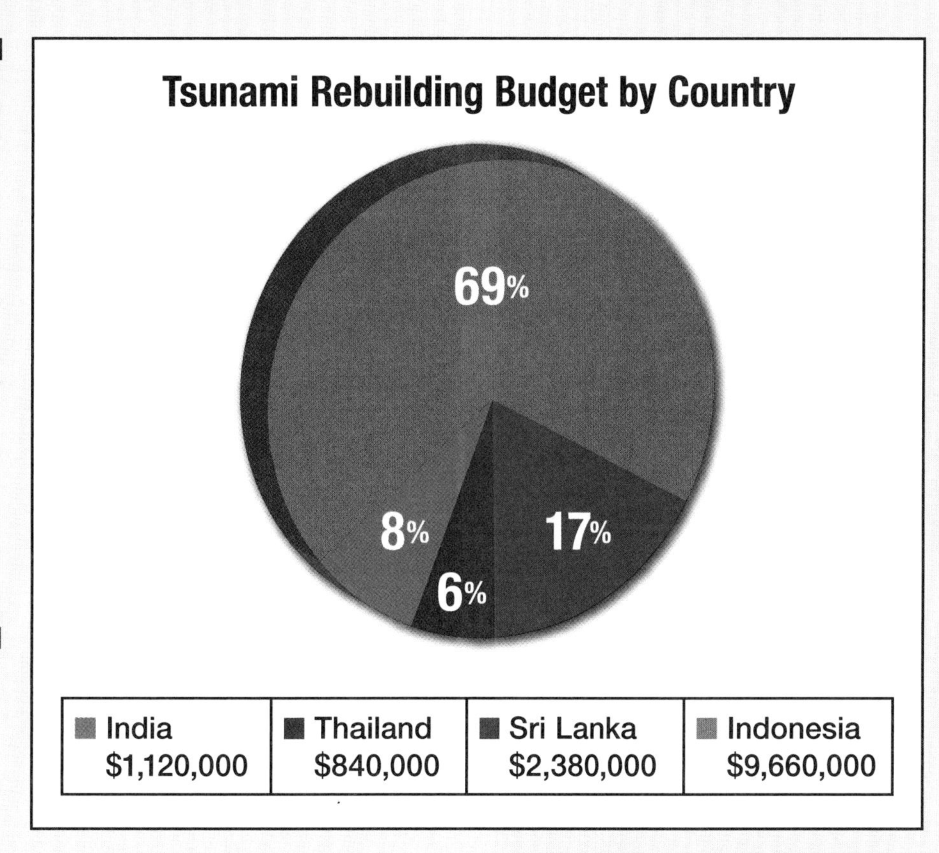

1. In which country did HFH spend the most money?
Ⓐ India
Ⓑ Indonesia
Ⓒ Sri Lanka
Ⓓ Thailand

2. Which country is represented by the color blue on the pie chart?
Ⓐ India
Ⓑ Indonesia
Ⓒ Sri Lanka
Ⓓ Thailand

3. In which country did HFH spend the least money?
Ⓐ India
Ⓑ Indonesia
Ⓒ Sri Lanka
Ⓓ Thailand

4. How much money did HFH spend in Sri Lanka compared to India?
Ⓐ about twice as much
Ⓑ about the same
Ⓒ about 4 times as much
Ⓓ about half as much

5. How much did HFH spend in Indonesia compared with the other 3 countries combined?
Ⓐ almost $4 million more
Ⓑ about $14 million more
Ⓒ more than $5 million more
Ⓓ about $3 million less

Comprehension

▶ **Fill in the circle next to the correct answer.**

1. The tsunami of 2004 began in ______________.

Ⓐ the Atlantic Ocean
Ⓑ Hawaii and Alaska
Ⓒ the Indian Ocean
Ⓓ South America

2. Where was Latha's family when the waves hit her village?

Ⓐ at the hospital
Ⓑ at the beach
Ⓒ at home
Ⓓ at the police station

Here's a tip.
For fill-in-the-blank questions, substitute each answer for the blank in the sentence. Then pick the best one.

3. Which of these events happened first?

Ⓐ Former presidents Bush and Clinton began raising money.
Ⓑ Volunteers built or repaired 4,000 homes.
Ⓒ Countries gave $4 billion.
Ⓓ News of the tsunami spread around the world.

4. Which event had not happened as of January 2006?

Ⓐ Habitat for Humanity begins rebuilding homes.
Ⓑ A tsunami warning system is complete.
Ⓒ Red Cross workers refocus their efforts.
Ⓓ Volunteers search for missing tsunami victims.

5. A tsunami is not likely to strike ______________.

Ⓐ on a mountain
Ⓑ near an ocean
Ⓒ in South Asia
Ⓓ in warm areas

Vocabulary

▶ **Fill in the circle next to the correct definition of the underlined word or words.**

1. The United States is in the Western Hemisphere.
   - Ⓐ area of the country
   - Ⓑ ocean zone
   - Ⓒ part of America
   - Ⓓ half of the earth

2. Building new homes was part of the process of recovering from the crisis.
   - Ⓐ big problem, part or stage
   - Ⓑ set of actions, big problem
   - Ⓒ big problem, set of actions
   - Ⓓ set of actions, half of the earth

3. A second tsunami would complicate the next phase of recovery!
   - Ⓐ correct, half of the earth
   - Ⓑ make more difficult, big problem
   - Ⓒ make more difficult, part or stage
   - Ⓓ set of actions, make more difficult

▶ **What does the prefix in the underlined word mean?**

4. If your first guess is inaccurate, you'll get another chance to guess right.
   - Ⓐ too
   - Ⓑ not
   - Ⓒ again
   - Ⓓ half

▶ **Which word below could you combine with the suffix *-ment* to form a real word? Fill in the circle next to the correct word.**

5. Ⓐ assist
   - Ⓑ process
   - Ⓒ invest
   - Ⓓ destroy

Short Answer

▶ **Use what you've read in this Workshop to answer the question below. Check your spelling and grammar.**

What do you think is the hardest part of recovering from the tsunami?

____

____

____

____

____

WORKSHOP 3

LITERATURE

Comprehension Focus
Story Elements

READINGS

1 ***Diamond Land*** >> Short Story

2 ***Nelson Mandela: In His Own Words*** >> Speech

LONG JOURNEY TO JUSTICE

It's the early 1990s in South Africa. A really unfair practice, apartheid, is a fact of life.

In the story "Diamond Land," Ayize's family has just lost most of their cattle, so Ayize wants to make money—fast. The diamond mines of South Africa are extremely dangerous. But that is where Ayize is headed.

When he gets to the mines, Ayize learns that the pink diamonds are worth most of all. Then he learns that the lives of black workers are the cheapest of all.

Will Ayize find his fortune? Or will he die trying?

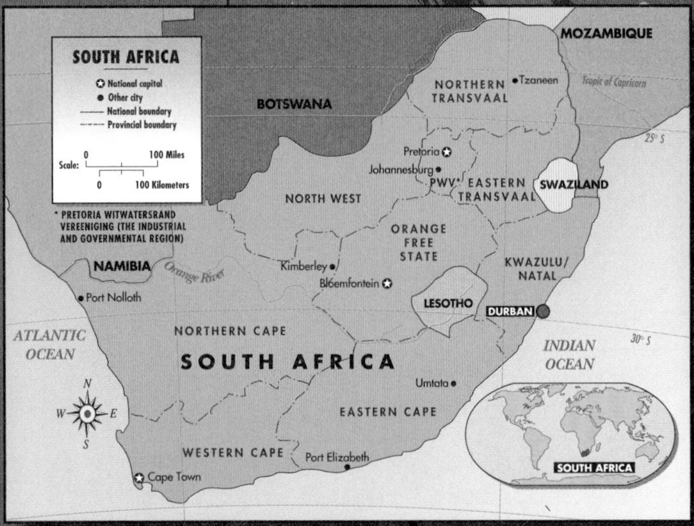

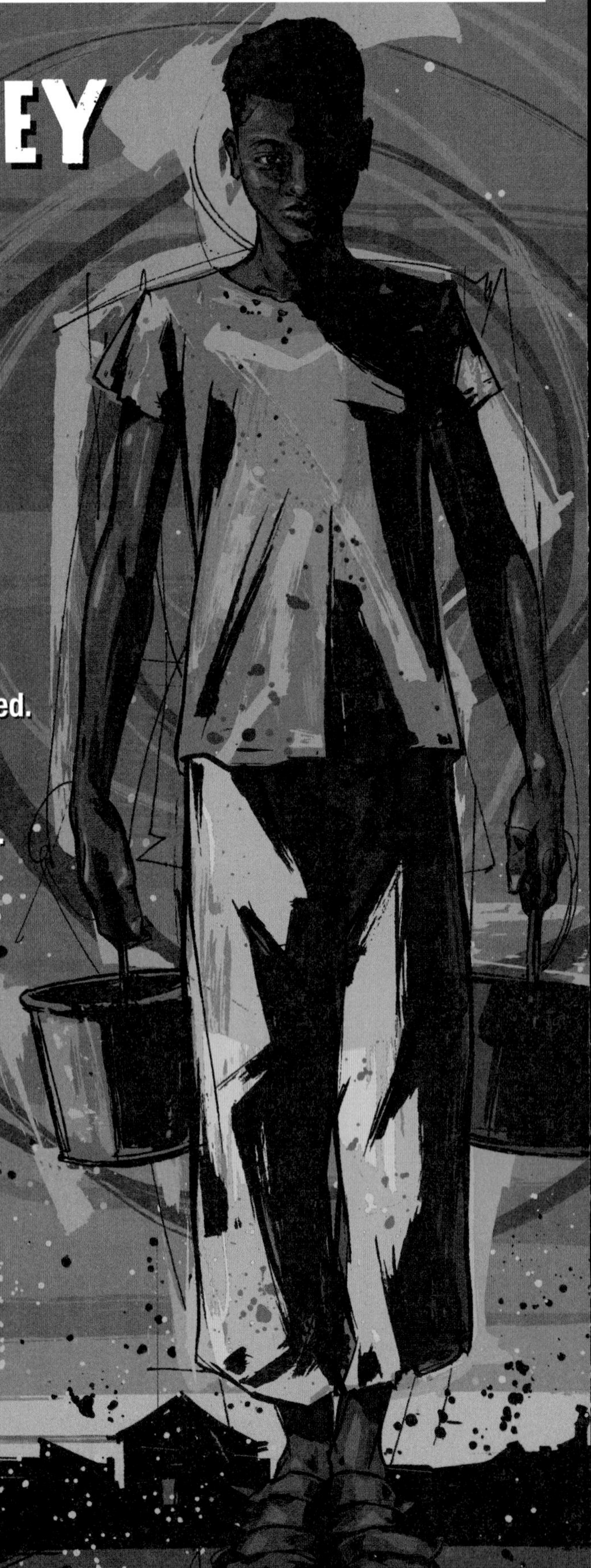

VOCABULARY BUILDER

Target Word ▶ Read the Target Words. Rate each one using the scale below.*	Meaning ▶ Read the Target Word meanings. Write in the missing ones.	Example ▶ Finish the Target Word examples below. Write in the missing ones.
access *ac•cess* *(noun)* ① ② ③		Graduating from high school will give me access to . . .
bias *bi•as* *(noun)* ① ② ③	prejudice	
conflict *con•flict* *(noun)* ① ② ③		When two people have a conflict, they should . . .
exploit *ex•ploit* *(verb)* ① ② ③	to treat someone unfairly in order to gain what you want	
rural *ru•ral* *(adjective)* ① ② ③		This house is located in a **rural** area.

***Rating Scale**

① = I don't know it at all.
② = I've seen it before.
③ = I know it and use it.

Comprehension Focus

Story Elements

A **short story** like "Diamond Land" is a brief piece of fiction. To understand a short story, look for four elements:

1. **Setting** is where and when the story takes place. This story takes place both in the rural homeland and the diamond mines of South Africa in the early 1990s.

2. **Characters** are the people in the story. There are several characters in this story.

Ayize,
a 16-year-old teen

Zindzi,
Ayize's future bride

Nkosi,
Ayize's friend at the mines

3. **Plot** is the sequence of events in a story. The plot contains a problem, or conflict, that the main character needs to solve. In "Diamond Land," Ayize needs to make money for his family, so he sets out for the diamond mines. The problem is that the mines promise not only money, but unfair treatment and danger, too.

4. **Theme** is the message about life that the author wants to express.

▶ **Turn the page to begin reading Ayize's story.**

Diamond Land

▶ Fill in this chart as you reread the story.

	Part 1 (pp. 60–63)	Part 2 (pp. 64–69)	Part 3 (pp. 70–73)
Setting	Time and Place: Afternoon; Ayize's family's pasture Time and Place:	Time and Place: Time and Place:	Time and Place: Time and Place:
Character	Who is the main character? Describe him/her:	How does the character change?	What is the character like now?
Plot Events	What happens at the beginning of the story?	What happens in the middle of the story?	How does the story end?
Theme	Author's message:		

Active Reading

Write What does the Dutch farmer's son find?

____

____

____

VOCABULARY BUILDER

Target Word

accumulate

ac•cu•mu•late (verb)

Rate it: ① ② ③

Meaning

____

____

____

Example

____

____

____

React

Was it good or bad for the Zulus that diamonds were discovered on their land? Explain your answer.

DIAMOND LAND

by Rita Williams-Garcia

Adapted from the novel *Diamond Land*

I stood on a large jagged rock and called out to my brothers. It was time to gather the cattle and bring them home. The Zulu sun would soon set over the hills.

My youngest brother, Joseph, climbed up on the rock. "Ayize," he called, "how big is our homeland?"

I told him, "As far as your eyes can see." I felt wise—like our father.

"As far as those trees?" he asked.

"Much farther," I said.

"As far as those hills?" He stretched his arm.

"Much, much farther," I said.

This game reminds us of the Zulu people. It reminds us that Zulu warriors were once powerful and that the Zulu had **accumulated** land that spread far and wide. Then, one day, a Dutch farmer's son found a huge stone on this land. The stone held light and all were amazed by its rare beauty. They called it a diamond.

Soon more Dutch, then the British, came in search of diamonds. The Zulus were mighty, but they could not win this conflict. In the end, the Zulus were pushed back into homelands much smaller than the land they once claimed.

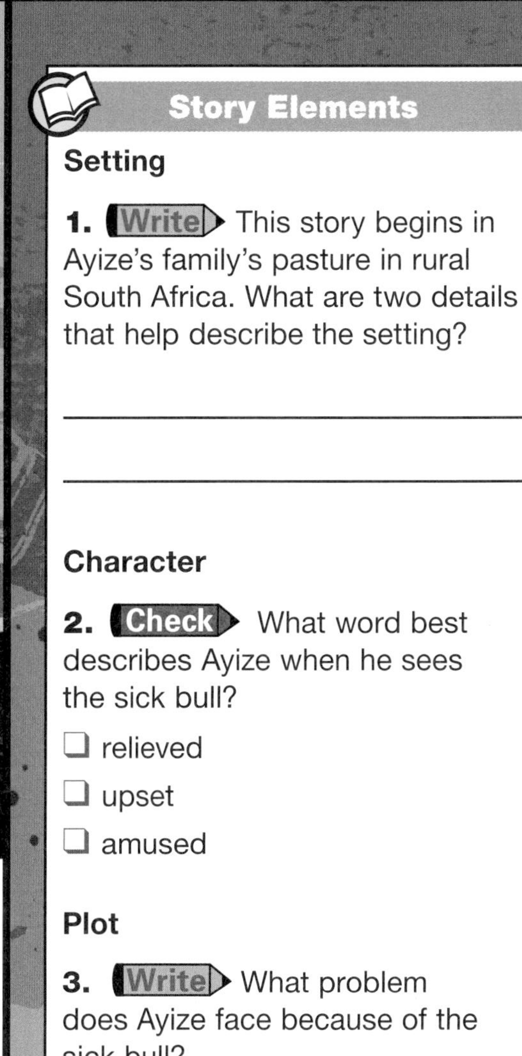

"Ayize! Ah-yee-zee! Come! Come!"

It was our brother Tuli, running up the hill.

"Tuli, what is it?" I asked.

Tuli was out of breath. "The red bull won't come!"

Tuli and I ran toward the river where the cattle drank. The red bull was down on his belly.

"No!" I said, and bent down to get a better look. The bull's eyes were thick with slime.

I pried open his mouth. His tongue was also black and full of slime.

"Tuli, get Father. Run home now!"

Within minutes my father came running with his rifle. "Stand away," he ordered.

I rose to my feet and stood next to my father.

The red bull moaned in agony. In two years he was to be given to my beloved Zindzi's family for *labola*. *Labola* means "bride price." It is a gift to the bride's family. ➜

Words to Know! **homeland** *(n.)* the country where you were born

Story Elements

Setting

1. **Write** This story begins in Ayize's family's pasture in rural South Africa. What are two details that help describe the setting?

____

____

Character

2. **Check** What word best describes Ayize when he sees the sick bull?

- ❑ relieved
- ❑ upset
- ❑ amused

Plot

3. **Write** What problem does Ayize face because of the sick bull?

____

____

____

____

____

____

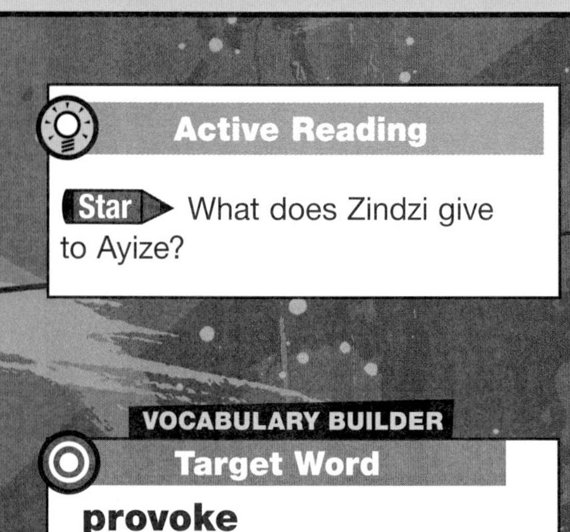

Active Reading

Star What does Zindzi give to Ayize?

VOCABULARY BUILDER

Target Word

provoke

pro•voke (verb)

Rate it: ① ② ③

Meaning

____

____

____

Example

____

____

____

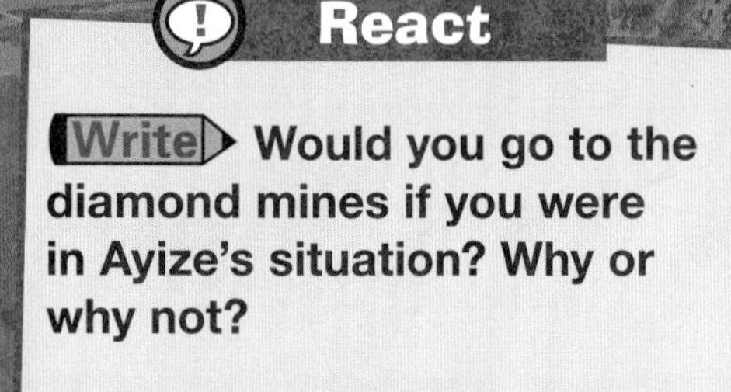

React

Write **Would you go to the diamond mines if you were in Ayize's situation? Why or why not?**

____

____

____

____

____

My father aimed the rifle and fired two shots. The other cows panicked and began to scatter. "We have to check the rest of the herd," my father told me.

One by one, we forced open their mouths to see their tongues. Then, carefully, we lifted their hooves.

My father waited until my brothers had gone, then he raised his rifle and shot the seven cows that were diseased.

Cows are valuable to our family, as valuable as money. What would we do with only two cows? How would we feed our family, or pay the bride price to Zindzi's family?

I thought Father shot our cows too quickly, but it was my fault. Shame stabbed me. Had I watched after the cows better, I might have seen their sickness earlier.

"Father," I said, "I'll replace the herd."

We walked in silence before he asked, "And how will you do this?"

I said, "I'll leave home for a time and work in the diamond mines."

My father said nothing more. This meant he agreed.

News spread quickly of my plans to work in the diamond mines. Neighbors came to give advice and to say good-bye. In the distance I saw Zindzi and her brothers. I greeted Zindzi's brothers first.

Her brothers warned me about the diamond mines. Many had gone to work in the mines, they said, and they returned sick or didn't return at all.

"I'll be all right," I told them. "I'm resolved to go." Then they gave Zindzi and me a moment to say our good-byes.

Zindzi was unlike any girl I knew. She was clever and beautiful. I only finished my one-to-seven schooling so I could see her in class each day.

"Don't worry, Zindzi. I'll earn the bride price soon," I told her.

Zindzi took a string of white beads from her belt. I was glad to see their white coloring. Her white beads said, "My thoughts stay with you."

Words to Know!	**rand** *(n.)* a unit of money in South Africa

“Go to the school before you set out for the mines,” my father advised. “You must learn more before you leave the homeland.” Then he gave me two hundred *rand.*

I slipped my knife in my belt and put the money in my pants pocket. I took the sack of food and drink that my mother gave me and left the hut.

The school wasn’t far. It was there that I had learned to read and speak English and Afrikaans.

Father Thomas, the priest, waved to me. He was once my teacher.

“To what do I owe this visit?”

“Father Thomas, I’ve come for advice. I have to find work in the diamond mines,” I told him.

The look of pleasure in his face fell flat, and was replaced by concern and disappointment.

“My son, many go in search of glittering diamonds, but they don’t find them. Instead, they lose their way home.”

“I don’t care for diamonds,” I said. “I care only for the money I can earn for cattle. I can earn a fortune.”

Again, Father Thomas shook his head. “My son, you will see. Blacks don’t gain wealth in the diamond mines.”

“Apartheid is almost over,” the priest went on. “But this land stays separated by biases between blacks and whites. Some diamond camps are better than others, but none are good,” Father Thomas emphasized. “There are squatter camps along the coast and rivers,” he explained. “They don’t follow laws. They use small children to do the dangerous work. Mines in Durban are better than squatter camps. But you’ll see that these mines are also dangerous. Remember, everything is black and white.”

I walked from the rural grassland into the woodland. Zulu soil was rich from rain and sun. Wild fig trees were everywhere, and I ate figs as I walked.

Then I heard a noise—a low growl. I worried that if I turned suddenly, I might **provoke** a wild beast. Slowly, I grabbed my knife handle.

But the growl turned out to be a rumbling truck. I felt foolish, but breathed easier.

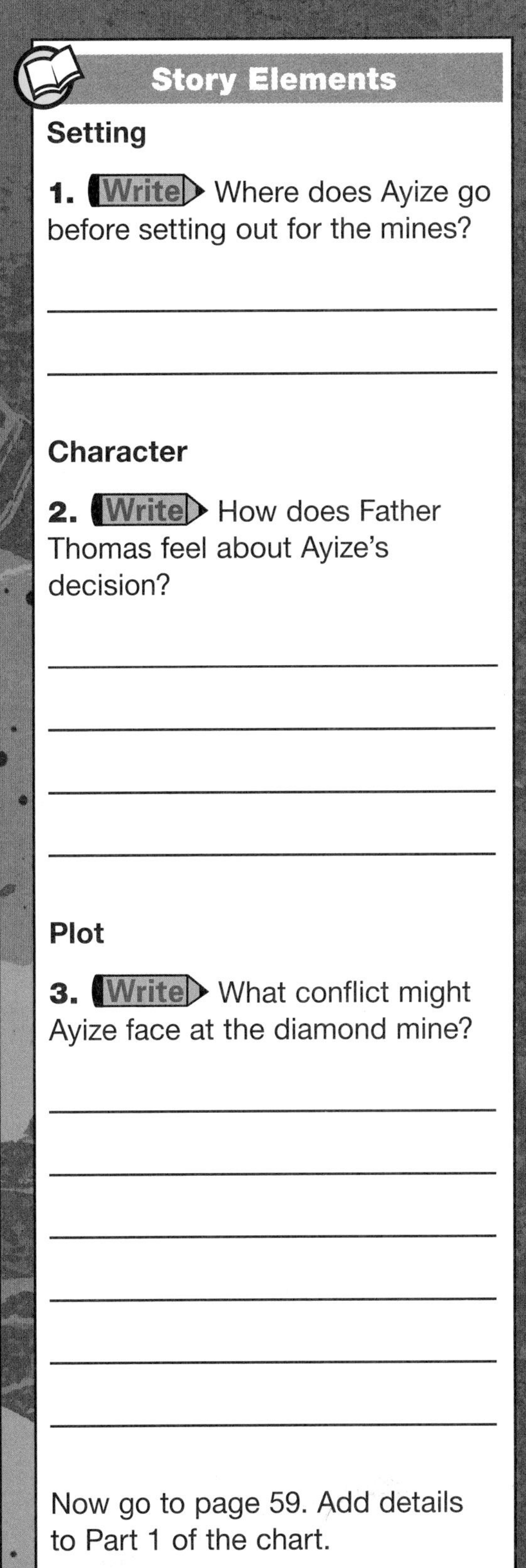

Story Elements

Setting

1. Write Where does Ayize go before setting out for the mines?

____

____

Character

2. Write How does Father Thomas feel about Ayize’s decision?

____

____

____

____

Plot

3. Write What conflict might Ayize face at the diamond mine?

____

____

____

____

____

____

Now go to page 59. Add details to Part 1 of the chart.

Active Reading

Write Who gives Ayize a ride to Shantytown?

______

______

______

VOCABULARY BUILDER

Target Word

detect

de•tect (verb)

Rate it: ① ② ③

Meaning

______

______

______

Example

______

______

______

React

Write **Do you think the children are being exploited? Explain your answer.**

______

______

______

______

The truck stopped near me, and a white man stuck his head out the window. "Where are you headed?"

I said, "I'm going to Durban."

"Hop in," he said.

The sign on the side of the truck said "Fritz the Furniture Maker."

"To Durban, you're going?" the large man asked.

"I'm going to work in the diamond mines," I said.

He whistled hot air.

"You look old enough," he said, "but it's very risky in the mines."

We drove along in his truck. As we climbed a steep hill, Fritz stopped the truck.

"Lad," he said, "look down there."

There seemed to be a camp down at the shore. Soldiers with rifles guarded holes by the beach. I saw children much younger than I digging by the rocks. As I stared at a hole, a boy rose out of it! A tube was attached to his mouth, and a rope was tied around his neck. He emptied his bucket into a larger bucket, gulped some air, and dove back into the hole. A little girl sprang up from another hole!

A soldier looked up at the road and **detected** us. He pointed his rifle in our direction.

Fritz grabbed the gears on the truck and pumped the gas with his large foot. The truck lurched forward. Fritz let out a laugh as we followed the bumpy dirt road.

"Those were squatters, lad, diving and digging for diamonds. Do you care to join up with them?"

We drove for many hours. Before sunset, we came to a place that Fritz called Shantytown. He stopped the truck and turned to me.

"This is where you want to be," he said.

In the distance, Shantytown shimmered the way I imagined diamonds would shimmer. As I drew near, I saw things more clearly. The shacks were made of wood with sheet metal for roofs. They sat side by side and on top of each other.

Words to Know! **lurched** *(v.)* moved in an unsteady way

Nearby, a group of people gathered at a fire, grilling meat. At least this smelled good and familiar to me. As I walked toward the fire a boy greeted me. He looked Zulu and seemed closer to my brother Coka's age—14 or 15. He wore a blue cap on his head. The white letters N and Y were sewn on his cap.

"You're new here," the boy said.

I nodded.

"I'm Nkosi," he said with pride. Nkosi means "ruler." Almost every Zulu home has a son who is named Nkosi.

"I'm Ayize," I said. "I came here from my rural homeland. I'm looking for work in the diamond mines."

"Are you alone?" he asked.

I hesitated, but answered, "Yes." After all, he was younger than I was.

"I need a roommate to share costs," Nkosi said. "I lost my roommate suddenly. That happens around here," he said. "I'll charge you only one hundred *rand*."

I wasn't eager to part with my money, but I needed shelter.

→

Story Elements

Setting

1. Circle ▶ How are the shacks at Shantytown described?

Character

2. Underline ▶ How does Nkosi feel about his name?

Plot

3. Write ▶ What important events happen in this part of the story?

____

____

____

____

Review: Sequence of Events

Write ▶ What happens after Ayize arrives at Shantytown?

____

____

____

____

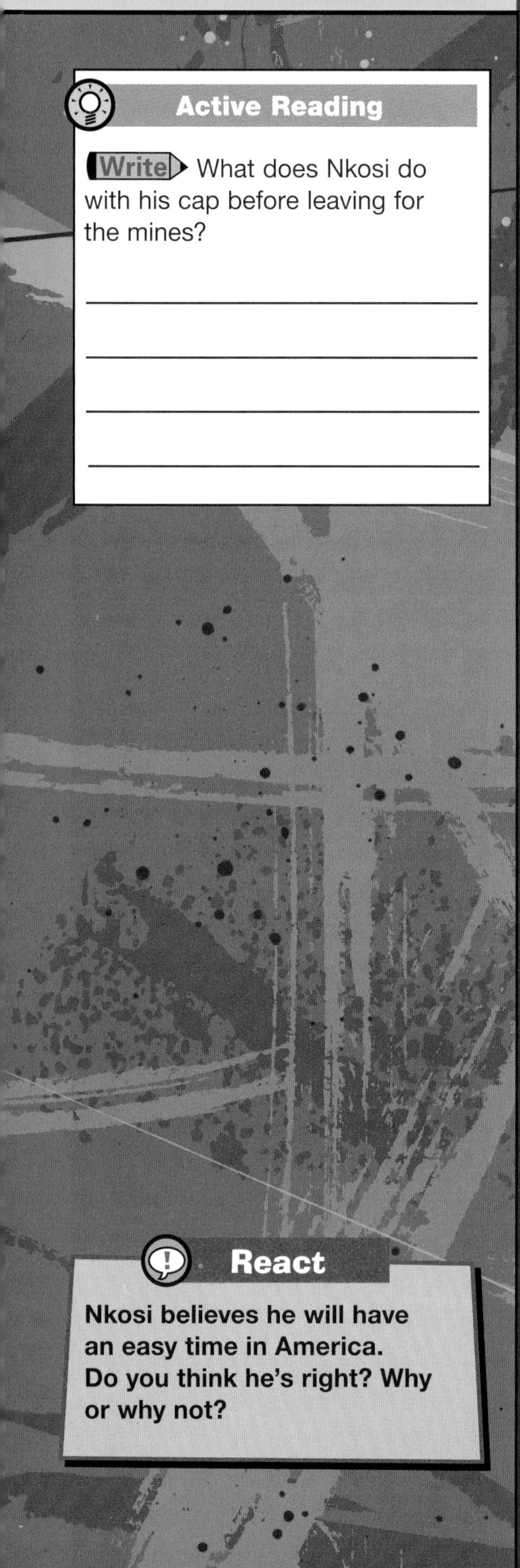

Active Reading

Write What does Nkosi do with his cap before leaving for the mines?

React

Nkosi believes he will have an easy time in America. Do you think he's right? Why or why not?

"Let me see the hut."

We walked to a small shack with a tin roof. Nkosi took a key from around his neck and unlocked the padlock. There was a blanket for his bed and two bricks for a table.

"Not bad," he said.

"Fifty *rand*," I said. We agreed on the fifty *rand*.

We returned to the barbecue and ate the rough chicken. I shared the drink my mother packed. While we ate, Nkosi caught me staring at his cap.

"It fell off of the white miners' truck one morning," he said. "Once I put it on my head, the white miner didn't want it." Nkosi laughed.

"What is this NY?" I asked.

A look of disbelief came over him. "You have not heard of the New York Yankees, America's best baseball team? I'm saving my money to go to America," Nkosi said.

I made a disbelieving sound. This boy was a dreamer.

Nkosi pointed to my beads. "A girl waits for you?"

I grunted.

"No one waits for me," he said. "No family, no bride. I'm free!"

"You're alone," I told him.

"No, my brother. I'm free to go where I choose." He tugged his NY cap. "When I make my fortune, I'll go to America. America has the best singers and rappers."

Then, Nkosi jumped to his feet. He pointed his hands as if they were guns and began shooting and chanting.

He looked funny. I laughed.

"Nkosi, what is that chanting?"

Nkosi was insulted. "I wasn't chanting. I was rapping. You know, the richest people in America are the blacks."

Even I didn't believe that.

"It's true," Nkosi said. "They play baseball and basketball. They sing and rap. Rappers and movie stars wear diamonds, Ayize—our diamonds."

This was too crazy to imagine.

"Do they own cows and land?" I asked.

Nkosi waved his hand at me. To him I was hopeless. He said we should sleep now because we had a long day of work in the mines ahead of us.

Before the sun rose, I felt a rumbling in the ground beneath me. Nkosi kicked me lightly with his foot and said, "Get up."

He removed his beloved cap from his head. He kissed it, then rolled it up in his blanket.

I followed him to the gravel road. Soon we were joined by a hundred black men and a few boys. As we walked down the road, trucks rushed by us, carrying white men.

We walked for almost five kilometers, until we found two trucks with long flat beds waiting for us.

"Run!" Nkosi shouted.

Without warning, the crowd ran, pushing and shoving. Everyone fought hard to find room on the trucks. We rode crushed together, with some men standing on the outside hanging onto the rails.

When we arrived at the camp, the whites had already begun to work. They had access to the good jobs. They drove the tractors and ran the heavy machines.

Nkosi and I stood on a long line with black workers. Each worker said his name and each time the boss made a mark in a book.

When it was my turn to speak, Nkosi cut in. "This is my brother, boss."

The white man looked at me with narrow eyes, then he glanced at Nkosi. Finally, he gave me a number.

"Don't bring anything into the camp—no food, no tools, nothing. If you want to buy food or drink, we take it from your pay. You leave how you come—with nothing."

Nkosi and I moved to another long line of black workers. We had to be searched before going into the work area.

I entered the mine and expected to see a diamond land, a place as bright and dazzling as the Zulu sun. Instead, there was a giant pit.

The black workers gathered in one area. The white workers set everything up first, Nkosi said. They blasted the dynamite to make tunnels. Many of these tunnels are too narrow for men. →

Words to Know! **beloved** *(adj.)* loved very much

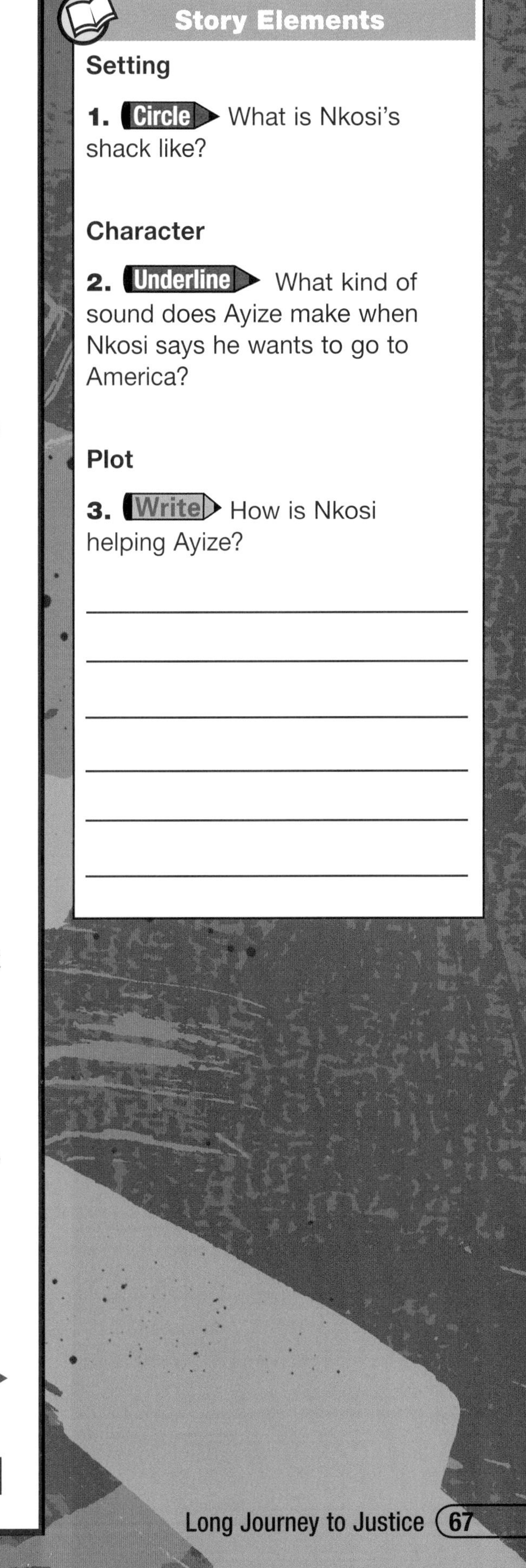

Story Elements

Setting

1. **Circle** What is Nkosi's shack like?

Character

2. **Underline** What kind of sound does Ayize make when Nkosi says he wants to go to America?

Plot

3. **Write** How is Nkosi helping Ayize?

____

____

____

____

____

____

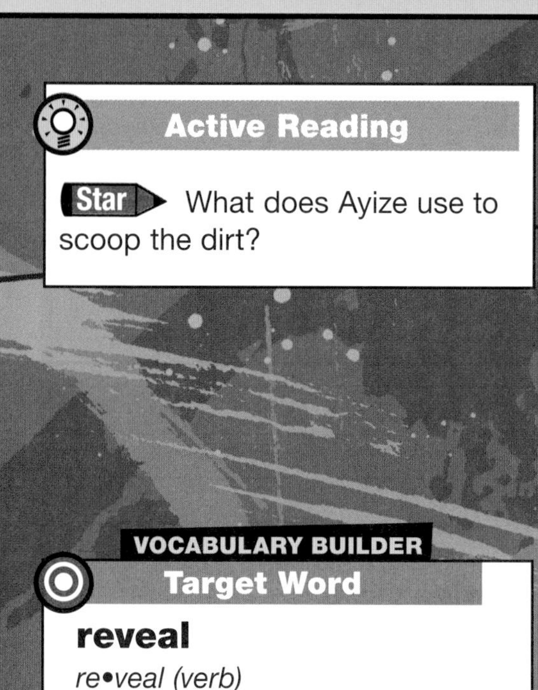

Active Reading

Star What does Ayize use to scoop the dirt?

VOCABULARY BUILDER

Target Word

reveal

re•veal (verb)

Rate it: ① ② ③

Meaning

____

____

____

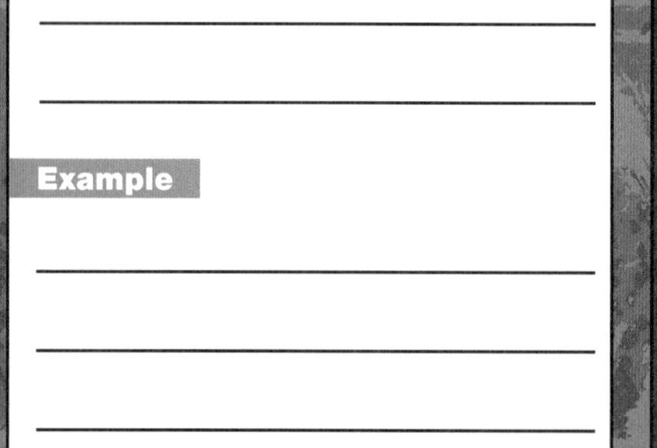

Example

____

____

____

React

Nkosi is being secretive. If you were Ayize, would you question Nkosi more? Why or why not?

"That's why they need children," Nkosi said. "They're small enough to fit in the tightest spaces. The black men come in last to do the hard labor."

I watched the workers with the powerful drills. Nkosi said they were searching for pipe, which is a kind of rock formation. "Some pipe is rich with diamonds, some have no diamonds at all," he told me.

Suddenly, the booming from the dynamite blasts stopped, and a loud whistle sounded. The children were led into the tunnels, and black men scurried down into the pit.

"Stick with me," Nkosi said. "We'll dig at the pink flag. The engineers detected pipe there. This rock is filled with diamonds—pink diamonds. The pink stones are rare. Diamond agents will pay top price for pink," he explained.

I followed Nkosi to the pink flag and did what he did. I scooped the dirt with my hands. Bend and scoop, bend and scoop. I kept up with this process until my cart was loaded. Then I pushed the cart along the tracks to another flag, where it was emptied into another bin. Then I came back and dug some more.

I opened the door of our shack. Nkosi sat under the lamp sewing his NY baseball cap. I startled him. When he jumped up, he looked like he was ready to fight me.

"You should knock first," he said.

"For fifty *rand*, I can just come in," I answered.

I put food on the brick table. Nkosi was glad to see the potatoes. We attacked the food that was still hot.

"What were you doing?" I asked, pointing to the cap.

"Just making some repairs," Nkosi said.

"Why?" I asked. The hat seemed almost new. It didn't look like it needed repairs.

"Stop asking so many questions!" he snapped at me. A drop of blood trickled down Nkosi's chin.

"Your mouth is bleeding," I said.

Nkosi kept eating his potatoes. "It's nothing. I cut my tongue."

"Cut your tongue? How?"

He said, "Stop worrying, little brother. One day I'll **reveal** to you how I cut my tongue, but not today."

Two weeks passed that I worked in the mines. I didn't get used to the smell, and my body ached from the hard work. Still, I remembered the children who fought to climb on the work truck. They dug rock until their fingers bled. They were exploited but they didn't complain. How could I?

"Who wants to earn one thousand *rand*?" the boss asked.

The boss's words set off a frenzy. All of the black workers leaped to their feet.

"Boss, Boss, pick me!" we shouted. We jumped and waved to be chosen.

Story Elements

Setting

1. Write Where does Nkosi lead Ayize to dig for diamonds?

____

____

Character

2. Underline Find one suspicious thing that Nkosi does.

Plot

3. Write What happens at the mines two weeks after Ayize starts working there?

____

____

____

____

____

____

Now go to page 59. Add details to Part 2 of the chart.

Active Reading

Star ▶ What sound does Ayize hear coming from the hole?

In spite of my jumping, the boss looked past me. He picked four workers, and Nkosi was one of them.

Nkosi beamed. "America, here I come."

The work whistle sounded. I climbed down into the pit.

A new hole had been dug near the center of the pit. I could see the four lucky blacks following the boss to the new hole. A rope was tied around each of them. Then, one by one, they vanished into the hole.

Suddenly I heard a terrible sound. "Aaaaiiiy!"

I jumped. It was a scream coming up from the hole. It was loud at first, then it faded away quickly. Both white and black workers gathered around the hole.

I tried to look and work at the same time. I counted three of the lucky workers coming out of the hole. Nkosi wasn't among them. My heart pounded as I ran to the hole.

"My brother! My brother!"

The boss said, "It was an accident. The rope broke."

"We have to get him!" I yelled.

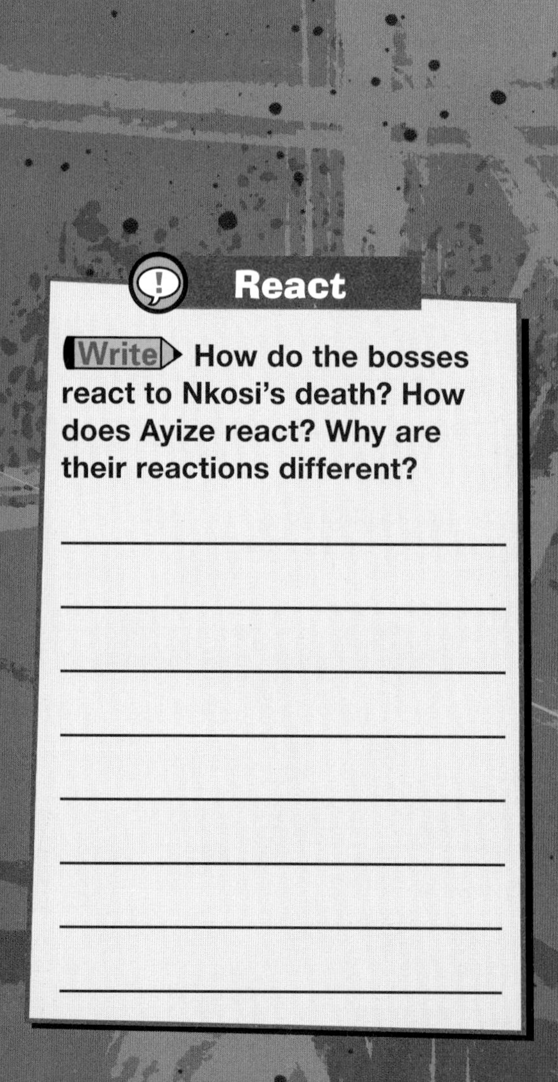

React

Write ▶ How do the bosses react to Nkosi's death? How does Ayize react? Why are their reactions different?

"He's gone," the boss said. "No one could survive that fall. He's gone."

How could Nkosi be gone, just like that?

"Get back to work, you!" The boss shoved me back toward my cart. I wanted to scream, but I held my tongue. I walked back to my cart, bent down, and started to dig.

Zulus don't cry or reveal their fear, I used to tell Joseph. Still, I cried on the long walk back to Shantytown. I wouldn't ride on the work truck with the others. I'd never ride the work truck or work in the mines again.

Let them keep their five hundred *rand*. Black life in the mines is no life at all. No one even tried to find Nkosi's body.

That night I fell down on Nkosi's blanket and slept until the sun rose. I had worked hard in the mines. And now I wouldn't get paid. But I didn't care—I wasn't going back.

I gathered the sack with my belongings and tied Zindzi's beads around my neck. I'd leave the shack as I had first entered it.

Yet I couldn't leave Nkosi's cap behind. His body was lying somewhere deep in that hole. This was the only true part of him that was left. I put the NY cap on my head and left Shantytown behind me.

I could still find work in a factory. I couldn't return home with less *rand* than I was given by my father. I headed for downtown Durban.

As I walked, Nkosi's cap bothered my head. Why did he love this cap so? I didn't understand. It scratched and jabbed. I took the cap off and looked inside. A band had been sewn around the edges. These were not machine stitches. They had been sewn by Nkosi. I felt hard lumps inside the band.

I stood still for a long time while my mind raced. Everything became as clear as diamonds. I would no longer search for a factory. Instead, I would look for a diamond agent.

→

Words to Know!	**agent** *(n.)* someone who arranges things for other people

Story Elements

Setting

1. Circle ▶ Where does Nkosi die?

Character

2. Write ▶ Why does Ayize decide to leave the diamond mines?

____

____

____

Plot

3. Write ▶ What does Ayize detect in Nkosi's baseball cap?

____

____

____

Review: Problem and Solution

1. Write ▶ What problem keeps Ayize from returning home?

____

____

____

2. Write ▶ How does Nkosi's hat solve this problem?

____

____

____

Active Reading

  Star How much *rand* does the agent give Ayize for the pink diamonds?

VOCABULARY BUILDER

Target Word

ingenious

in•ge•nious (adjective)

Rate it: ① ② ③

Meaning

___

___

___

Example

___

___

___

React

Write **Nkosi stole pink diamonds from the mines. Do you think he was right or wrong to do that? Why?**

___

___

___

___

___

___

In downtown Durban, I had to be careful. I didn't want to be stopped for any reason. The police would be biased against me. After a lot of walking, I found an agent.

I said in Afrikaans, "I've something to sell."

"Let me see," he said.

I removed Nkosi's cap. I undid Nkosi's stitches slowly and pushed the stones along the band. Out of the small opening they fell.

They were pink stones with some traces of blood—Nkosi's blood. He had found the pink stones the engineers couldn't find. He had been hiding them in his mouth, smuggling them out of the camp. His plan was **ingenious**.

The diamond agent looked at me. He put the pink stones on a scale and looked at me hard.

"Steal these stones, did you?"

"No," I said. Nkosi couldn't answer the same, but I could.

He looked at the stones and said, "Eight thousand *rand*."

"Only eight thousand *rand* for the pink stones?" Didn't Nkosi say the pink stones were rare?

The diamond agent called another man over. The other man looked at the stones. He went to a room in the back and returned with cash.

"Fifteen thousand *rand*," he said.

Quickly, I took the money and left with haste. The diamond agent could still call the police. My heart pounded as I walked.

I kept the faces of Zindzi, my family, and Nkosi with me. They would guide me to the homeland.

Epilogue

Even with enough *rand* to buy cows, Zindzi and I waited to marry. I had much to learn from my father about being a man and a rancher. Ten years later, I accomplished my goal. I had my own *kraal*, filled with cattle.

Often I remember Nkosi and his dream to see America. It saddens me that he didn't live to see the growing changes in South Africa. Shortly after Nkosi's death, apartheid ended.

South Africans elected our first black president, Nelson Mandela. As president, Nelson Mandela rewrote many of the old laws that had exploited people.

The diamond and gold mines have changed, but not enough. Fewer mines employ children, but some still do. More companies follow safety laws. Yet, the mines remain dangerous, and traces of apartheid remain between black and white miners. As long as the world craves diamonds, these ugly holes will be dug in our land.

While I tend cattle, my thoughts jab me. I ask myself the same questions. Do people know the cost of the diamonds that they wear? Can they see the blood on the stones? END

Words to Know!	**epilogue** *(n.)* a speech or piece of writing added to the end of a play, story, or poem

Story Elements

Setting

1. Circle ▶ Where does Ayize go after selling the diamonds?

Character

2. Underline ▶ What questions does Ayize ask himself while he's tending his cattle?

Theme

3. Check ▶ Which do you think is the author's main message?

- ❑ All people deserve justice and respect.
- ❑ Dignity is more important than money.
- ❑ Hard work is always rewarded.
- ❑ Never trust a stranger.

Now go to page 59. Complete Part 3 of the chart and the theme.

Skills Check

1. Write ▶ What does Ayize do with Nkosi's diamonds?

____

____

2. Write ▶ What changes come to South Africa soon after Nkosi's death?

____

____

Active Reading

Write ▸ On what occasion did Mandela give this speech?

Nelson Mandela is known for his moving and inspiring speeches.

NELSON MANDELA
In His Own Words

In 1994, Nelson Mandela was elected the first black president in South Africa's history. His job was difficult—to unite a country that had been torn apart by apartheid for over forty years. More than a billion people around the world watched on television as Mandela delivered his inaugural speech.

React

Write ▸ **What sentence or passage from this speech is the most inspirational to you? Underline it. Then explain why it inspires you.**

Inaugural Speech as President of South Africa, Pretoria, May 10, 1994

Your Royal Highnesses, Distinguished Guests, Comrades, and Friends.

Today, all of us do, by our presence here, and by our celebrations in other parts of our country and the world, confer glory and hope to newborn liberty.

Out of the experience of an extraordinary human disaster that lasted too long, must be born a society of which all humanity will be proud.

Our daily deeds as ordinary South Africans must produce an actual South African reality that will reinforce humanity's belief in justice, strengthen its confidence in the nobility of the human soul, and sustain all our hopes for a glorious life for all.

All this we owe both to ourselves and to the peoples of the world who are so well represented here today. . . .

We dedicate this day to all the heroes and heroines in this country and the rest of the world who sacrificed in many ways and surrendered their lives so that we could be free.

Their dreams have become reality. Freedom is their reward. . . .

We understand it still that there is no easy road to freedom.

We know it well that none of us acting alone can achieve success.

We must therefore act together as a united people, for national reconciliation, for nation building, for the birth of a new world.

Let there be justice for all.

Let there be peace for all.

Let there be work, bread, water, and salt for all.

Let each know that for each the body, the mind, and the soul have been freed to fulfill themselves.

Never, never, and never again shall it be that this beautiful land will again experience the oppression of one by another. . . .

The sun shall never set on so glorious a human achievement!

Let freedom reign.

God bless Africa!

I thank you. END

Literary Elements: Repetition

Repetition is words, phrases, or sentences that are used over and over again. Repetition is one of the most powerful elements in speeches.

Underline Find the phrases in Mandela's speech that repeat.

Literary Elements: Theme

Theme is the message about life that the author wants to express.

Write How does this speech remind you of the themes of justice and equality in the story "Diamond Land"?

____

____

____

____

____

____

____

TAKE THE WORD CHALLENGE

Start

1 Describe.

Describe. Describe a conflict each of these pairs of people could have.

____
parent and teenager

____
boss and new employee

____
brother and sister

____
two best friends

2 Rank them.

Rank them. Which of these would you most want to get access to? Come up with a choice of your own.

1 = want it the most

4 = want it the least

_____ the backstage of a big concert

_____ a pro locker room

_____ a movie set

_____ other: ______________

____

3 Verb Endings

A **verb ending** can be added to a verb to show when an action takes place. To show that an action happened in the past, you can often add *-ed*. To show that an action happens in the present, you can often add *-ing*. If a verb ends with an *e*, it is usually dropped before adding *-ed* or *-ing*.

I often *walk* my dog.

Yesterday I *walked* my dog.

Right now, I am *walking* my dog.

Yesterday I **played** basketball, but today I am **playing** soccer.

Add the verb. Use the correct verb ending.

1. At practice yesterday, our coach __________ his secret strategy. (reveal)
2. Sometimes, I can __________ a hint of a smile on his face. (detect)
3. Because of her job, she is __________ money to buy a car. (accumulate)

4 Check two.

Check two. Which two statements below reveal a bias?

- ❑ "She's too pretty to be nice."
- ❑ "He's rich so I know that he never has problems."
- ❑ "She reminds me of someone I know."

5 Write.

Write. Choose the correct word to fill in each blank.

Rural areas typically have few __________ (buildings/trees).

In a typical rural area, people might have __________ (apartments/farms).

Towns in rural areas tend to be __________ (noisy/quiet).

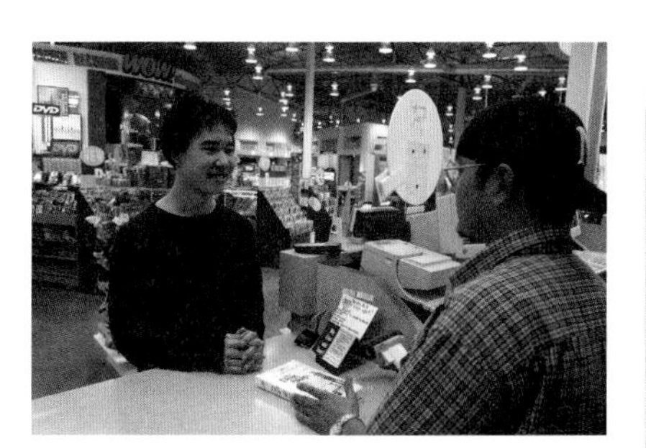

6

Fill in. Complete the sentences with ingenious and accumulate.

Matt has an ___________ plan to ___________ CDs. He will get a job in a music store and use his discount to buy music. Yes, his plan to ___________ CDs is ___________.

7

Decide. Which of these would provoke you to anger?

VA = very angry
SA = sort of angry
NA = not angry

_____ finding out that a friend gossiped about you

_____ having someone insult a family member

_____ seeing a dog mistreated

_____ being called a bad name

_____ a rainy afternoon

What is one other thing that really provokes you?

____

____

8 Word Families

A **word family** is a group of words that share the same base word and have related meanings, such as *create* and *creation*. To *create* is to make something. A *creation* is what someone has made.

Which sentences use words that come from the same word family as *detect*?

- ❑ It's important for every house to have a smoke detector.
- ❑ I had to return the jeans because they had a defect.
- ❑ The detective wasn't sure he could solve the case, but he would try.

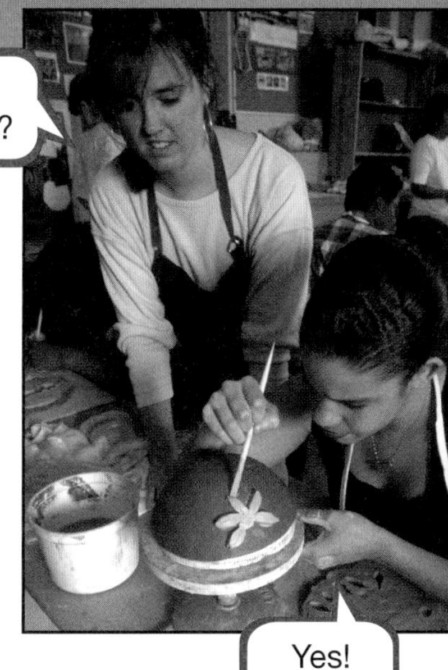

9

Check. You're trying to learn more about someone. Choose the two things that would reveal the most about a person.

- ❑ their journal
- ❑ their room
- ❑ their clothes
- ❑ their conversations with their best friend

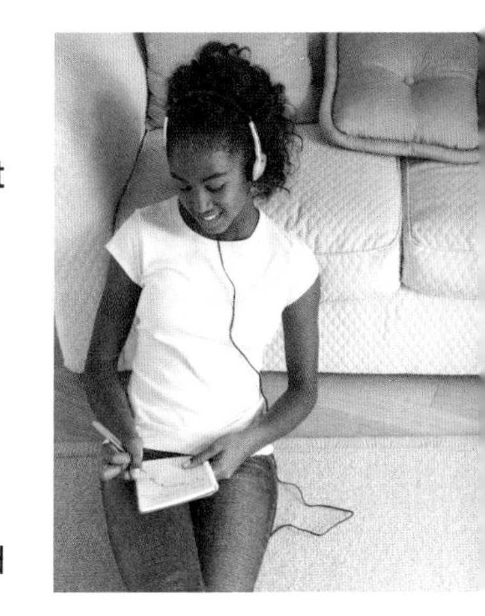

10

Think. Read the sentence. Then answer the questions.

Nadia was paid $30 for an eight-hour babysitting job.

Do you think she was exploited or treated fairly?

❑ exploited ❑ treated fairly

Explain why you think Nadia was exploited or treated fairly.

____

____

Finish

Writing Focus

Literature Response

In a **literature response**, a reader relates a piece of literature to his or her life.

▶ **Read Simone's literature response to "Diamond Land."**

Student Model

A Literature Response to "Diamond Land"

by Simone Clarke

Like Ayize, I have been treated unfairly. It all started when I was leaving a store and the security alarm went off. After that, two security guards took me to a room and started yelling at me. One even said she might arrest me. I tried to explain that I didn't steal anything, but they wouldn't listen. In the end, I gave them access to my bags. They searched them and let me go. They said they have a lot of conflicts with teens. Neither of the guards apologized for wrongly accusing me. Overall, I felt they weren't fair. People shouldn't have biases against teenagers.

Parts of a Literature Response

▶ **Find these parts of Simone's literature response.**

1. Underline the sentence that **relates the writer's experience** to Ayize.
2. Check three important **details** that describe the experience.
3. Number these details in the **time order** they happened.
4. Circle the **linking words** that connect the details.
5. Put a star before the sentence that **sums up** the writer's ideas and feelings.

Brainstorm

▶ Read the writing prompt at the top of the idea web. Then use the boxes to help you brainstorm your ideas.

Writing Prompt:

Tell about a time when you were treated unfairly, like Ayize.

At School

In Your Neighborhood

At Home

With Friends

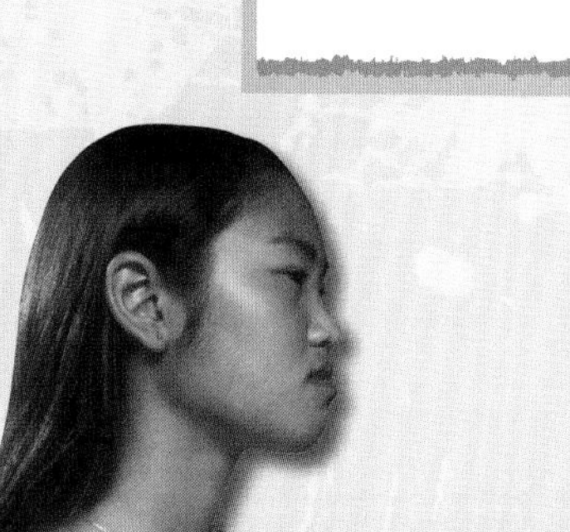

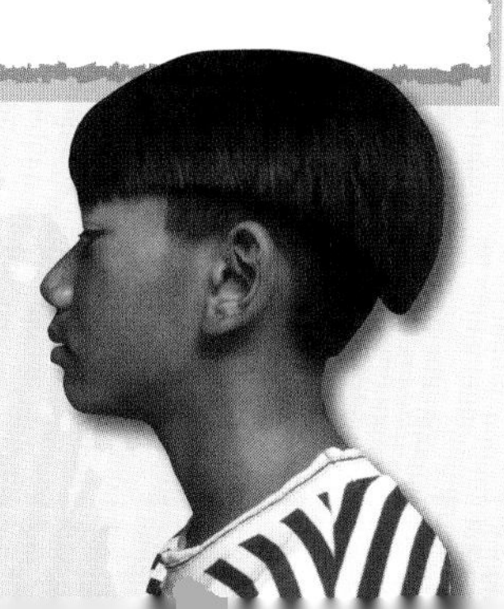

Plan Your Paragraph

Writing Prompt: Tell about a time when you were treated unfairly, like Ayize.

▶ **Use this chart to plan and organize your paragraph.**

Word Choices

____

____

____

____

____

Introduce the Topic
- *Like Ayize, I . . .*
- *A time when . . .*
- *There was a time when . . .*

Detail 1
- *It all started when . . .*
- *First, . . .*
- *First of all, . . .*

Detail 2
- *After that, . . .*
- *When . . .*
- *Next, . . .*

Detail 3
- *In the end, . . .*
- *Finally, . . .*
- *It got better after . . .*

Conclusion
- *Overall, I felt . . .*
- *That's why . . .*
- *I felt like . . .*

Write Your Paragraph

▶ **Use this writing frame to write a first draft of your paragraph.**

____
(title)

Like Ayize, I ______________________________________

It all started when ______________________________________

After that, ______________________________________

In the end, ______________________________________

Overall, I felt ______________________________________

Revise

▶ **Rate your paragraph. Then have a writing partner rate it.**

Scoring Guide			
weak	okay	good	strong
1	2	3	4

1. Does the beginning **relate the writer's experience** to Ayize?

Self 1 2 3 4
Partner 1 2 3 4

2. Are there **details** that describe the experience?

Self 1 2 3 4
Partner 1 2 3 4

3. Are the details arranged in the **time order** they happened?

Self 1 2 3 4
Partner 1 2 3 4

4. Do **linking words** connect the details?

Self 1 2 3 4
Partner 1 2 3 4

5. Does the ending **sum up** the writer's ideas and feelings?

Self 1 2 3 4
Partner 1 2 3 4

▶ Now revise your paragraph to make it stronger.

Grammar Correcting Run-On Sentences

A run-on sentence is made up of two complete thoughts that are incorrectly joined together.

- To fix a run-on sentence, separate the ideas into two complete sentences.
- Or, insert a comma and a connecting word between the thoughts.

Example

Run-on sentence:	Ayize needed money he went to the mines.
Complete sentences:	Ayize needed money. He went to the mines.
Complete sentence:	Ayize needed money, so he went to the mines.

▶ **Put an R next to the run-on sentences. Put a C next to the complete sentences.**

1. Many cows were sick they died. R
2. Ayize left for the mines his father was concerned. ________
3. Father Thomas had advice, and he shared it with Ayize. ________
4. Fritz picked up Ayize he took him to Shantytown. ________
5. Ayize met Nkosi they became friends. ________
6. Ayize returned home, but he never forgot the mines. ________

▶ **Rewrite the run-on sentences below as complete sentences.**

7. Ayize was leaving neighbors came to say goodbye.

____

8. Zindzi gave Ayize a necklace he wore it all the time.

____

9. Nkosi had a plan he wanted to go to America.

____

10. Ayize found Nkosi's diamonds he sold them and went home.

____

Edit *Take a close look at each of the sentences in your draft on page 81. Are any of them run-on sentences? If so, fix them.*

Usage USING CORRECT WORD ORDER

The **order of words** in a sentence must make sense.

- An adjective comes before the noun it describes.
- A helping verb comes just before the main verb in a statement.

Example

Correct	Incorrect
Zindzi gave Ayize white beads.	Zindzi gave Ayize beads white.
He realized why Nkosi was sewing.	He realized why was Nkosi sewing.

▶ **Find and correct five errors in this paragraph.**

Student Model

Like Ayize, I've been treated unfairly. In my rurral town, mowing lawns is a big business. First, my best friend and I went into business together mowing lawns I worked really hard to get customers. After that, we worked all summer, even during weather hot. In the end, he exploitted me, taking all the money we earned. Overall, I felt angry really, but I have come to forgive him.

Check and Correct

- ☐ Circle two spelling errors and correct them.
- ☐ Underline two word order errors and correct them.
- ☐ Correct one run-on sentence.

Look at the sentences in your own draft on page 81. Do they all use correct word order? If not, fix them.

Final Draft/Present

▶ **Write a final draft of your paragraph on paper or the computer. Check it again and correct any errors before you present it.**

Meet the Author

RITA WILLIAMS-GARCIA

Rita Williams-Garcia has always loved writing. She was born in Queens, New York, but her family moved frequently. As a child and teen, she kept journals and wrote stories constantly. At age 14, her dedication paid off when she sold her first story.

Most of Williams-Garcia's stories focus on the experiences of urban teens. However, in recent years, she has begun writing about teens in other countries. What inspired her to write "Diamond Land"?

"My birthstone is a diamond," says Williams-Garcia. "But when my boyfriend proposed marriage, he did not give me a diamond ring. He said that Africans die every day mining diamonds.

"Eventually, I married someone else. He did give me a diamond ring. But when it was stolen, I didn't ask him to replace it. I remembered what I had been told about Africans and diamonds."

No matter what she is writing about, Rita Williams-Garcia's stories are inspired by real teens and real issues.

"I only want to write the story that I am dying to tell."

Ask Yourself

1. **Underline** What happened when Williams-Garcia was 14 years old?
2. **Circle** What do most of Williams-Garcia's novels and short stories focus on?
3. Name one book you have read that has realistic teen characters. What made the characters seem realistic?

____

____

____

Reading an Author Home Page

Where can you learn more about Rita Williams-Garcia? Authors often have Web sites. The home page of a Web site is its main page. The home page connects you to other pages. Check out the home page of Rita Williams-Garcia's Web site below.

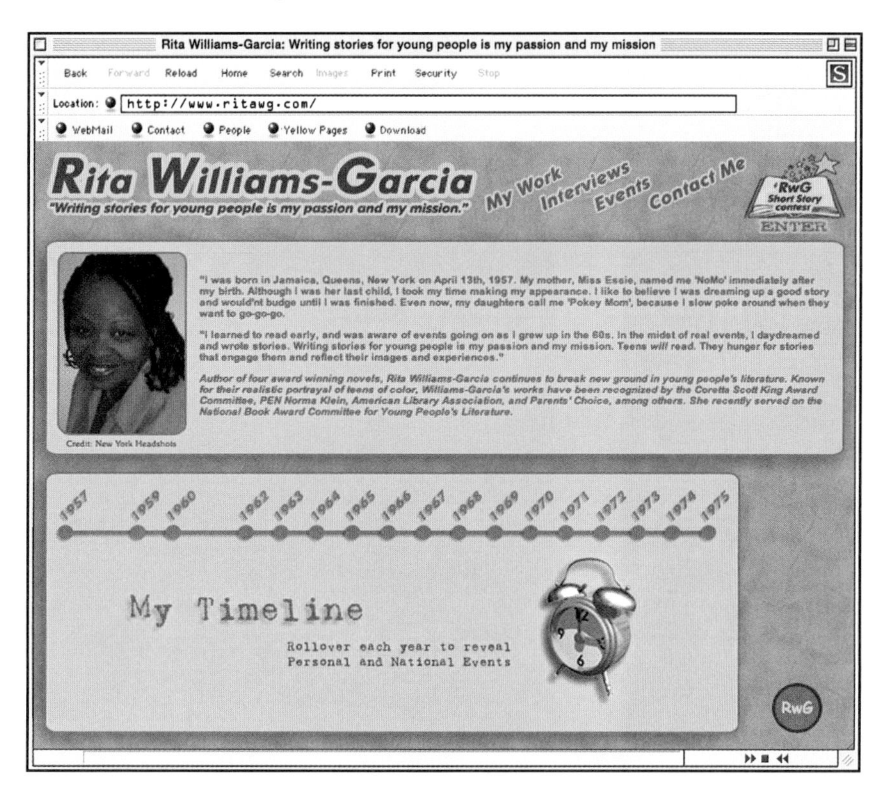

▶ **Fill in the circle next to the correct answer.**

1. What is this Web site about?

Ⓐ Queens, New York
Ⓑ Rita Williams-Garcia
Ⓒ diamonds
Ⓓ short story contests

2. What is the address of this Web site?

Ⓐ www.ritawg.com
Ⓑ www.mywork.com
Ⓒ www.enter.com
Ⓓ www.writingstories.com

3. Which button would you click to find out about the work the author has written?

Ⓐ My Work
Ⓑ Interviews
Ⓒ Events
Ⓓ Contact Me

4. What will you probably see if you click "Contact Me"?

Ⓐ book reviews
Ⓑ an online store
Ⓒ the author's email address
Ⓓ contest information

5. Which is a reason to visit this Web site?

Ⓐ to find out how Rita Williams-Garcia's stories end
Ⓑ to learn how to use the Internet
Ⓒ to read about American history
Ⓓ to learn more about Rita Williams-Garcia

Comprehension

▶ **Fill in the circle next to the correct answer.**

1. Where does "Diamond Land" take place?
Ⓐ northern Africa
Ⓑ New York
Ⓒ South Africa
Ⓓ a coal mine

2. Based on this story, you can tell that Ayize is

________________.

Ⓐ responsible and courageous
Ⓑ lazy and foolish
Ⓒ carefree and funny
Ⓓ sneaky and untrustworthy

3. What is the most important event in the story?
Ⓐ Ayize talks to Father Thomas.
Ⓑ A man gives Ayize a ride to Shantytown.
Ⓒ Zindzi gives Ayize a necklace.
Ⓓ Nkosi dies in the mines.

4. Which of the following events happens first?
Ⓐ Ayize leaves to work in the mines.
Ⓑ Ayize and Zindzi get married.
Ⓒ Ayize's family loses most of their cattle.
Ⓓ Ayize finds Nkosi's diamonds.

5. The overall message of this story is

________________.

Ⓐ to never work in the mines
Ⓑ that all people deserve justice and respect
Ⓒ to avoid hitchhiking
Ⓓ to be mistrustful of everyone

Here's a tip.
For short-answer questions, restate the question in your answer. This helps focus your answer.

Vocabulary

▶ **Fill in the circle next to the correct definition of the underlined word.**

1. Ayize's family lived in a rural part of South Africa.
   - Ⓐ countryside
   - Ⓑ modern
   - Ⓒ city
   - Ⓓ dangerous

2. Ayize and Father Thomas had a conflict about whether or not Ayize should go.
   - Ⓐ secret
   - Ⓑ joke
   - Ⓒ understanding
   - Ⓓ disagreement

3. Many white people in South Africa had a bias against black people.
   - Ⓐ strong friendship
   - Ⓑ forgetfulness
   - Ⓒ prejudice
   - Ⓓ good feeling

▶ **Choose the correct form of the underlined verb.**

4. Diamond mine bosses had exploit the black workers.
   - Ⓐ exploiting
   - Ⓑ exploits
   - Ⓒ exploited
   - Ⓓ correct as is

▶ **Choose the correct word to fill in the blank.**

5. Nelson Mandela has worked to make opportunities ____________ to everyone.
   - Ⓐ accessibility
   - Ⓑ accessible
   - Ⓒ access
   - Ⓓ inaccessible

Short Answer

▶ **Use what you've read in this Workshop to answer the question below. Check your spelling and grammar.**

Do you think Nkosi would have wanted Ayize to sell his diamonds? Explain.

____

____

____

____

____

WORKSHOP 4

NONFICTION

Comprehension Focus
Summarize

READINGS

1 ***Welcome to the Crime Lab*** >> Encyclopedia Article
2 ***Body of Evidence*** >> Magazine Article
3 ***DNA Analysis: The Key to Solving Crimes*** >> Science Text

CRIME LAB SCIENCE

No matter how clever, careful, and precise criminals are, they almost always leave evidence at the crime scene. Their shoes leave prints. Their tools and weapons leave telltale marks. Even their bodies shed skin cells and strands of hair.

In the past, such evidence could be difficult to trace to a suspect. But in today's crime labs, forensic scientists turn the tiniest scraps of evidence into giant clues through DNA analysis and other techniques. And often those clues are exactly what it takes to bring a criminal to justice.

VOCABULARY BUILDER

Target Word ▶ Read the Target Words. Rate each one using the scale below.*	Meaning ▶ Read the Target Word meanings. Write in the missing ones.	Example ▶ Finish the Target Word examples below. Write in the missing ones.
analysis *a•nal•y•sis* *(noun)* ① ② ③		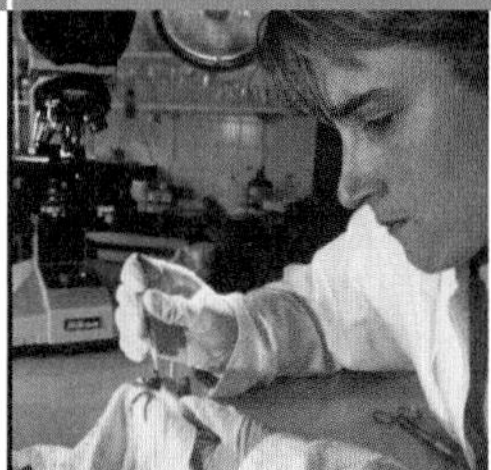 DNA **analysis** is an important tool for solving crimes.
evidence *ev•i•dence* *(noun)* ① ② ③	information and facts that help prove something	
precise *pre•cise* *(adjective)* ① ② ③		I am very precise about how I . . .
technique *tech•nique* *(noun)* ① ② ③	a special method or way of doing something	
verify *ver•i•fy* *(verb)* ① ② ③		I will verify the movie times by . . .

***Rating Scale**

① = I don't know it at all.
② = I've seen it before.
③ = I know it and use it.

The Big Idea

Write What is this article mainly about?

______

______

______

VOCABULARY BUILDER

Target Word

extract

ex•tract (verb)

Rate it: ① ② ③

Meaning

______

______

______

Example

______

______

______

React

Are you a good match for a crime lab job? What would you like about it? What would you not like about it?

Welcome to the Crime Lab

A crime lab is where forensic scientists test the evidence found at crime scenes. In a modern-day crime lab, a single drop of blood can be all the evidence that's needed for a team of scientists to solve a crime.

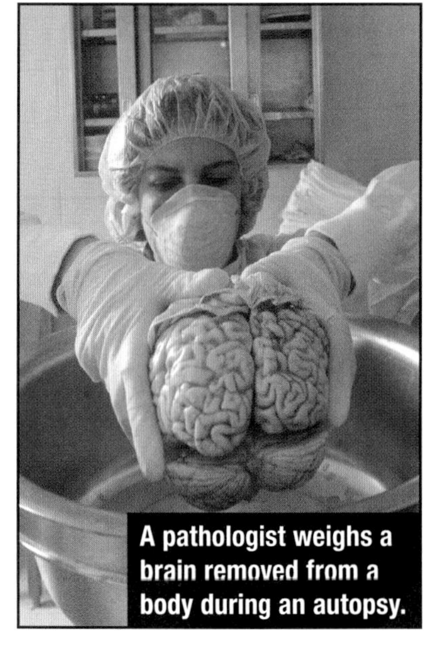

A pathologist weighs a brain removed from a body during an autopsy.

A crime lab is made up of smaller labs, including the autopsy room, the toxicology lab, and the forensic biology lab.

Scientists who work in the autopsy room are called pathologists. They examine bodies for clues to the cause of death. First, they dissect the internal organs and take samples of body fluids and tissues. Then they give the samples to the toxicology and forensic biology labs.

In the toxicology lab, toxicologists test the samples for alcohol, drugs, and poison. Their tests can accurately determine the amounts and types of substances present in a victim's body at the time of death.

Forensic biologists use the samples for DNA analysis. DNA is a molecule in the body that carries unique genetic information. Forensic biologists **extract** DNA from the samples. They use it to verify a victim's identity, or match a suspect to a crime.

Thanks to crime lab science, extracting and analyzing evidence is faster and more efficient now than ever before. So is catching criminals. END

Words to Know! **internal** *(adj.)* existing inside someone

Comprehension Focus

Summarize

A **summary** is a short statement of the most important ideas in a reading. To summarize:

- Find the topic of the text.
- Look for the most important details about the topic.
- Restate the topic and important details in a short summary. Use your own words.

▶ **Fill in this chart with the topic and important details in "Welcome to the Crime Lab."**

Topic

____

____

____

Details

1. *Pathologists work in the autopsy room to examine bodies for the cause of death.*

2. ______________________________

3. ______________________________

Summarize

▶ **Now summarize the article. Check that you:**

❑ state the topic

❑ give important details about the topic

❑ use your own words

The Big Idea

Write What is this article mainly about?

____

____

____

VOCABULARY BUILDER

Target Word

superficial

su•per•fi•cial (adjective)

Rate it: ① ② ③

Meaning

____

____

____

Example

____

____

____

React

What clue do you think is most important in the case so far? Tell how this clue could help solve the crime.

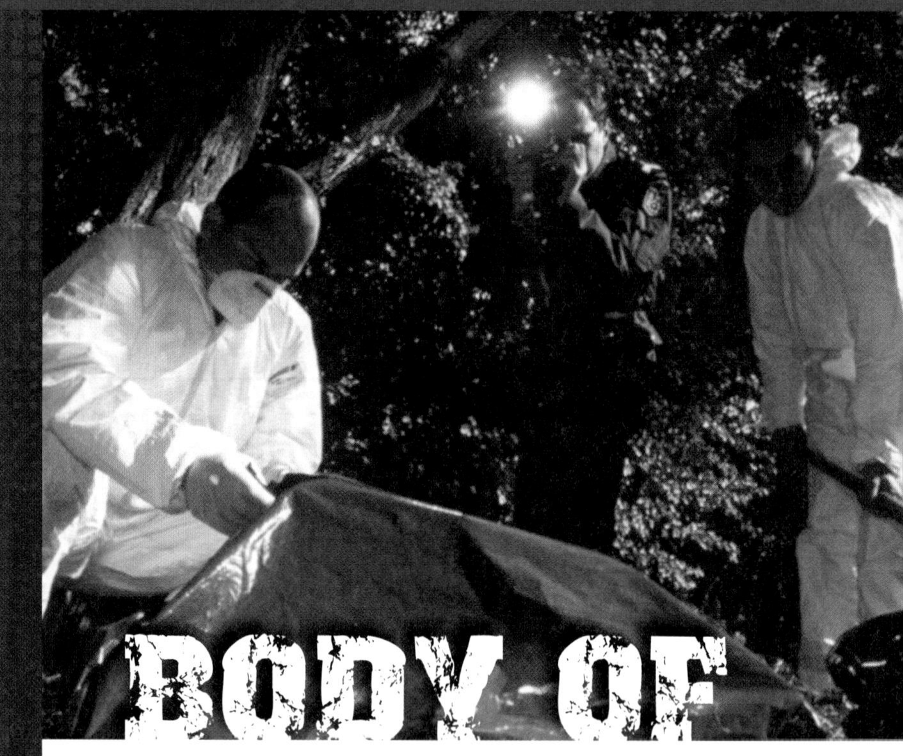

BODY OF EVIDENCE

Pathologists examine a body and uncover a web of lies, deceit—and murder.

On February 13, 2000, at around 1:00 P.M., a man named Bob Dorotik went running in southern California and never came back. At 7:45 P.M., his wife, Jane, called the police and reported him missing. About nine hours later, at 4:36 A.M. on February 14, the police found Bob's body lying in a patch of poison oak along his favorite jogging path. There was blood on Bob's face and wounds on the back of his head. A black, braided rope dangled from his neck. Clearly, Bob Dorotik had been murdered.

TIMELINE OF THE DOROTIK MURDER

2-13-00; 7:45 P.M.
Jane Dorotik reports her husband missing.

2-14-00; 4:36 A.M.
Investigators find Bob Dorotik's body in a patch of poison oak.

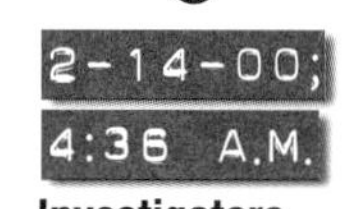

Time of Death

When pathologists from the crime lab arrived at the scene at 4:45 P.M., they looked for evidence that would reveal the time of death. They verified that Bob's body was cold to the touch and in full rigor mortis.

Rigor mortis (Latin for "rigidity in death") is a temporary stiffness in the body. It usually begins 1 to 3 hours after death as a consequence of chemical changes in the muscles. It starts in the face and neck. Within about 12 hours, it spreads to the entire body. After roughly 36 hours, the muscles soften again as the body begins to decompose.

The pathologists concluded that Bob had been dead for more than 12 hours, but probably less than 36 hours.

The Autopsy Room

At 9:30 A.M. on February 15, the pathologists performed a five-hour, detailed autopsy of Bob's corpse, beginning on the outside. They noted the precise size, shape, and color of every mark on his body. They detected seven areas of multiple cuts and bruises on his head, rope marks on his neck, and more than a dozen **superficial** injuries.

One clue was especially interesting. The pathologists found a small piece of Bob's scalp lying directly on the skin of his chest. Since the piece of scalp was found under Bob's shirt and not on top of it, it was possible that the killer had murdered Bob first, and then put the running clothes on his dead body. This called into question whether Bob had really gone running, as Jane had told the police. →

Words to Know! **decompose** *(v.)* to decay

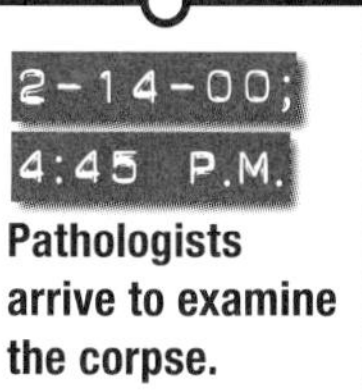

Pathologists arrive to examine the corpse.

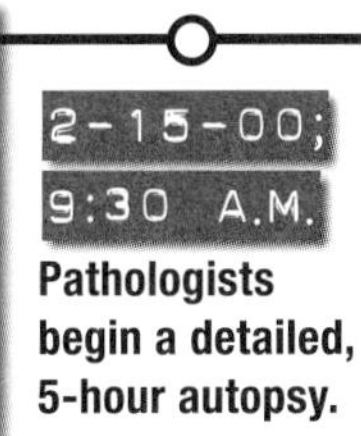

Pathologists begin a detailed, 5-hour autopsy.

Summarize

1. **Write** What is the topic of the section "Time of Death"?

___

___

___

___

2. **Underline** Find two details in "Time of Death" that relate to the topic.

3. Summarize the section in your own words. Tell your summary to a partner.

4. **Write** What is the topic of the section "The Autopsy Room"?

___

___

___

___

5. **Underline** Find two details in "The Autopsy Room" that relate to the topic.

6. Summarize the section in your own words. Tell your summary to a partner.

Active Reading

Underline What important clue did Bob's stomach hold?

VOCABULARY BUILDER

Target Word

theory

the•o•ry (noun)

Rate it: ① ② ③

Meaning

___

___

___

Example

___

___

___

Under the Skin

Next, the pathologists cut into Bob's body to search for more clues. They studied and weighed every major organ. The brain injuries confirmed the **theory** that head trauma was the cause of death. The stomach also revealed an important clue: undigested red meat.

Jane had told investigators that Bob ate steak for dinner on February 12. She also said she saw Bob alive the following afternoon. But an analysis of Bob's stomach contents told a different tale.

The undigested steak in Bob's stomach proved that he was killed soon after he ate. If Bob had eaten the steak in the evening, as Jane said, she could not have seen him alive the next afternoon.

The Suspect

The pathologists' discoveries didn't prove that Jane was the killer, but they gave investigators reasons to form a theory about her guilt. First, someone had put Bob's running clothes on his body after his death, and Jane had access to those clothes. Further, the condition of Bob's stomach contents suggested that Jane was lying about the last time she saw him alive.

With the help of other forensic scientists and crime lab techniques, investigators accumulated enough evidence to arrest Jane on February 17. On June 12, 2001, a jury found her guilty and she was later sentenced to 25 years in prison. Jane, who has been working to prove her innocence since her arrest, is currently in prison in California. END

Words to Know! **trauma** *(n.)* a severe injury

React

Write Do you think Jane is guilty or innocent? State your verdict and give one good reason to support it.

___

___

___

___

___

2-15-00

Pathologists find undigested steak in Dorotik's stomach.

2-17-00

Jane Dorotik is arrested for first-degree murder.

Comprehension Focus

Summarize

▶ **Fill in this chart with the topic and important details in "Body of Evidence."**

Details

1. ______________________________

____

____

2. ______________________________

____

____

3. ______________________________

____

____

Summarize

▶ **Now tell your summary to a partner. Check that you:**

- ❑ state the topic
- ❑ give important details about the topic
- ❑ use your own words

The Big Idea

Write What is this article mainly about?

___

___

___

VOCABULARY BUILDER

Target Word

consist

con•sist (verb)

Rate it:  ① ② ③

Meaning

___

___

___

Example

___

___

___

React

In solving a crime, do you think DNA analysis or eyewitness accounts are more accurate? Explain your answer.

DNA ANALYSIS: The Key to Solving Crimes

Adapted from *Forensics* by Richard Platt

DNA analysis has become a crucial weapon in the fight against crime.

Police catch a shoplifter and take a saliva sample from inside his mouth. Investigators find that the DNA in the sample precisely matches DNA evidence from an unsolved murder committed years earlier. It may sound impossible, but it happens. Thanks to DNA analysis, which was invented in 1984, solving crimes is easier than ever before.

DNA and Identity

DNA, or deoxyribonucleic acid, is a molecule found in every cell in the human body. It **consists** of genes and repeated patterns of proteins.

Genes, which determine what people look like, come from both parents. The repeated patterns of proteins in DNA also come from both parents. The order of these patterns and the number of times they repeat are unique to each person. (The only exception

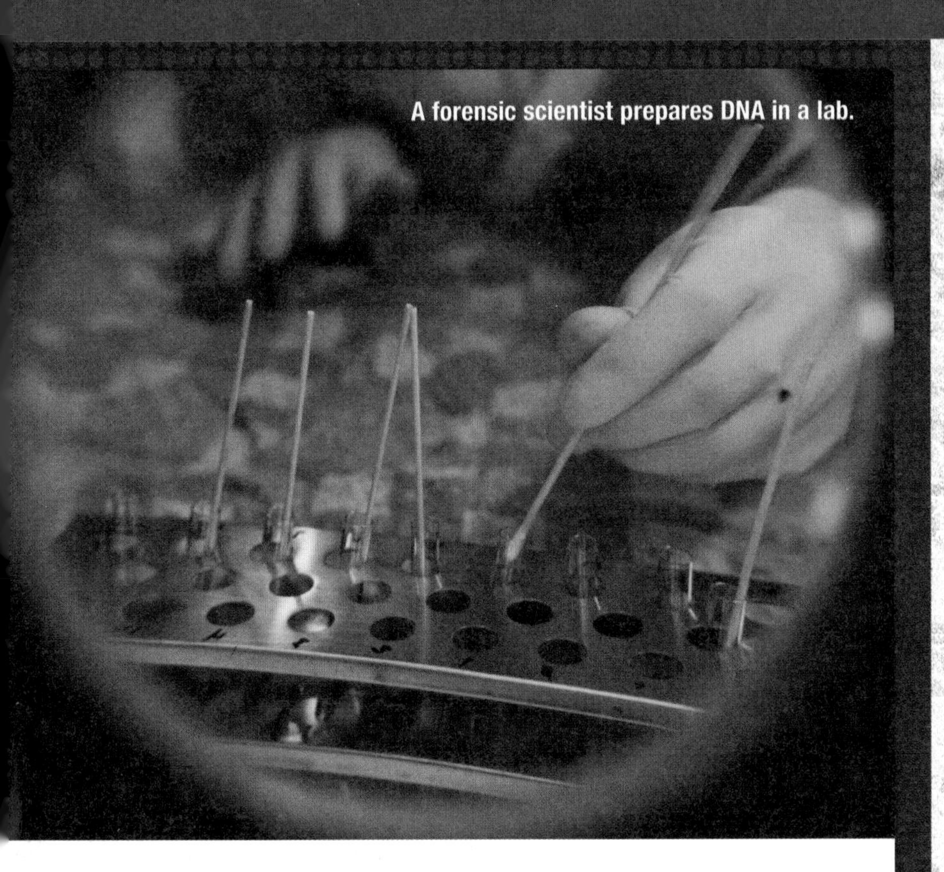

A forensic scientist prepares DNA in a lab.

to this is identical twins, who share the same DNA.) Because each person's DNA is unique, DNA analysis can be used to identify people.

Extracting DNA

DNA can be found in blood, saliva, and other body fluids and tissues. If crime scene investigators find a drop of blood, they collect the sample on a cotton swab. The swab is stored in a sterilized tube with a preservative. The tube is chilled to keep the DNA from decaying before it is analyzed.

Forensic scientists at the crime lab extract the DNA from the sample. This allows them to compare the DNA with a suspect's DNA to verify whether the suspect was at the crime scene. In order to make the comparison, scientists mix the extracted DNA with special chemicals that multiply its repeated patterns until there is enough material to test. ➜

Words to Know!	**sterilized** *(adj.)* made free from germs

Summarize

1. **Write** What is the topic of "DNA and Identity"?

____

____

____

2. **Underline** Find two details in "DNA and Identity" that relate to the topic.

3. Summarize the section in your own words. Tell your summary to a partner.

4. **Write** What is the topic of the section "Extracting DNA"?

____

____

____

5. **Underline** Find two details in "Extracting DNA" that relate to the topic.

6. Summarize the section in your own words. Tell your summary to a partner.

Review: Sequence of Events

Circle In the section "Extracting DNA," what happens to a sample after it is collected on a swab?

Active Reading

  Circle What is the final step in DNA analysis?

VOCABULARY BUILDER

Target Word

utilize

u•til•ize (verb)

Rate it: ① ② ③

Meaning

___

___

___

Example

___

___

___

React

Write **A small percentage of trials send innocent people to jail. How could a person be proved innocent through DNA analysis?**

___

___

___

___

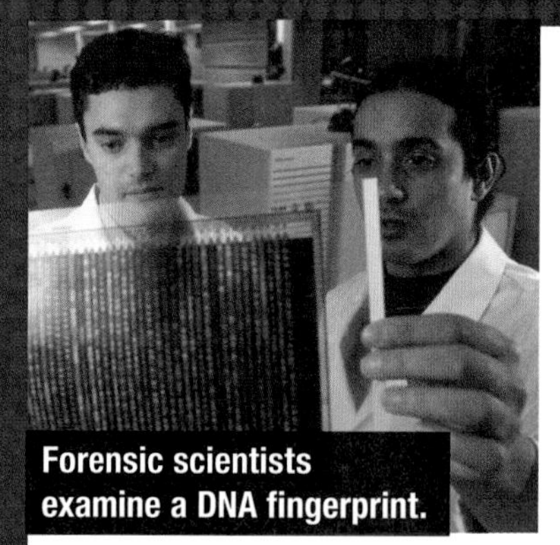

Forensic scientists examine a DNA fingerprint.

A DNA Fingerprint

Next, scientists use a special technique to mark each repeated protein pattern with dye. Then they put the patterns in a tube. A sensor in the tube reads the patterns and sends the data to a computer. The computer creates a precise DNA profile, or "fingerprint," that identifies the person to whom the DNA belongs.

The final step in DNA analysis is to compare the crime scene profile to a suspect's profile. If there is no suspect, detectives look for a match in a computer database that contains thc DNA profiles of known criminals. This database, called CODIS (Combined DNA Index System), stores more than a million profiles. If a match is made between the lab's profile and a profile in CODIS, investigators may have identified a suspect in their case.

Imperfect Proof

Investigators **utilize** DNA analysis to match suspects to crimes. They can also use it to exonerate people who have been wrongly accused. The Innocence Project is a group established specifically to reexamine evidence in cases of possible wrongful convictions. But just how accurate is DNA analysis?

Although DNA tests are very precise, they are not foolproof. Crime scene samples can be polluted with DNA from other sources. Human error in the lab can also contribute to inaccurate matches.

Despite these issues, DNA analysis is a ground-breaking technique that has forever changed the way crimes are investigated—and solved. END

Words to Know! **exonerate** *(v.)* to free from blame

 TEXT FEATURE **Reading a Diagram**

THE STRUCTURE OF DNA

In the **nucleus** of each human cell, there are 46 **chromosomes** (23 from each parent). Each chromosome is made of two strands of DNA connected by chemicals called **base pairs**. The **DNA strands** form the shape of a spiral ladder, called a **double helix**. The base pairs are the rungs of the ladder. Base pairs are part of the proteins that make a person's DNA unique.

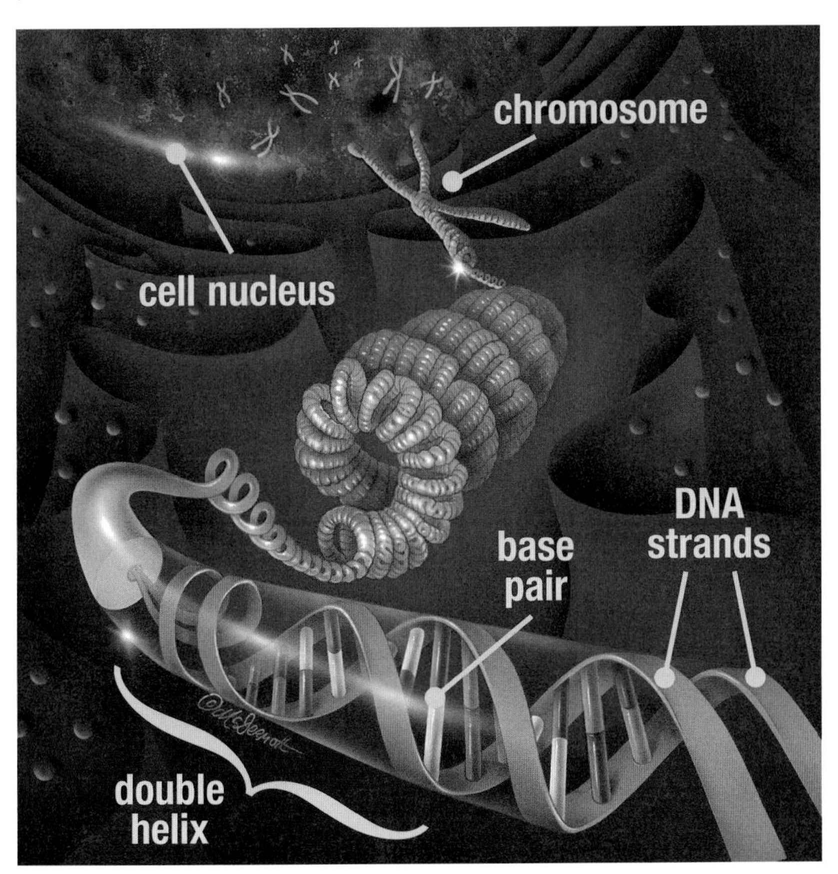

A diagram can give a detailed view of something of scientific interest.

1. What connects the two strands of DNA?
   Ⓐ chromosomes Ⓒ base pairs
   Ⓑ a double helix Ⓓ the cell nucleus

2. What shape do the strands of DNA and the base pairs form?
   Ⓐ a spiral ladder Ⓒ a circle
   Ⓑ a line Ⓓ an "x"

3. What does a double helix consist of?

____

 **Summarize**

1. **Write** What is the topic of the section "A DNA Fingerprint"?

____
____
____
____

2. **Underline** Find two details in "A DNA Fingerprint" that relate to the topic.

3. Summarize the section in your own words. Tell your summary to a partner.

Skills Check

1. **Write** What is the topic of the section "Imperfect Proof"?

____
____
____
____

2. **Underline** Find two details in "Imperfect Proof" that relate to the topic.

3. Write a summary of this section on a separate sheet of paper.

TAKE THE WORD CHALLENGE

Start

1

Decide. Write ***P*** (for personal) next to the analysis you might tell a friend. Write ***N*** (for newspaper) next to the analysis you might find in a newspaper.

_____ "The movie reminded me of my family."

_____ "The movie brilliantly explored bad relationships."

2

Circle. Which of these utilizes more energy?

swimming	*or*	birdwatching
reading	*or*	running

Which of these utilizes less energy?

lounging	*or*	leaping
eating	*or*	sleeping

3 Using a Dictionary

Guide words are the words on the top of dictionary pages. They tell the first and last words listed on those pages.

murmur ▸ mustache

mur·mur (mur-mur) ***verb***
1. To talk very quietly.
2. To make a quiet, low, continuous sound. *The wind murmured in the trees.*
▹ ***verb*** **murmuring, murmured** ▹ ***noun*** **murmur**

mus·cle (muhss-uhl) ***noun***
1. One of the parts of your body that produces movement. Your muscles are attached to your skeleton and pull on your bones to make them move. *The diagram shows the muscles that move your arm.*
2. Strength or power. *This job requires muscle.*
Muscle sounds like **mussel.**

upper arm muscles

biceps (contract to bend arm)
tendons (attach muscle to bone)
triceps (contract to straighten arm)

Write these Target Words next to the words that could be their guide words:

consist	extract	verify

Guide Words	Target Words
ventilate, vertical	__________
extinct, eyewitness	__________
considerable, consult	__________

4

Decide. Which of these things can you use to verify your identity? Write ***Y*** if you can use it. Write ***N*** if you can't.

_____ A driver's license

_____ A note from a friend

_____ An envelope addressed to you

_____ A passport

_____ A picture ID

5

Complete the sentences. Fill in each blank with the correct form of consist from below.

consistency **consists** **inconsistent**

My theory is that my brother stole the pie. The evidence __________ of a substance with a sticky __________ and a trail of crumbs. But the evidence is __________ with my theory because the trail leads to my sister's room.

6 Advise. What is a good technique for making friends?

____

____

____

____

____

____

____

7 Describe. What is your theory about the "crime" scene above?

____

____

____

____

____

____

____

You are a unique **individual** because of your **individual** clothing style!

8 Multiple-Meaning Words

Multiple-meaning words are words that have more than one meaning.

Read the definitions of these multiple-meaning words. Use them to fill in the blanks below.

extract: 1. *(verb)* to take or pull something out
2. *(noun)* a product prepared by extracting

superficial: 1. *(adjective)* on the surface, not deep
2. *(adjective)* shallow, of no substance

contact: 1. *(verb)* to get in touch with
2. *(noun)* the state of touching or connecting

1. I tried to __________ the information from him but he only gave me __________ answers to my questions.

2. Let's __________ the grocery store to see if they have the vanilla __________ we need to make cookies.

3. She was a very __________ person who only cared about making __________ with celebrities.

9 Check them. Which of these things might be evidence in a murder trial?

- ☐ a gun
- ☐ a TV show
- ☐ blood stains
- ☐ fingerprints

10 Complete the sentences. Fill in each blank with the correct form of precise from below.

precisely **precision** **imprecise**

It was important to measure the chemicals __________. A(n) __________ measurement might result in an explosion. So I needed a lab partner who worked with __________.

Finish

Writing Focus

Expository Summary

A **summary** gives the most important ideas and details from a reading.

▶ **Read Carlos's summary of "Welcome to the Crime Lab."**

Student Model

Summary of
"Welcome to the Crime Lab"
By Carlos Santiago

"Welcome to the Crime Lab" describes the labs where forensic scientists investigate evidence found at crime scenes. First, the article tells about the autopsy room, where scientists called pathologists dissect the bodies of victims to determine the cause of death. Next, it describes the toxicology lab, where scientists test for alcohol, drugs, or poisons in victims' bodies. The article also explains how forensic biologists analyze DNA samples. All these people help identify criminals by using forensic techniques in a crime lab.

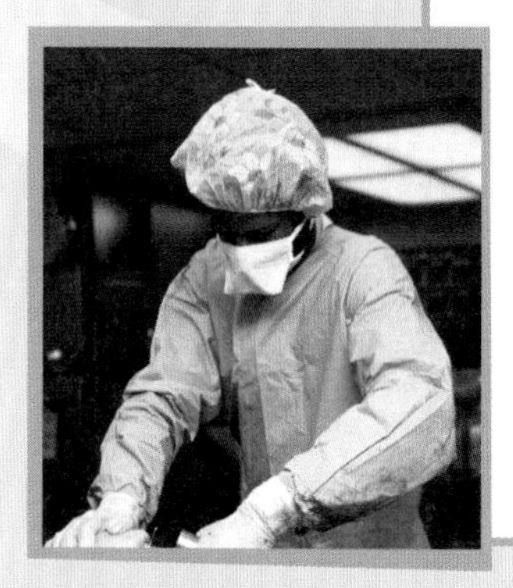

Parts of an Expository Summary

▶ **Find these parts of Carlos's expository summary paragraph.**

1. Underline the sentence that states the **topic of the reading**.
2. Check three **important details**.
3. Circle the **linking words** that connect the details.
4. Reread to see that the summary is in the **writer's own words**.
5. Decide if the summary is **brief, but complete**.

Brainstorm

▶ **Read the writing prompt in the middle of the idea web. Then use the boxes to help you organize your ideas.**

Important Detail

Important Detail

Writing Prompt:

Write a paragraph that summarizes the article "Body of Evidence."

Important Detail

Important Detail

Plan Your Paragraph

Writing Prompt: Write a paragraph that summarizes the article "Body of Evidence."

▶ **Use this chart to plan and organize your paragraph.**

Word Choices

____

____

____

____

____

Topic

- *The article "Body of Evidence" . . .*
- *The scientists in the crime lab . . .*
- *"Body of Evidence" describes . . .*

First Important Detail

- *First, the article . . .*
- *The first analysis of evidence . . .*
- *To begin with, . . .*

Second Important Detail

- *Next, . . .*
- *Another important point is . . .*
- *In addition, . . .*

Third Important Detail

- *The article also . . .*
- *The most important part . . .*
- *Another important factor . . .*

Last Important Detail

- *Finally, . . .*
- *The last important point is that . . .*
- *In summary, . . .*

Write Your Paragraph

▶ **Use this writing frame to write a first draft of your paragraph.**

____
(title)

The article "Body of Evidence" describes ______________________________

First, the article describes ______________________________

Then, ______________________________

The article also ______________________________

Finally, the article ______________________________

Revise

▶ **Rate your paragraph. Then have a writing partner rate it.**

Scoring Guide			
weak	okay	good	strong
1	2	3	4

1. Does the first sentence state the **topic of the reading**?

Self	1	2	3	4
Partner	1	2	3	4

2. Does the summary contain only **important details**?

Self	1	2	3	4
Partner	1	2	3	4

3. Do **linking words** connect the details?

Self	1	2	3	4
Partner	1	2	3	4

4. Is the summary written in the **writer's own words**?

Self	1	2	3	4
Partner	1	2	3	4

5. Is the summary **brief, but complete**?

Self	1	2	3	4
Partner	1	2	3	4

▶ Now revise your paragraph to make it stronger.

Grammar Using Correct Verb Tense

The **tense** of a verb shows when the action happens.

- A **present-tense verb** shows action that is happening now.
- A **past-tense verb** shows action that took place in the past. Most past-tense verbs end in *-ed*.

Example

Present-Tense Verb	Past-Tense Verb
The scientist examines the evidence.	The scientist examined the body.
Biologists extract DNA from samples.	Biologists extracted DNA yesterday.

▶ **Identify the tense of the verb in each sentence below by writing present or past on the line to the right.**

1. Pathologists performed an autopsy in the crime lab. ______past______
2. They dissected the internal organs of the body. ____________
3. Scientists study trace evidence. ____________
4. The evidence proved the identity of the criminal. ____________
5. A forensic scientist uses a microscope. ____________
6. The police announced the solution to the mystery. ____________

▶ **Rewrite the sentences below using the past tense of the verb.**

7. Investigators and pathologists together solve the crime.

____

8. Crime labs include many different types of labs.

____

9. Who works on the case in the toxicology lab?

____

10. The lab reports its findings to the police.

____

Take a close look at each of the sentences in your draft on page 105. Do they all use correct verb tense? Fix the ones that don't.

Mechanics Using Commas in a Series

Items in a series are separated by **commas**.

- A series is a list of the same kinds of words.
- Commas follow every item in the series except the last one.

Example

Correct	Incorrect
Blood, skin, and DNA are all studied in a crime lab.	Blood skin and DNA are all studied in a crime lab.

▶ **Find and correct five errors in this paragraph.**

Student Model

The article "Welcome to the Crime Lab" describes the scientists' techniques and tools in a crime lab. First, it told about the room where autopsies are performed on bodys. Next, it goes to the toxicology lab where tests are done to see if drugs alcohol or poison are in victims' blood. Then it talks about the lab where DNA is analised. All these parts of a crime lab are important to solving crimes.

Check and Correct

- ❑ Circle two spelling errors and correct them.
- ❑ Insert two missing commas.
- ❑ Correct one verb-tense error.

Edit *Look at the sentences in your own draft on page 105. Do they all use commas in a series correctly? Fix the ones that don't.*

Final Draft/Present

▶ **Write a final draft of your paragraph on paper or the computer. Check it again and correct any errors before you present it.**

Careers

Criminology Researcher

As a Ph.D student in Criminology, Sylvia Valenzuela is part researcher and part investigator. She studies trends in violence and homicide in the home. She has also done research into juvenile delinquency. "My ultimate goal," Sylvia says, "is to become a principal investigator and lead a research project of my own."

Name: Sylvia Valenzuela

Hometown: Huntington Beach, California

Job: Criminology Researcher

Duties:
- researches trends in criminology
- interviews subjects for studies in criminology

Skills:
- analyzing data
- multitasking
- staying flexible, because things are always changing in her field

Similar Jobs:
- clinical researcher
- analyst for a crime-solving agency
- college professor

Sylvia Valenzuela interviews a subject for a crime study.

Pay: $40,000 and up

Education: Bachelor's Degree or Master's Degree in Criminal Justice

Ask Yourself

1. **Underline** How much education does this job require?
2. **Circle** Which of Sylvia's duties requires good communications skills?
3. How much do you want this job?
   - ❑ I don't want it.
   - ❑ I might want it.
   - ❑ I really want it.

Analyzing Data

Analyzing evidence in a crime lab requires careful observation. Here's a look at how criminologists match *latent prints* (fingerprints found at a crime scene) to fingerprints taken from suspects. Follow the steps below to analyze fingerprints.

▶ **STEP 1. The latent print below was found at the scene of a robbery. Identify which class, or type, it is by comparing it to the prints from the fingerprint chart. Which one does it look most like? Put a check mark on the line next to right loop or whorl below.**

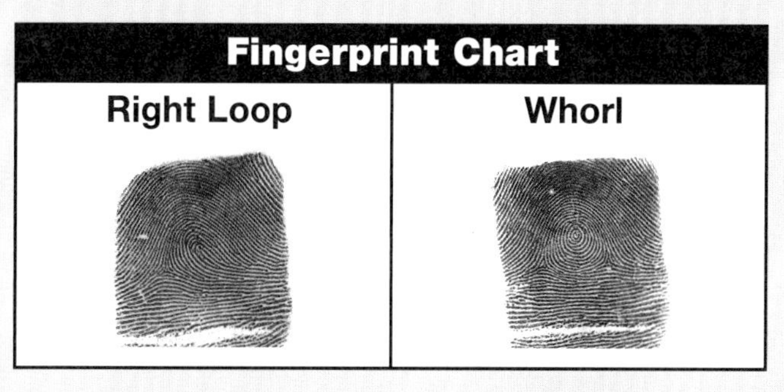

________________ right loop   **________________ whorl**

▶ **STEP 2. The fingerprints below were taken from the two main suspects in the robbery. Identify the class that each pair of prints belongs to by comparing them to the fingerprint chart in STEP 1. Check the right answer for each suspect.**

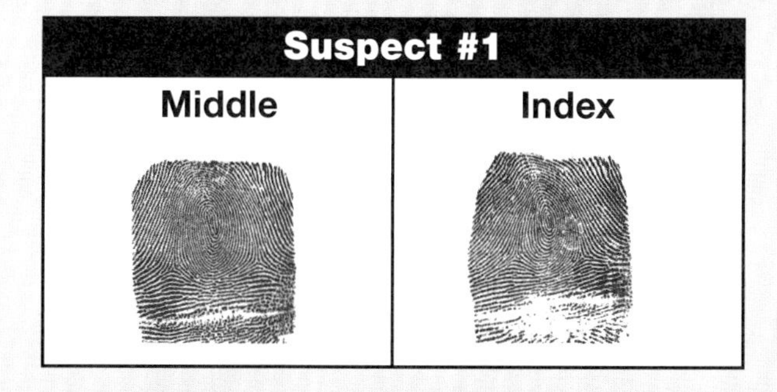

Suspect #1 ________________ right loop   **________________ whorl**

Suspect #2 ________________ right loop   **________________ whorl**

▶ **STEP 3. Which suspect's prints are of the same class as the latent print? __________**

Now, compare those two prints to the latent print. Look carefully at the lines, or friction ridges, in each print. Observe where they curve, break, or split into two lines. Which print looks most like the latent print?

________________ middle   **________________ index**

Comprehension

▶ **Fill in the circle next to the correct answer.**

1. A crime lab tests mainly the ____________.

Ⓐ blood samples of criminals
Ⓑ accuracy of interviews with crime scene witnesses
Ⓒ evidence found at a crime scene
Ⓓ statements given by the suspect

Here's a tip.
When taking a test with passages, read the questions first. You'll know what to watch for while reading.

2. The final step in DNA analysis is to ____________.

Ⓐ compare the crime scene DNA to a suspect's DNA
Ⓑ send it to the toxicology lab
Ⓒ use a cotton swab to obtain a sample
Ⓓ extract DNA from the sample

3. Which sentence gives the best summary of what happens in the autopsy room?

Ⓐ Toxicologists test samples for alcohol and poisonous drugs.
Ⓑ Forensic scientists examine evidence like mud and skin cells.
Ⓒ Detectives interview crime suspects.
Ⓓ Pathologists examine dead bodies for the cause of death.

4. Which important detail would be included in a summary of the case of Bob Dorotik?

Ⓐ Within 12 hours, rigor mortis spreads to the entire body.
Ⓑ Bob's stomach held an important clue: undigested red meat.
Ⓒ Bob liked to jog.
Ⓓ Rigor mortis is temporary stiffness after death.

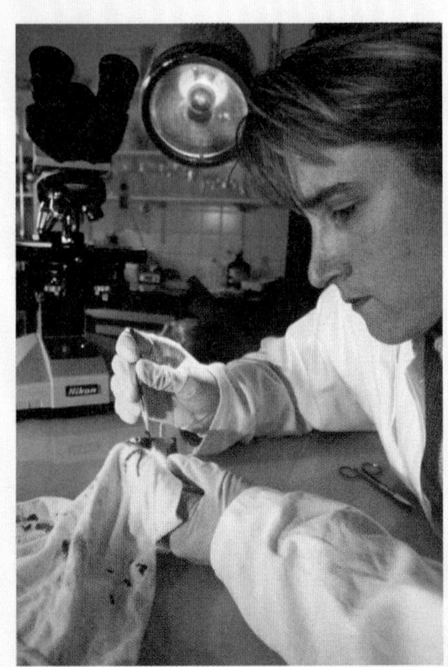

5. DNA analysis is an important crime-solving tool because ____________.

Ⓐ fingerprints can be matched to those of a known criminal
Ⓑ it can establish the time of death
Ⓒ DNA is unique to individuals, except in the case of identical twins
Ⓓ it shows the level of poison in the blood

Vocabulary

▶ **Fill in the circle next to the correct definition of the underlined word.**

1. The scientist did an analysis of the victim's blood.
   Ⓐ careful examination
   Ⓑ new idea
   Ⓒ small amount
   Ⓓ illustration

2. The evidence was used to identify the murderer.
   Ⓐ special method
   Ⓑ kind of poison
   Ⓒ information that helps prove something
   Ⓓ detailed study of something

3. The autopsy verified the precise time of death.
   Ⓐ proved true; exact
   Ⓑ killed; well-known
   Ⓒ analyzed; tiny
   Ⓓ suspected; unusual

▶ **Choose the correct definition for the underlined multiple-meaning word.**

4. The pathologist extracts DNA in order to analyze it.
   Ⓐ inserts
   Ⓑ takes out
   Ⓒ colors
   Ⓓ destroys

▶ **Which are the most likely dictionary guide words for the underlined word?**

5. Scientists use a special technique to extract DNA.
   Ⓐ tenant and tiger
   Ⓑ swoon and table
   Ⓒ teach and telephone
   Ⓓ trial and umbrella

Short Answer

▶ **Use what you've read in this Workshop to answer the question below. Check your spelling and grammar.**

Describe one technique used in a crime lab and tell how it can help solve a crime.

____

____

____

____

WORKSHOP 5

NONFICTION

Comprehension Focus
Fact and Opinion

WIRED FOR TROUBLE

Are you addicted to email? Is your cell phone glued to your ear? Do you and your friends text and instant message (IM) constantly?

It's hard to imagine life without technology. But sometimes it can hurt you as much as it helps. Cell phones provoke trouble in the classroom. Bullies harass their victims through email, blogs, text messages, and IMs. And what happens when kids spend all their time online?

Take a look at the troubling side of technology!

VOCABULARY BUILDER

Target Word ▶ Read the Target Words. Rate each one using the scale below.*	Meaning ▶ Read the Target Word meaning. Write in the missing ones.	Example ▶ Finish the Target Word examples below. Write in the missing ones.
appropriate *ap•pro•pri•ate* *(adjective)* ① ② ③		At a movie theater, it's not appropriate to . . .
critic *crit•ic* *(noun)* ① ② ③	someone whose job is to judge something, or someone who judges something harshly.	
proportion *pro•por•tion* *(noun)* ① ② ③		I ate a large **proportion** of that pizza!
simultaneously *si•mul•ta•ne•ous•ly* *(adverb)* ① ② ③	at the same time	
technology *tech•nol•o•gy* *(noun)* ① ② ③		One form of technology I use every day is . . .

***Rating Scale**

①=I don't know it at all.
②=I've seen it before.
③=I know it and use it.

The Big Idea

Write What is this debate mainly about?

____

____

____

VOCABULARY BUILDER

Target Word

conclude

con•clude (verb)

Rate it: ① ② ③

Meaning

____

____

____

Example

____

____

____

React

Do you think cell phones should be banned from schools? Explain your opinion.

Should Schools Ban Cell Phones?

More than half of American teens carry cell phones. But in cities like New York, schools have banned cell phones. Supporters of bans say cell phones are disruptive in class. Critics say students need their phones. Here's how two students answered the question.

YES Ringing phones disrupt class. Kids use text messages to cheat. Some students use camera phones to invade people's privacy. These are the reasons that I believe schools should ban cell phones.

Most schools have phones in the office. When appropriate, parents and children can contact each other through school. Office phones are also adequate for emergencies.

Sure, cell phones are convenient. But at school, the disruptions they cause outweigh the convenience they offer.

Rasheed Jones, 14

NO School violence and medical crises can happen at any time. Students need cell phones to contact their families or 911 in case of emergency.

It's also important that teens learn to use cell phones appropriately. Students who bring phones to school can learn when it's okay to use them.

Finally, cell phones make life easier when practice runs late, or your mom gets stuck in traffic. For all these reasons, I've **concluded** that schools should not ban cell phones.

Kristy Clark, 13

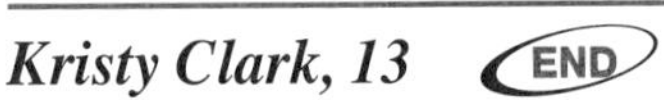

Words to Know! **disrupt** *(v.)* stop or break up

Comprehension Focus

Fact and Opinion

A **fact** is a statement that can be proven true. An **opinion** is a statement of someone's personal feeling or belief. An opinion can also express a judgment—the conclusion someone reaches after thinking something over.

- To identify a fact, ask: Can this statement be proven true? How or where could I check whether it is true?
- To identify an opinion, ask: Is this someone's feeling, belief, or judgment? To recognize opinions, look for signal words, such as *think*, *believe*, *best*, *worst*, *appropriate*, and *unfair*.

▶ **Use this chart to identify facts and opinions from "Should Schools Ban Cell Phones?"**

Statement	Fact or Opinion?	How Do I Know?
More than half of American teens carry cell phones.	fact	Studies or surveys can show whether this is true.
Cell phones are disruptive in class.		
Most schools have phones in the office.		
It's important that teens learn to be responsible cell phone users.		

The Big Idea

Write ▶ What is this article mainly about?

____

____

____

VOCABULARY BUILDER

Target Word

manipulate

ma•nip•u•late (verb)

Rate it:   ③

Meaning

____

____

____

Example

____

____

____

React

Why might it be easier to bully someone by email and instant message than in person?

Cyberbullies

Technology is supposed to make life easier. But critics say it can make kids' lives tougher than ever.

A New Way to Bully

Bullying is nothing new. But in recent years, a new breed of bullies has emerged. Called cyberbullies, they are young—mostly 9 to 16—and technologically savvy. And they are exploiting their skills in disturbing and inappropriate ways, experts feel.

Armed with cell phones and computers, cyberbullies aren't confined to hassling their victims at school or on the street corner. Instead, they use technology to inflict pain from afar.

For one victim, a

minor conflict with a friend provoked an ugly attack. Joanne, 14, argued with a friend at a sleepover. For the next three months, she received a steady stream of threatening emails and ugly comments on her blog. "It was a nightmare," Joanne says. "I dreaded going on my computer."

A Growing Problem

As a larger proportion of kids go online, experiences like Joanne's are becoming common. In 2005, an Internet safety group took a survey. Of the 3,000 kids who responded, half said that they or their friends were victims—or perpetrators—of cyberbullying. In Westchester County, NY, officials held a meeting to address the problem. All but six of the 200 students who attended had been involved in some form of cyberbullying.

Cyberbullies' techniques can be ingenious. They impersonate other teens online and send phony messages to friends and classmates. They forward private emails and embarrassing photos to hundreds of people. Through email and IMs, they spread gossip and **manipulate** friends into fighting with each other.

Experts say any kid with access to technology can be a cyberbully. You don't need to be strong to intimidate someone online. You don't even need to identify yourself.

That anonymity might be the most alarming element of cyberbullying. Because they don't have to face their victims, cyberbullies are often nastier than other bullies.

"People say worse things online than to your face," claims one victim of cyberbullying.

Words to Know! perpetrator *(n.)* someone who has done wrong

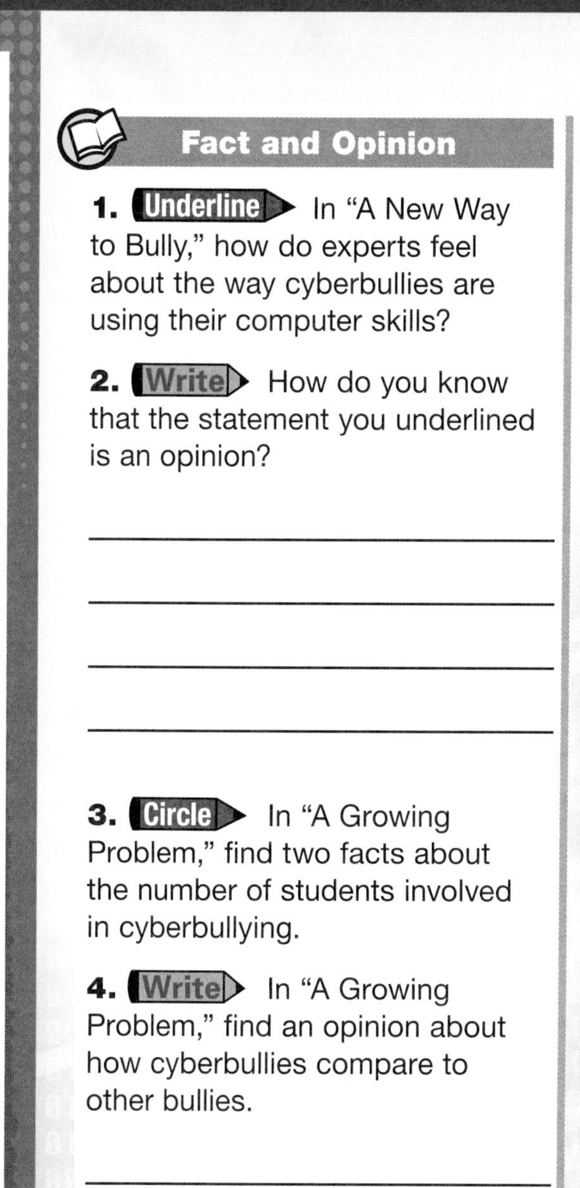

Fact and Opinion

1. **Underline** In "A New Way to Bully," how do experts feel about the way cyberbullies are using their computer skills?

2. **Write** How do you know that the statement you underlined is an opinion?

____

____

____

____

3. **Circle** In "A Growing Problem," find two facts about the number of students involved in cyberbullying.

4. **Write** In "A Growing Problem," find an opinion about how cyberbullies compare to other bullies.

____

____

____

____

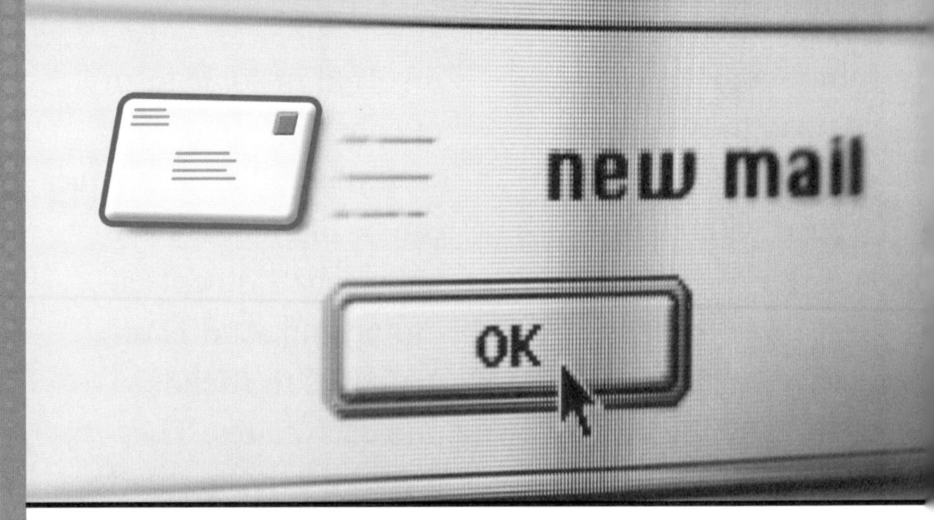

Active Reading

Underline What is a common form of cyberbullying among boys?

VOCABULARY BUILDER

Target Word

aspect

as•pect (noun)

Rate it: ① ② ③

Meaning

____

____

____

Example

____

____

____

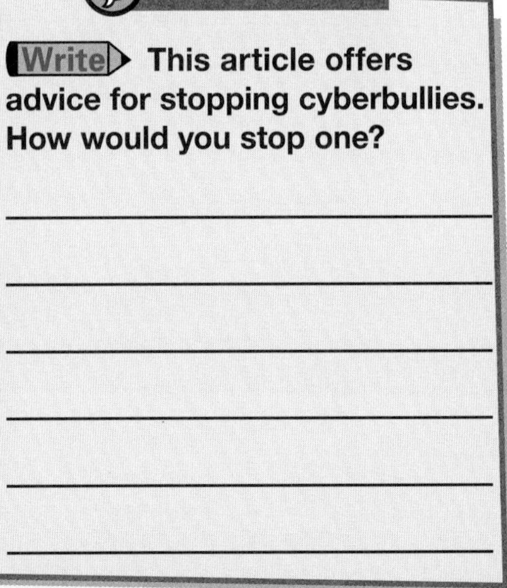

React

Write **This article offers advice for stopping cyberbullies. How would you stop one?**

____

____

____

____

____

____

Across Gender Lines

Both boys and girls can be cyberbullies, but they tend to participate in different **aspects** of bullying. Girls often mock victims' looks. They are harsher critics than boys, victims feel.

A common form of cyberbullying among boys occurs on gaming sites. Bullies called "griefers" hassle other players. When Michael, 13, outplayed another boy, griefers tracked him down online. They sent IMs threatening to beat him up.

Making It Stop

What can you do to stop a cyberbully?

An Internet safety group has this advice. First, try to ignore bullies. Block their screen names.

If that doesn't work, save the evidence. Tell an adult what's happening. Surveys show many victims don't tell their parents, for fear of being barred from the Internet. Nonetheless, keeping quiet is not a good idea.

If you've never had an online altercation, try to keep it that way. Don't chat with strangers. Change your passwords often. Never give out passwords or personal information. One way to stop cyberbullies is to prevent them from getting started. END

Words to Know! **altercation** *(n.)* fight or quarrel

Comprehension Focus

Fact and Opinion

▶ Use this chart to identify facts and opinions from "Across Gender Lines" and "Making It Stop."

Statement	Fact or Opinion?	How Do I Know?
Girl cyberbullies are harsher critics than boys.	opinion	This statement expresses a judgment about girl cyberbullies.
Cyberbullies who hassle online gamers are called "griefers."		
Surveys show many victims of cyberbullying don't tell their parents.		
Keeping quiet about cyberbullying is not a good idea.		

TROUBLE AT YOUR FINGERTIPS

The Big Idea

Write What is this article mainly about?

____

____

____

VOCABULARY BUILDER

Target Word

negative

neg•a•tive (adjective)

Rate it: ① ② ③

Meaning

____

____

____

Example

____

____

____

React

Compare yourself to the teens who answered the survey. How long could you go without technology? What would you miss most about it?

In 2005, researchers at Johns Hopkins University conducted a study to find out how technology is affecting teenagers' lives.

The results may alarm you.

>> Hooked on Technology

As of 2005, almost nine out of ten teens were online. More than half had cell phones. Recently, a survey of more than 1,000 students ages 12 to 17 revealed the **negative** aspects of teens' love of technology. Huge numbers of teens spend an inappropriate proportion of their time online or on the phone. Forty percent of students surveyed say they stay logged onto the Internet for a week or more at a time. Sixty-two percent said they can't live without technology for more than a few days. One in four said they hate to be disconnected for even one minute!

These results are shocking and disturbing, researchers feel. They say that students who spend so much time "connected" often suffer harsh consequences. These teens tend to have brief attention spans, limited patience, and difficulty thinking independently. Indeed, 81 percent of students surveyed say they call their parents to ask questions, rather than finding answers for themselves. Over half said they get frustrated if they can't reach someone immediately. →

Words to Know! **brief** *(adj.)* short

Fact and Opinion

1. **Underline** Find a fact about how many students were surveyed.

2. **Write** How do you know the statement you found is a fact?

____

____

3. **Circle** Find a sentence that tells how researchers feel about the survey results.

4. **Star** How do you know that this statement is an opinion?

Review: Summarize

Find the topic and important details in the section "Hooked on Technology." Then, turn to a partner and summarize the section.

Active Reading

Circle ▶ Find two reasons that some teens go over the minute plans on their cell phones.

VOCABULARY BUILDER

Target Word

modify

mod•i•fy (verb)

Rate it: ① ② ③

Meaning

____

____

____

Example

____

____

____

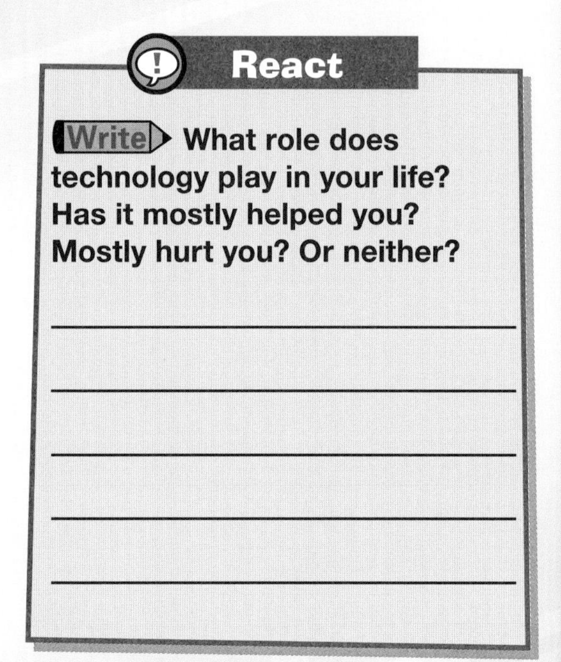

React

Write ▶ **What role does technology play in your life? Has it mostly helped you? Mostly hurt you? Or neither?**

____

____

____

____

____

>> One Student's Story

Experts say relying too much on technology can impair your ability to function on your own. Stephanie, 16, is a case in point. When she gets home from school, she goes online immediately—sometimes until 3 A.M. Often, she is simultaneously on the phone. "I'm way too dependent on my cell phone," she admits. Recently, Stephanie traveled to a country where her phone didn't work. "One afternoon I was shopping, and I couldn't decide what to buy," she recalls. "I felt helpless. I thought, if my cell worked here, I could just ask my friends."

Habits like Stephanie's aren't just brain-deadening. As she can verify, they're expensive! Stephanie owes her parents $2,000 in excess phone charges. And she is not alone. Fifty-two percent of survey respondents say they've gone over their cell phone's minute plans. They either talk too much or send too many text messages.

>> Out of Focus

For teens like Stephanie, the amount of information they take in through technology is overwhelming. Too many activities compete for their attention, so they often do several things simultaneously. Often, it's their school performance that suffers. Forty-four percent of teens surveyed send text messages during class. One in three are easily distracted from homework. A whopping 97 percent say they always watch TV or surf the Internet while studying.

Teens even find it tough to invest time in other leisure activities. "Sometimes I'd like to read a book," says Tony, 15. "But 'disconnecting' is scary.

Words to Know! **impair** *(v.)* damage or make less good

I'm afraid I'm missing what my friends are talking about online."

Are you addicted to technology? Resolve to **modify** your behavior. These tips may help:

1. **Log off for at least a half hour a day.**
2. **Turn off your cell phone during class.**
3. **IM with only one or two people at a time.**
4. **Set your email to register new messages only every half hour.**
5. **Turn off your phone when you're with friends.**

By dedicating your attention to one thing at a time, you'll do better at everything! END

TEXT FEATURE Reading a Bar Graph

WHAT TEENS DO ONLINE

Below are percentages of U.S. teens who do these online activities:

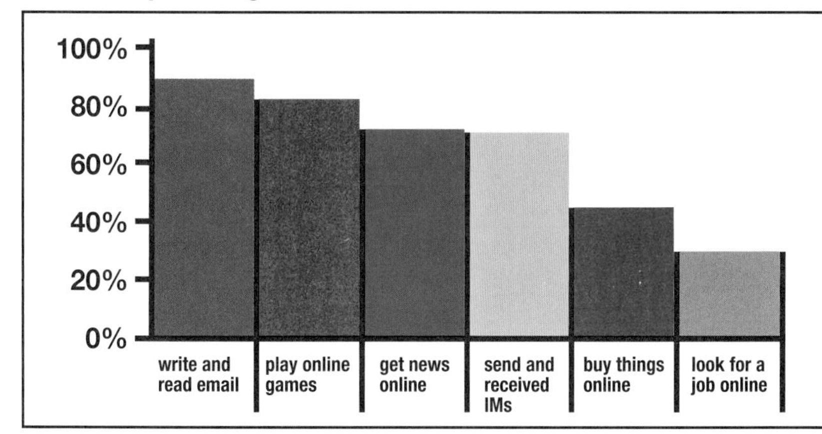

A bar graph shows how different pieces of information relate to each other.

1. What information does this bar graph show?

Ⓐ what percentage of their time teens spend online

Ⓑ what percentage of teens own their own computers

Ⓒ what percentage of teens do different activities online

2. What percentage of teens write and read email?

Ⓐ about 90% Ⓒ almost 80%

Ⓑ 99% Ⓓ half

3. Do more teens shop online or get news online?

____

Source: Pew Internet & American Life Project

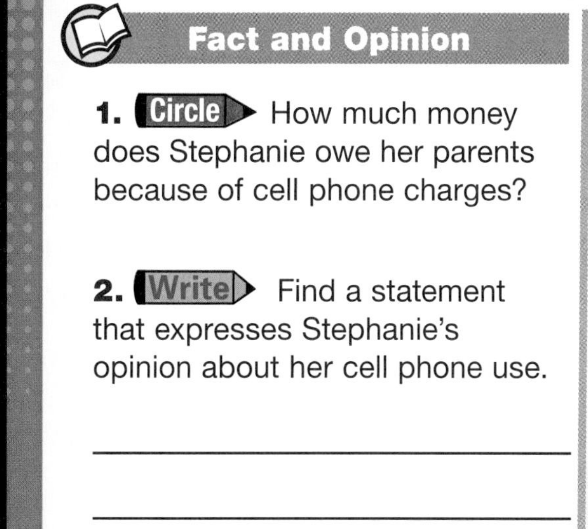

Fact and Opinion

1. **Circle** How much money does Stephanie owe her parents because of cell phone charges?

2. **Write** Find a statement that expresses Stephanie's opinion about her cell phone use.

____

____

____

____

____

____

Skills Check

1. **Circle** How many teens say they send text messages in class?

2. **Write** Find two more facts about teens, technology, and homework.

- ______________________________

____

____

- ______________________________

____

____

TAKE THE WORD CHALLENGE

Start

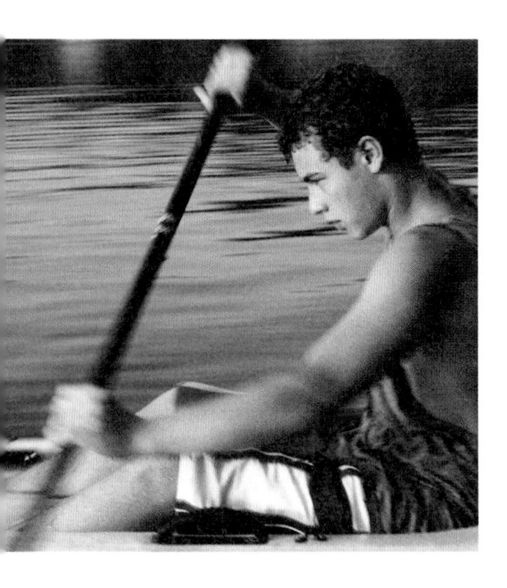

1 Think about it. Where is it appropriate to wear a swimsuit? Write ***A*** for *appropriate* or ***I*** for *inappropriate* next to each place listed below.

_____ at school

_____ on the beach

_____ at a football game

_____ in the grocery store

_____ to a party

2 Evaluate. What's your opinion? Become a music critic, a movie critic, and a literary critic. Fill in your choice for each category below:

____
Year's worst song

____
Year's best movie

____
Year's most interesting book

3 Homophones

Homophones are words that sound alike but have different meanings and spellings. Examples are *flower* and *flour* or *threw* and *through*.

Match each word to its homophone below.

bored	cell	haul

board: _______________________

hall: _______________________

sell: _______________________

Fill in the sentences with two new homophones.

Can you help me remove the__________ from this CD?

It's the new album by my favorite __________ .

4 Evaluate. Are the following negative or positive ways to use technology? Write ***N*** or ***P*** next to each way.

_____ To email a love note to your crush

_____ To play video games with people in other cities

_____ To look up information for a report

_____ To send a threatening IM to that kid who called you a name at school

_____ To buy gifts online for all your friends

_____ To hassle a gamer who beat you at your favorite game

5

Circle one in each row. Which one takes up a larger proportion of your time?

playing sports ***OR*** watching movies

studying ***OR*** hanging out with friends

riding in a car ***OR*** walking

6

Evaluate. What are two things you can conclude about the girl pictured below?

Conclusion 1: ______________________

____

Conclusion 2: ______________________

____

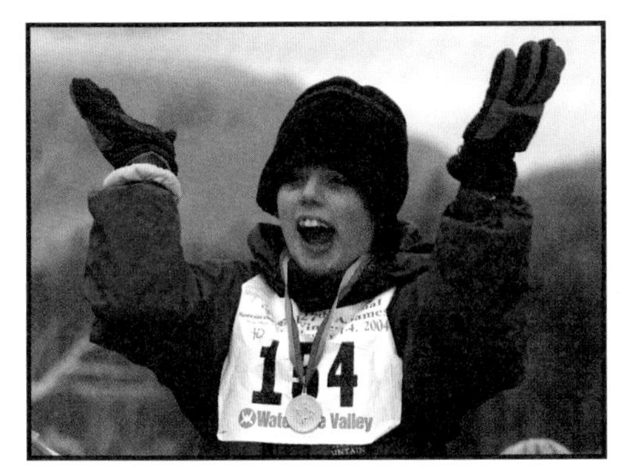

7

Complete the sentences. Fill in each blank with the correct form of manipulate from below.

manipulate
manipulator
manipulation

Only a real ____________ would try to cause trouble between friends by sending fake emails. That kind of ____________ is totally mean and wrong. I hope no one ever tries to ____________ me that way.

8 Compound Words

I'll check the **guidebook** when we get to the **campground**.

A **compound word** is made up of two smaller words. For example:

over + turn = *overturn*

Draw a line to separate these compound words into two words.

bedroom	**cupcake**	**campground**
homework	**guidebook**	**daydream**

Use four of the compound words above to fill in the blanks in the sentences below.

I was in my ____________ doing my ____________. My paper was due the next day. But I found it hard to focus. I kept having this ____________ about eating a ____________.

9

Explain. What aspect of your life would you most like to modify? Why?

____

____

10

Complete the sentences. Fill in each blank with the correct form of modify from below.

modify | **modified** | **modification**

Last year, my sister ____________ her bike so it would go faster. This year, I want her to help me ____________ mine. She is an expert at bike ____________!

Finish

Writing Focus

Persuasive Paragraph

A **persuasive paragraph** tries to convince the reader to share the writer's opinions.

▶ **Read Sam's paragraph about text messaging.**

Student Model

Say No to Text Messaging

by Sam Lee

I strongly believe that the worst problem teens have with technology is text messaging. First of all, many students send and receive text messages during class, when they're supposed to be learning. A second reason is that texting has become a substitute for talking. Having a real conversation is a more appropriate way to communicate with friends. The most important problem with text messaging is that it gets many teens into money trouble. When the cell phone bill comes, they have gone over their limit and are hit with big charges. In conclusion, I think teens should think twice before becoming slaves to text messaging.

Parts of a Persuasive Paragraph

▶ **Find these parts of Sam's persuasive paragraph.**

1. Underline the sentence that states the writer's **opinion**.
2. Check three **reasons** that support the opinion.
3. Put a box around the reason you think is **strongest**.
4. Circle the **linking words** that connect the ideas.
5. Put a star before the sentence that **restates** the writer's opinion.

Brainstorm

▶ **Read the writing prompt in the middle of the idea web. Then use the boxes to help you brainstorm your ideas.**

Email Trouble

Cell Phone Trouble

Writing Prompt:
Which type of technology gets teens in the biggest trouble? Write a persuasive paragraph about it.

Internet Trouble

Trouble with Other Technology

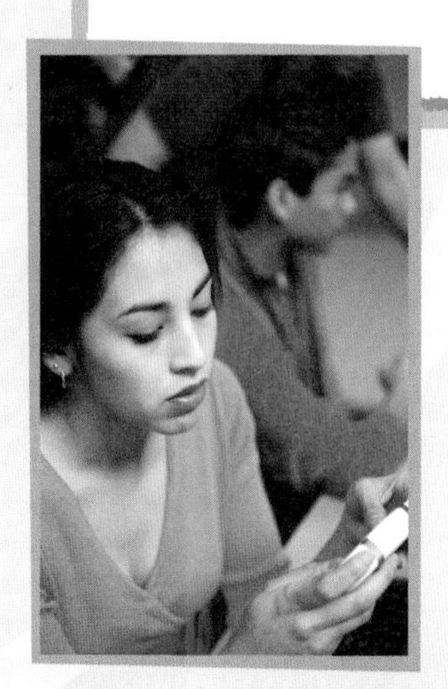

Plan Your Paragraph

Writing Prompt: Which type of technology gets teens in the most trouble? Write a paragraph about why you think so.

▶ **Use this chart to plan and organize your paragraph.**

Word Choices

____

____

____

____

____

Your Opinion

- *I strongly believe that . . .*
- *Many teens have problems . . .*
- *The worst problem with technology . . .*

Reason 1

- *First of all, . . .*
- *The first reason . . .*
- *To begin with, . . .*

Reason 2

- *A second reason is that . . .*
- *In addition, . . .*
- *Another important point . . .*

Reason 3

- *The most important problem is . . .*
- *Finally, . . .*
- *Most of all, . . .*

Ending

- *In conclusion, . . .*
- *To sum up, . . .*
- *For these reasons,*

Write Your Paragraph

▶ **Use this writing frame to write a first draft of your paragraph.**

____
(title)

I strongly believe that ______________________
____
____
____

First of all, ________________________________
____
____
____

A second reason is that ______________________
____
____
____

The most important problem is _______________
____
____
____

In conclusion, ______________________________
____
____
____
____

Revise

▶ **Rate your paragraph. Then have a writing partner rate it.**

Scoring Guide			
weak	okay	good	strong
1	2	3	4

1. Does the first sentence clearly state the writer's **opinion**?

Self	1	2	3	4
Partner	1	2	3	4

2. Is the opinion supported by several **reasons**?

Self	1	2	3	4
Partner	1	2	3	4

3. Are the reasons given **strong** and **convincing**?

Self	1	2	3	4
Partner	1	2	3	4

4. Do **linking words** connect the ideas?

Self	1	2	3	4
Partner	1	2	3	4

5. Does the concluding sentence **restate** the writer's opinion?

Self	1	2	3	4
Partner	1	2	3	4

▶ **Now revise your paragraph to make it stronger.**

Grammar Using Irregular Verbs

Most past-tense verbs end in *–ed.* **Irregular verbs** do not.

- You must remember the different spellings of irregular past-tense verbs.
- The verb *to be* is a common irregular verb. Its present-tense forms are I am, you are, he/she is. Its past-tense forms are I was, you were, he was.

Example

Present-Tense Verb	Past-Tense Verb
I am online right now.	I was online yesterday.
Hector sends lots of emails.	He sent me a message today.
She knows his cell now.	She knew his old number.

► **Circle the correct past-tense verb in each sentence below.**

1. They [**bring** **brought**] their laptops to yesterday's assembly.
2. I was upset when someone [**steal stole**] my new cell phone.
3. After her last cell phone bill, she [**begin began**] to talk less.
4. The quiet girl [**became become**] a bully online.
5. My digital camera [**break broke**] when I dropped it.
6. He [**forget forgot**] to check his email last night.

► **Rewrite the sentences below using the past-tense form of the verb.**

7. Her cell phone **ring** in the middle of the concert.

____

8. Everyone in class **see** the inappropriate email.

____

9. I **give** my old computer to my little brother.

____

10. My friend **speak** so fast that I couldn't understand him.

____

Look at the sentences in your own draft on page 129. Do all sentences use correct verb forms? Fix the ones that don't.

Mechanics Using Commas With Introductory Words

A **comma** follows an opening word or phrase at the beginning of a sentence.

- *Yes, No, Next,* and *Later* are examples of opening words.
- *In addition* and *After a while* are examples of opening phrases.

Example

Correct	Incorrect
Later, they emailed each other.	Later they emailed each other.
In addition, my phone broke.	In addition my phone broke.

▶ **Find and correct five errors in this paragraph.**

Student Model

A big problem with tekhnology is teens using cell phones in public. First of all teens disturb other people with their conversations. There loud voices are so inappropriate. Another problem is when they try to talk and simultaneously do something else. I was almost ran over by a kid on a skateboard talking on his cell phone. In addition teens talk about private things in public. I overheard one boy say terrible things about his girlfriend in the mall. That's my opinion!

Check and Correct

- ❑ Circle two spelling errors and correct them.
- ❑ Underline one verb-tense error and correct it.
- ❑ Insert two missing commas.

Look at the sentences in your own draft on page 129. Are opening phrases and words followed by commas? Fix the ones that aren't.

Final Draft/Present

▶ **Write a final draft of your paragraph on paper or the computer. Check it again and correct any errors before you present it.**

Careers

Cell Phone Salesperson

More than 150 million people in the United States own a cell phone. Paul Nguyen sells cell phones for a living. He is the manager at Unicell Communications in Chicago, Illinois. Every day, he helps people pick out new phones or purchase gadgets for their phones. Paul loves his job and sees it as a service to his community. "Cell phones are a growing technology," he says. "And I enjoy helping people learn how to use them."

Name: Paul Nguyen

Hometown: Chicago, Illinois

Job: Cell Phone Salesperson

Duties:
- Repair phones
- Sell phones to customers
- Activate new cell phone accounts
- Manage part-time employees
- Design advertising brochures

Skills:
- Communicating and negotiating
- Providing customer service
- Solving problems creatively
- Keeping up with the latest technology

Similar Jobs:
- Sales Manager
- Technology Advisor

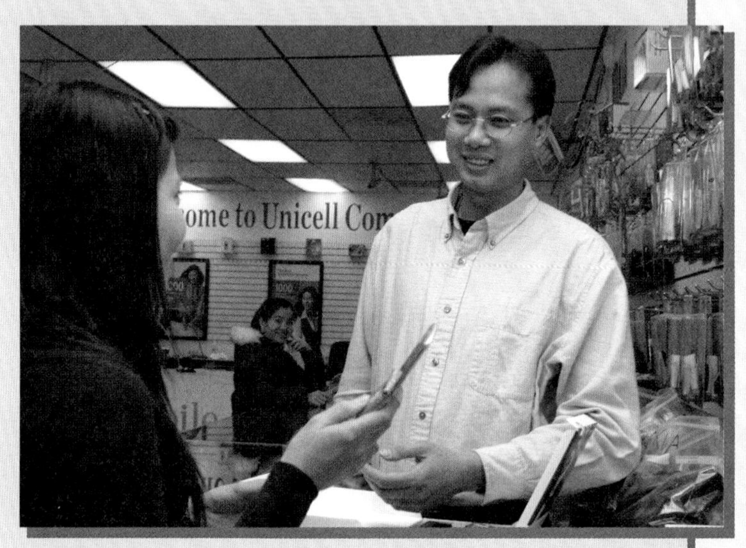

A customer asks Paul for advice before buying a new phone.

Pay: $22,000 to $35,000 per year

Education: High School Degree

Ask Yourself

1. **Circle** Find one thing you would enjoy about this job.
2. **Underline** Find one thing that would make this job difficult for you.
3. How much do you want this job?
   - ❑ I don't want it.
   - ❑ I might want it.
   - ❑ I really want it.

Real-World Skills

Choosing a Cell-Phone Minutes Plan

Using more minutes than your cell phone plan allows is expensive! But you don't want to pay for more than you need. When Paul Nguyen sells a new phone, he helps the customer choose an appropriate minute plan. Read and compare these three monthly plans. Then answer the questions below.

	(Per Month)	Weekdays	Weeknights	Weekends	Texting
Plan A	$25	250 minutes	no extra minutes	unlimited minutes	0 messages
Plan B	$40	600 minutes	unlimited minutes	unlimited minutes	20 messages
Plan C	$60	1500 minutes	unlimited minutes	unlimited minutes	50 messages

Charge for using extra minutes: 40 cents per minute (all plans)
Charge for sending extra text messages: 20 cents per message (all plans)

▶ **Fill in the circle next to each correct answer.**

1. What is the charge for using extra minutes?
Ⓐ 40 cents per minute
Ⓑ $40 per minute
Ⓒ 20 cents per minute
Ⓓ $25 per minute

2. If you spend 1000 weekday minutes on the phone every month, which is the best plan for you?
Ⓐ any of the plans
Ⓑ Plan A
Ⓒ Plan B
Ⓓ Plan C

3. Which plan gives you no extra weeknight minutes?
Ⓐ Plan A
Ⓑ Plan B
Ⓒ Plan C
Ⓓ both Plan B and Plan C

4. Which plan lets you send 20 text messages without an extra charge?
Ⓐ Plan A
Ⓑ Plan B
Ⓒ none of the plans
Ⓓ both Plan A and Plan B

5. What is the charge for using 100 extra minutes on any plan?
Ⓐ nothing
Ⓑ $25
Ⓒ $40
Ⓓ $60

Comprehension

► **Fill in the circle next to the correct answer.**

1. Another kind of technology that could be included in this article is __________.

Ⓐ a microwave
Ⓑ a blow dryer
Ⓒ a digital watch
Ⓓ a video-game player

Here's a tip.
You can answer some questions by looking directly in the text. For other questions, you have to combine what you already know with what you've read.

2. Which sentence gives the best summary of "Cyberbullies"?

Ⓐ Cyberbullies steal other kids' screen names.
Ⓑ Blogs are dangerous for teens to use.
Ⓒ Cyberbullies use technology as a weapon to hurt others.
Ⓓ Traditional bullies are meaner than cyberbullies.

3. Which of the following statements is an opinion?

Ⓐ Many teenagers use the Internet after school.
Ⓑ Most schools have telephones in the office.
Ⓒ You should never use a cell phone during class.
Ⓓ A survey showed technology can have negative effects.

4. How could the following fact be checked? *Sixty-five percent of students in our class are connected to the Internet at home.*

Ⓐ by looking in an encyclopedia
Ⓑ by taking a survey of the class
Ⓒ by looking on the Internet
Ⓓ by asking the teacher's opinion

5. What was the author's purpose for writing "Trouble at Your Fingertips"?

Ⓐ to inform readers about problems teens have with technology
Ⓑ to entertain readers with humorous stories about teens and technology
Ⓒ to persuade readers to stop using cell phones and email
Ⓓ to inform readers about the problem of cyberbullying

Vocabulary

▶ **Fill in the circle next to the correct definition of the underlined word.**

1. I can use two kinds of technology simultaneously.
   Ⓐ devices, at different times
   Ⓑ electronic products, at the same time
   Ⓒ repairmen, in the same way
   Ⓓ suitable, quickly

2. What proportion of your day do you spend on a telephone or cell phone?
   Ⓐ height and width
   Ⓑ proper amount
   Ⓒ number of minutes
   Ⓓ part or share

3. Critics say cell phones are not appropriate in class.
   Ⓐ people against, suitable
   Ⓑ incorrect people, noisy
   Ⓒ teachers, distracting
   Ⓓ people in favor of, useful

▶ **Fill in the circle next to the correct answer.**

4. Which two words are homophones?
   Ⓐ phone/fond
   Ⓑ critic/critical
   Ⓒ cell/sell
   Ⓓ trouble/double

5. Which word is a compound word?
   Ⓐ simultaneously
   Ⓑ cyberbullies
   Ⓒ manipulating
   Ⓓ dependent

Short Answer

▶ **Use what you've read in this Workshop to answer the question below. Check your spelling and grammar.**

Should there be laws against cyberbullying? Explain why or why not.

____

____

____

____

WORKSHOP 6

LITERATURE

Comprehension Focus
Story Elements

READINGS
1 ***To Build a Fire*** >> Short Story
2 ***from "Staying Alive"*** >> Poetry

Facing the Elements

What does it take to stay alive in the harshest places on earth? In "To Build a Fire," you'll read about one man's journey through the frozen wilderness of the Yukon Territory in Canada. Will he make it to camp, or freeze to death trying?

"To Build a Fire" is one of Jack London's most famous stories. He wrote it after traveling in the Yukon, where he saw the struggle with nature firsthand. London survived his adventures, but many others didn't.

Can anyone really prepare for nature's most extreme conditions? Get ready to face the elements.

Jack London wrote stories of survival that are considered American classics.

VOCABULARY BUILDER

Target Word ▶ Read the Target Words. Rate each one using the scale below.*	Meaning ▶ Read the Target Word meanings. Write in the missing ones.	Example ▶ Finish the Target Word examples below. Write in the missing ones.
elements *el•e•ments* *(noun)* ① ② ③		Always be prepared to face the **elements**. 
hostile *hos•tile* *(adjective)* ① ② ③	very unfriendly	
instinct *in•stinct* *(noun)* ① ② ③		In an emergency, my instinct would be to . . .
reaction *re•ac•tion* *(noun)* ① ② ③	an action in response to something	
sufficient *suf•fi•cient* *(adjective)* ① ② ③		I need sufficient ______ in order to . . .

*Rating Scale

① = I don't know it at all.
② = I've seen it before.
③ = I know it and use it.

Comprehension Focus

Story Elements

A **short story** like "To Build a Fire" is a brief piece of fiction. To understand a short story, look for four elements:

1. **Setting** is where and when the story takes place. This story takes place in the Yukon Territory of northern Canada in the early 1900s.

2. **Characters** are the people in the story. There are two characters in this story.

the man,
a logger in the Yukon

the dog,
a big, gray husky

3. **Plot** is the sequence of events in a story. The plot contains a problem, or conflict, that the main character needs to solve. In "To Build a Fire," the main character and a dog set out on a journey in the bitter cold. The man must figure out how to survive when he becomes weary and frostbitten. What price will he pay for facing the elements?

4. **Theme** is the message about life that the author wants to express.

▶ **Turn the page to begin reading the man's story.**

To Build a Fire

► **Fill in this chart as you reread the story.**

	Part 1 (pp. 140–141)	Part 2 (pp. 142–145)	Part 3 (pp. 146–149)
Setting	Time and Place: 9:00 A.M.; near the Yukon River Time and Place:	Time and Place: Time and Place:	Time and Place: Time and Place:
Character	Who is the main character? Describe him/her:	How does the character change?	What is the character like now?
Plot Events	What happens at the beginning of the story?	What happens in the middle of the story?	How does the story end?
Theme	Author's message:		

Active Reading

Write Why is the Yukon River hidden from sight?

VOCABULARY BUILDER

Target Word

eventually

e•ven•tu•al•ly (adverb)

Rate it:  

Meaning

Example

React

Would you be prepared to survive in the cold wilderness? Why or why not?

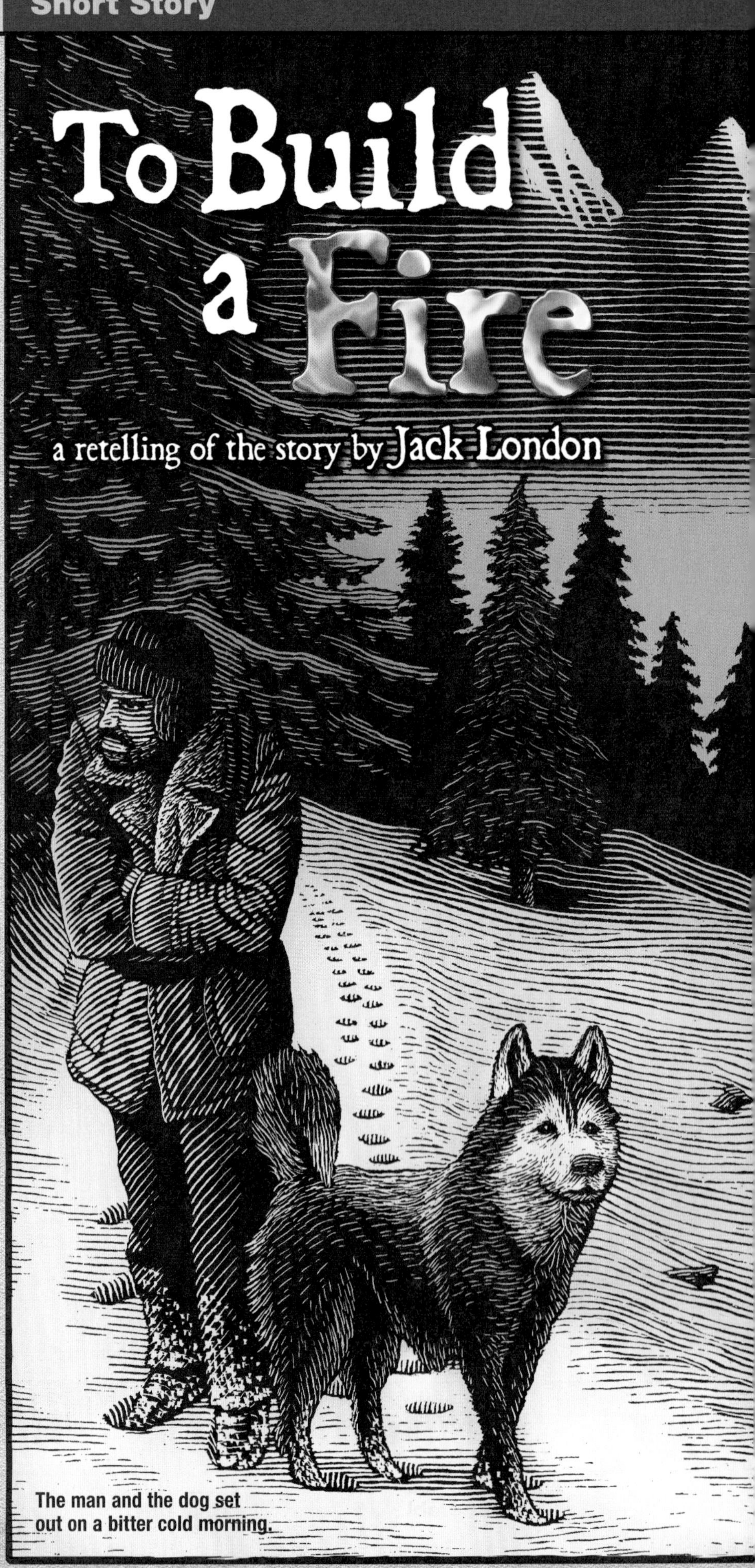

To Build a Fire

a retelling of the story by Jack London

The man and the dog set out on a bitter cold morning.

Day had broken cold and gray—exceedingly cold and gray. It was still cold and gray when the man left the main Yukon trail and climbed a high bank to a smaller trail that led eastward. It was a steep bank, and he paused for breath at the top, excusing the act by glancing at his watch.

It was nine o'clock, but there was no sun this far north. It was a clear day, yet there was a subtle gloom that made the day dark without the light of the sun. Despite the gloom, the man did not feel worried. It had been days since he had seen the sun and he knew that more days must pass before **eventually** he would see it above the skyline again.

The man looked back to where the Yukon River lay a mile wide and hidden under three feet of ice. On top of this ice were as many feet of snow. North and south, as far as he could see, was pure white. But all of it—the mysterious trail, the absent sun, the tremendous cold, and the strangeness and weirdness of it all—made no impression on the man.

The trouble was that the man was without imagination. He was quick and alert in the things in life, but only in the things, and not in their meanings. To him, fifty degrees below zero simply meant a danger of frostbite and the need for warm clothes. It did not lead him to think about how vulnerable he was in this frozen wilderness. Nor did it lead him to have humility about his place in the universe. ➜

Words to Know! **vulnerable** *(adj.)* easily harmed or attacked

Story Elements

Setting

1. Circle Find a sentence or phrase that describes the day.

Character

2. Underline Find a sentence that tells how the man feels about the gloomy day.

Plot

3. Write At the beginning of the story, the man has left the main trail. What kind of trail is he on now?

____

____

____

Now go to page 139. Add details to Part 1 of the chart.

Active Reading

Star What does the man forget to do before eating?

VOCABULARY BUILDER

Target Word

assume

as•sume (verb)

Rate it: ① ② ③

Meaning

____

____

____

Example

____

____

____

React

Do you think the dog should stay with the man? Or should it go back to the camp? Explain your answer.

The dog was wiser about the cold than the man, and its instinct told it that it was too cold to travel.

He turned and spat, and was startled by a sharp crackle. He knew that at fifty below spit crackled on the snow, but this spit had crackled in the air, which meant that it was colder than fifty below.

But it did not matter. He was bound for the old mine near Henderson Creek, where his friends were already gathered. He had come a different way, alone, to check on the chances of getting out logs in the spring.

The man **assumed** that by six o'clock, he would be in camp. A fire would be going, and a hot supper would be ready. He had his lunch with him, under his shirt. In this weather the only way to keep food from freezing was to place it against naked skin.

He plunged along the trail among the big spruce trees. At his heel trotted a dog, a big native husky, gray-coated and not noticeably different from its brother, the wild wolf.

The animal was depressed by the tremendous cold. The dog was wiser about the cold than the man, and its instinct told it that it was too cold to travel. In reality, it was not just 50 below, but 75 degrees below zero. The dog knew that the man should not brave the elements in such cold but should instead go to camp or seek shelter and build a fire. The dog had learned fire and it wanted fire. Or else it wanted to burrow under the snow and cuddle in its own warmth, away from the air.

The dog's muzzle and eyelashes were white with frost from its frozen breath. The man's red beard and mustache were frozen, too. He was chewing tobacco, and the juice had formed an amber-colored ice beard on his chin.

Words to Know!	**plunged** *(v.)* moved through with force

Soon, the man and the dog were warming up by the fire.

At 12:30 the man and the dog reached the fork of the creek, the man pleased at the speed they had made. He stopped, unbuttoned his jacket, and took out his lunch. His fingers were exposed to the freezing air for only a few seconds, but instantly they turned numb. He struck them against his leg and tried to take a bite of biscuit and bacon. But he could not eat because his ice beard prevented him.

Suddenly he realized that he had forgotten to build a fire and thaw out. He chuckled at his foolishness, found some twigs, and got out his matches. He soon had a roaring fire, in the heat of which he thawed the ice from his face and ate. The dog stretched out close to the fire.

Story Elements

Setting

1. **Circle** Where is the man going?

Write Where does he stop at 12:30?

____

____

Character

2. **Write** What does the dog's instinct tell it about the weather?

____

____

____

____

Plot

3. **Write** List two important events that happen in this part of the story.

1. ______________________________

____

____

2. ______________________________

____

____

Active Reading

Star The old man at Sulphur Creek gives the man two pieces of advice. What is one of them?

VOCABULARY BUILDER

Target Word

temporary

tem•po•rar•y (adjective)

Rate it: ① ② ③

Meaning

____

____

____

Example

____

____

____

React

Write **Some people say that humans can never conquer nature. Is this man winning his battle against nature? Explain your answer.**

____

____

____

When he had finished eating, the man pulled on his mittens and started out again. The dog yearned to go back to the fire. The man did not understand the seriousness of the cold, but the dog had inherited the knowledge from its ancestors. It knew how foolish it was to walk in such fearful cold. But it did not try to express its doubt to the man. It was not concerned with his welfare, but only with its own. Still, when the man whistled and spoke with the sound of whiplashes, the dog's reaction was to follow him.

There were hidden springs under the snow and ice, springs that bubbled out from the hillsides. They never froze, and they were deadly traps. They hid pools of water that might be three feet deep. Up until now, the man had seen no signs of any of these springs.

Then it happened. At a place where the soft, unbroken snow looked solid, the man broke through, wetting himself halfway to the knees.

Words to Know!	**yearned** *(v.)* wanted something very much

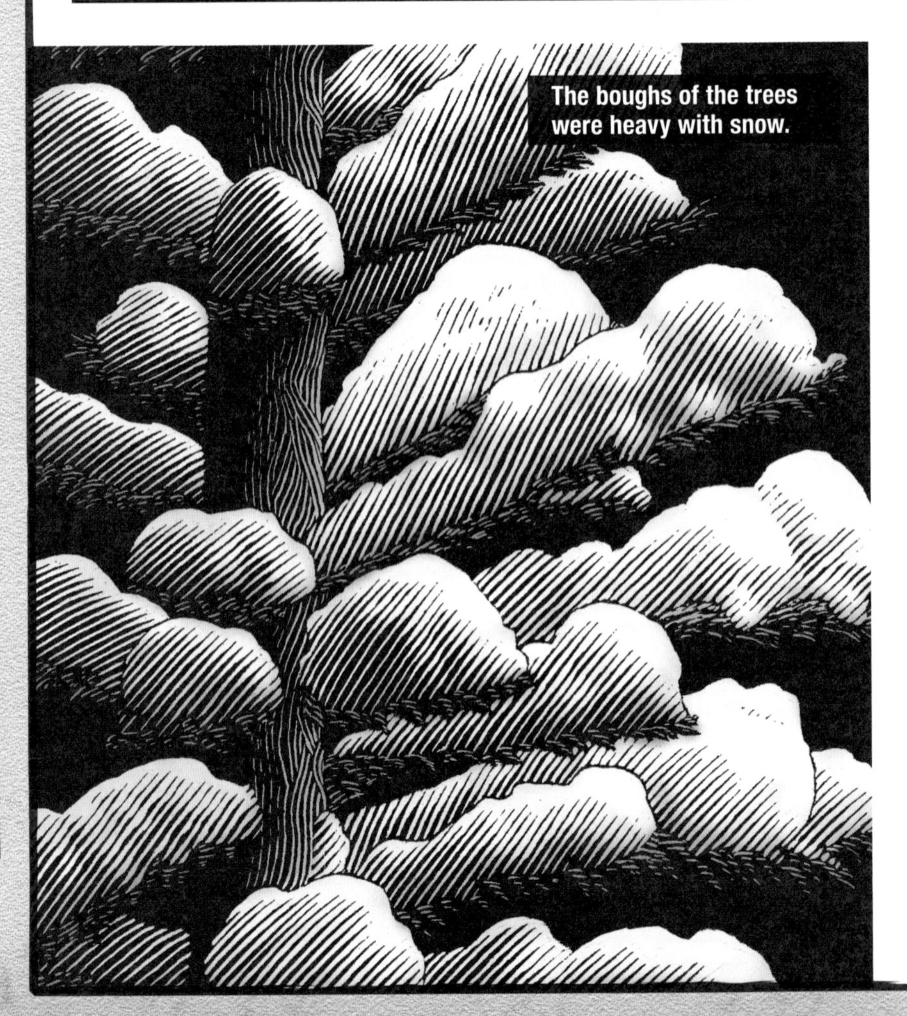

The boughs of the trees were heavy with snow.

Already, all sensation had left his feet, his fingers were numb, and his nose and cheeks were freezing.

He cursed. This would delay him an hour, since now he would have to build a fire and dry out. He climbed the bank and found a sufficient amount of dry firewood. He worked slowly and carefully, with great concentration, knowing his danger. At 75 below zero, a man must not fail in his first attempt to build a fire. An old man on Sulphur Creek had told him that, and now he was thankful for the advice. Already, all sensation had left his feet, his fingers were numb, and his nose and cheeks were freezing.

The man struck a match, and soon the fire started. He was relieved to be safe, but he remembered the words of the old-timer. The man had been very serious in laying down the law that no man must travel alone in the Klondike after it got to be fifty below. Well, here he was. He had had the accident, he was alone, and he had saved himself. The break in his journey would only be **temporary**. All a man had to do was to keep his head, and he would be all right.

Still, it was surprising how fast his cheeks and nose were freezing. And his fingers were now lifeless. When he touched a twig, he had to look to see whether he had hold of it.

He started to untie his moccasins, which were coated with ice. His socks were like sheaths of iron, and the moccasin strings were like rods of twisted steel. He drew his knife, but before he could cut the strings, it happened.

He should have known better, building the fire under a spruce tree. The tree had a weight of snow on its boughs. Now, high up in the tree, a bough dropped its load of snow, which fell on the boughs beneath, breaking them. The snow fell like an avalanche on the man and the fire. The fire was blotted out!

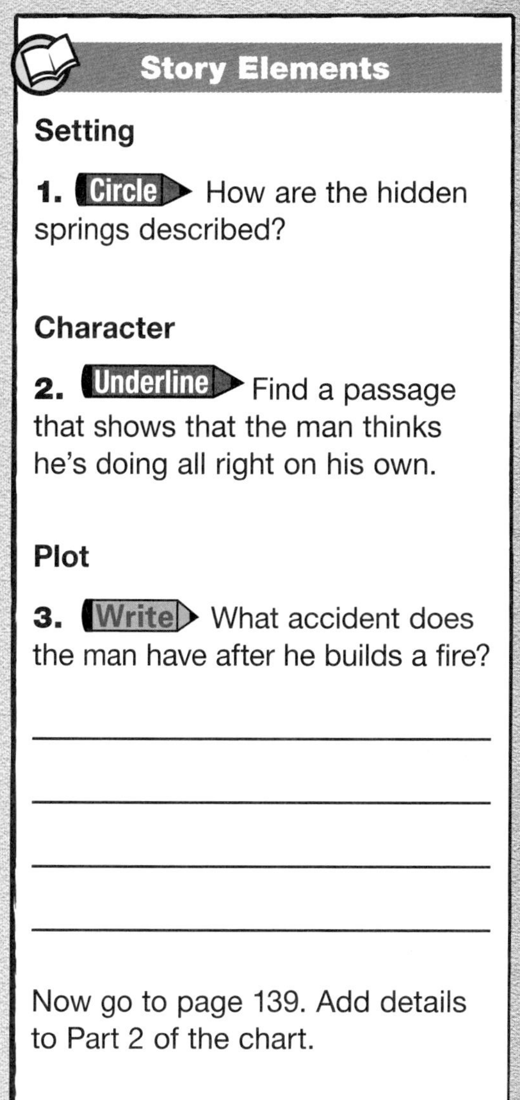

Story Elements

Setting

1. Circle ▶ How are the hidden springs described?

Character

2. Underline ▶ Find a passage that shows that the man thinks he's doing all right on his own.

Plot

3. Write ▶ What accident does the man have after he builds a fire?

____

____

____

____

Now go to page 139. Add details to Part 2 of the chart.

Review: Fact and Opinion

Write ▶ Write whether each statement is a fact or an opinion.

1. The man is foolish.

____

2. The temperature is 75 degrees below zero.

____

Active Reading

Star How do the man's fingers feel?

VOCABULARY BUILDER

Target Word

speculate
spec•u•late (verb)

Rate it: ① ② ③

Meaning

____

____

____

Example

____

____

____

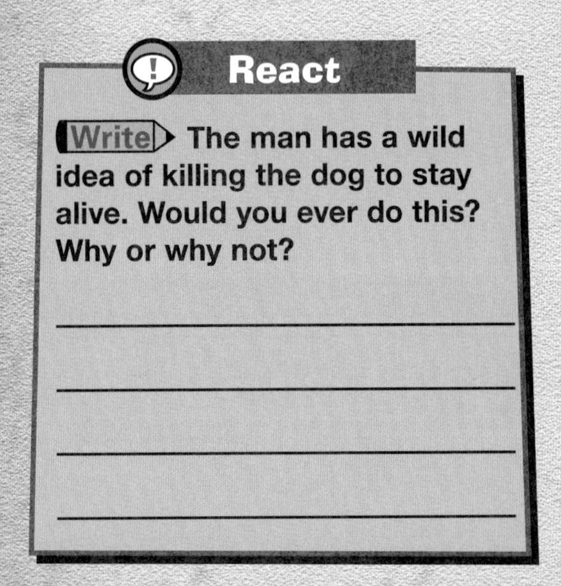

The dog sat in the snow, its wolf-brush of a tail curled warmly over its feet, and the man felt a surge of envy.

The man's reaction was complete shock. It was as if he had heard his own sentence of death. He stared at the spot where the fire had been. Then he grew very calm. Perhaps the old-timer on Sulphur Creek was right. He should have had a trail mate. Well, he must build the fire over again. Even if he succeeded, he would probably lose some toes, as his feet were badly frozen now.

He gathered grass and twigs. The dog sat and watched him, with yearning in its eyes. It looked upon him as the fire-provider, and the fire was slow in coming.

The man reached in his pocket for a piece of bark. He could not feel it with his fingers. He could hear it rustling as he fumbled for it, but he could not get hold of it. He knew that his feet were freezing, and he fought against panic. He thrashed and beat his arms and hands. The dog sat in the snow, its wolf-brush of a tail curled warmly over its feet, and the man felt a surge of envy.

A faint tingling began in his beaten fingers. Then it turned into a stinging ache. The man stripped the mitten from his right hand and got out the bark. But his fingers were already going numb again, and he could not separate one of his matches from the others. He managed to get the whole bunch of matches between the heels of his hands and carried the bunch to his mouth.

He got one match and dropped it in his lap. But he could not pick it up. Then he devised a way. He picked it up in his teeth and scratched it on his leg. Twenty times he scratched, before he succeeded in lighting it. As it flamed, he held the match with his teeth to the bark. The burning sulphur caused him to cough. The match fell in the snow.

Words to Know! **devised** *(v.)* planned

At last, he caught the whole bunch of matches between his hands and scratched them along his leg. They flared into flame—seventy sulphur matches at once. He held them to the birch bark. Then, with the heels of his hands, he placed grasses and twigs on the flame. But he grew more awkward, and a large piece of green moss fell on the little fire, causing it to go out. The fire-provider had failed to make a fire.

His eyes fell on the dog, and a wild idea came into his head. He began to **speculate** about how he could survive. He would kill the dog and bury his hands in the warm body until the numbness went. Then he could build another fire. ➔

The man awkwardly held a handful of matches.

Story Elements

Setting

1. Write What effect is the cold weather having on the man?

____

____

____

____

Character

2. Write How is the man's outlook on his situation changing?

____

____

____

____

Plot

3. Write List two important events that happen in this part of the story.

1. __________________________

____

____

2. __________________________

____

____

The man knew he was losing his battle with the deep, frozen wilderness. He sat up and thought of meeting death with dignity.

He called the dog to him, but his voice betrayed a strange note of fear that frightened the animal. It sensed danger. It flattened its ears down, its demeanor becoming slightly hostile. Its restless, hunching movements and the liftings and shiftings of its forefeet became more pronounced. It would not come to the man.

He crawled toward the dog, his arms flashing out to it. But his hands would not clutch because there was neither bend nor feeling in his fingers. Before the dog could get away, he circled its body with his arms. He sat in the snow, while it snarled and whined and struggled.

Then he realized that he could not kill the dog with his helpless hands. He released it, and it plunged wildly away with its tail between its legs, still snarling.

Now the man knew that it was a matter of life and death, with the chances against him. In a panic, he turned and ran up the old, dim trail. The dog kept up with him. Maybe, if he ran on, his feet would thaw out, and he would reach camp and the boys. However, his theory had one flaw—he lacked sufficient **endurance**. Several times he stumbled, and finally he tottered, crumpled up, and fell. The dog curled its tail over its forefeet and sat in front of him, eager and intent.

The man knew he was losing his battle with the deep, frozen wilderness. He sat up and thought of meeting death with dignity. However, the thought did not come to him in quite such terms. It merely occurred to him that he was making a fool of himself. He was bound to freeze anyway, so he might as well take it decently. With this newfound peace of mind came drowsiness. A good

Words to Know!	**demeanor** *(n.)* the way in which a person or animal behaves

Active Reading

Star What happens when the man tries to run up the trail?

VOCABULARY BUILDER — Target Word

endurance
en•dur•ance (noun)

Rate it: ① ② ③

Meaning

____

____

____

Example

____

____

____

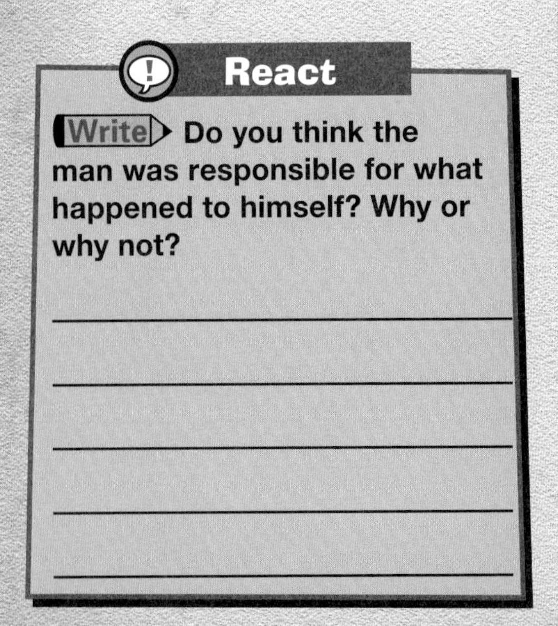

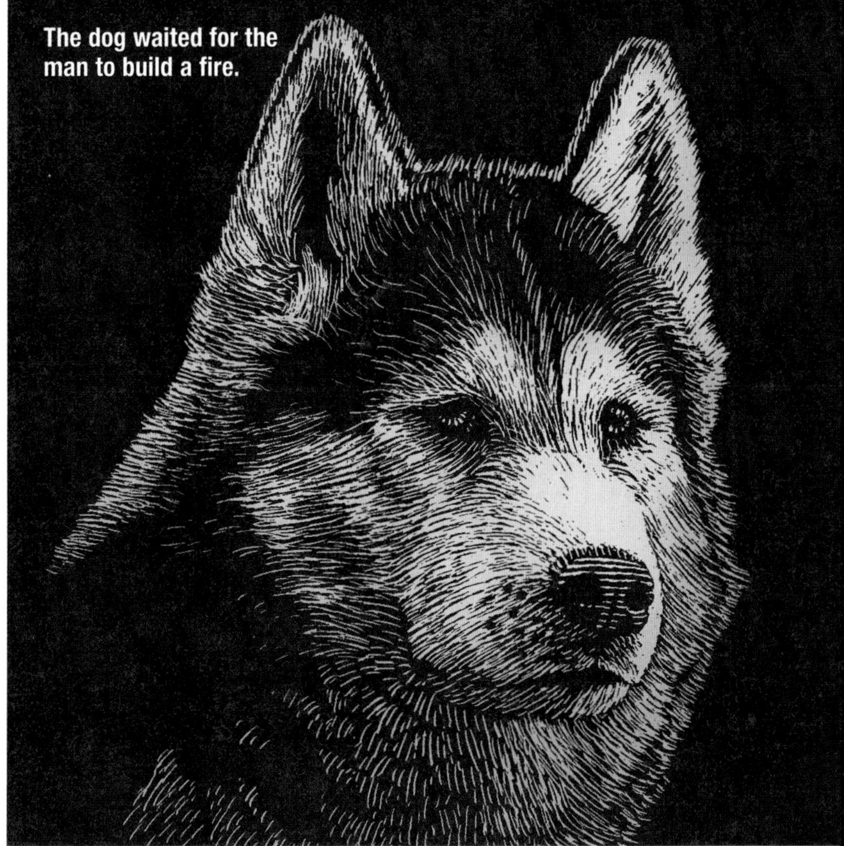

The dog waited for the man to build a fire.

idea, he thought, to sleep off to death. Freezing was not as bad as people thought. There were lots of ways to die. He pictured the boys finding his body the next day. Then he drifted on from this to a vision of the old-timer on Sulphur Creek.

"You were right, old hoss; you were right," the man mumbled to the old-timer of Sulphur Creek.

Then the man drifted off into what seemed to him the most comfortable and satisfying sleep he had ever known. The dog sat facing him and waited. The brief day drew to a close in the long, slow twilight. There were no signs that a fire would be made. Never had the dog known a man to sit like that in the snow and make no fire. It whined, but the man remained silent. It crept close to the man and caught the scent of death. Instinctively, the animal bristled and backed away.

A little longer it delayed, howling under the stars that danced and shone brightly in the cold sky. Then it turned and trotted up the trail in the direction of the camp, where it knew there were other food-providers and fire-providers. END

Story Elements

Setting

1. Write What time span does this story cover?

____

____

Character

2. Write How does the man feel as he is losing consciousness?

____

____

Theme

3. Check Which do you think is the author's main message?

- ❑ Nature's elements can be hostile.
- ❑ Don't be too proud to admit you need help.
- ❑ Always be prepared.

Now go to page 139. Complete Part 3 of the chart and the theme.

Skills Check

1. Write Why is the man unable to kill the dog?

____

____

2. Write What does the dog do at the end of the story?

____

____

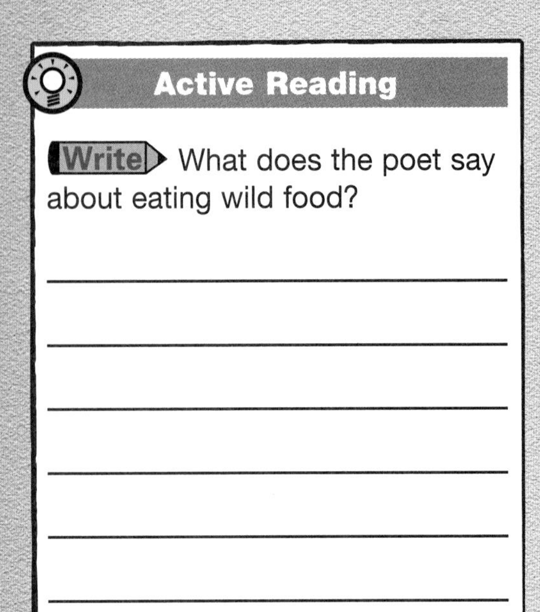

Active Reading

Write What does the poet say about eating wild food?

React

Write Where might *you* become lost? How would you reach safety?

from

STAYING ALIVE

by David Wagoner

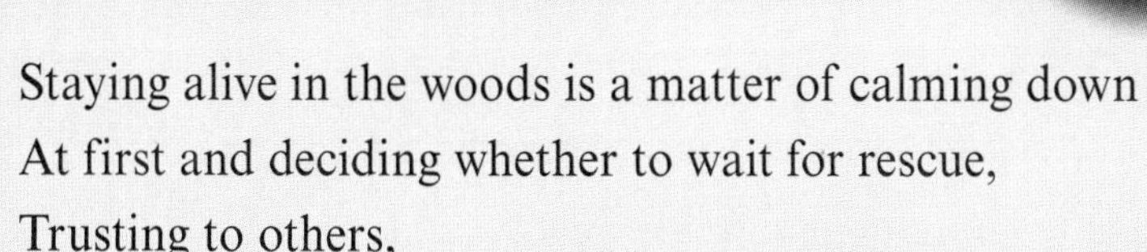

Staying alive in the woods is a matter of calming down
At first and deciding whether to wait for rescue,
Trusting to others,
Or simply to start walking and walking in one direction
Till you come out—or something happens to stop you.
By far the safer choice
Is to settle down where you are, and try to make a living
Off the land, camping near water, away from shadows.

Eat no white berries;
Spit out all bitterness.
If you have no matches, a stick and a fire-bow
Will keep you warmer,
Or the crystal of your watch, filled with water, held up to the sun
Will do the same in time. In case of snow
Drifting toward winter,
Don't try to stay awake through the night, afraid of freezing—
The bottom of your mind knows all about zero;
It will turn you over
And shake you till you waken.

If you hurt yourself, no one will comfort you
Or take your temperature,
So stumbling, wading, and climbing are as dangerous as flying.
But if you decide, at last, you must break through
In spite of all danger,
Think of yourself by time and not by distance, counting
Wherever you're going by how long it takes you;
No other measure
Will bring you safe to nightfall. Follow no streams: they run
Under the ground or fall into wilder country.

Poetic Elements: Free Verse

Free verse is poetry that does not have regular patterns of rhyme and rhythm.

Many poems have rhyming words at the end of each line. They also follow a specific rhythm.

1. **Circle** Look at the first five lines of the poem. Circle the last word that appears in each line.

2. **Check** Does this section of the poem have a regular pattern of rhyme and rhythm?

❑ Yes

❑ No

Active Reading

Write What is the body signal that means you want to be picked up?

Remember the stars
And moss when your mind runs into circles. If it should rain
Or the fog should roll the horizon in around you,
Hold still for hours
Or days if you must, or weeks, for seeing is believing
In the wilderness. And if you find a pathway,
Wheel, rut, or fence, wire,
Retrace it left or right: someone knew where he was going
Once upon a time, and you can follow
Hopefully, somewhere,
Just in case. There may even come, on some uncanny evening,
A time when you're warm and dry, well fed, not thirsty,
Uninjured, without fear,
When nothing, either good or bad, is happening.
This is called staying alive. It's temporary.

What occurs after
Is doubtful. You must always be ready for something to
 come bursting
Through the far edge of a clearing, running toward you,
Grinning from ear to ear
And hoarse with welcome. Or something crossing and hovering
Overhead, as light as air, like a break in the sky,
Wondering what you are.

React

Write Would the man in "To Build a Fire" have followed this poet's advice? Explain your answer.

Here you are face to face with the problem of recognition.
Having no time to make smoke, too much to say,
You should have a mirror
With a tiny hole in the back for better aiming, for reflecting
Whatever disaster you can think of, to show
The way you suffer.

These body signals have universal meaning: If you are lying
Flat on your back with arms outstretched behind you,
You say you require
Emergency treatment; if you are standing erect and holding
Arms horizontal, you mean you are not ready;
If you hold them over
Your head, you want to be picked up. Three of anything
Is a sign of distress. Afterward, if you see
No ropes, no ladders,
No maps or messages falling, no searchlights or trails blazing,
Then, chances are, you should be prepared to burrow
Deep for a deep winter. END

Words to Know! **distress** *(n.)* the need for help

Literary Elements: Mood

Mood is the general feeling that an author creates.

1. **Check** Which word do you think best describes the mood of this poem?

- ❑ serious
- ❑ carefree
- ❑ funny
- ❑ scary

2. **Circle** Find three words or phrases that help create the mood.

Literary Elements: Symbol

A **symbol** is something that has meaning in itself, but also stands for something else. For example, the sun can be a symbol for warmth and happiness.

Some details in this poem could be meant as symbols for life's struggles.

Write Think about what these words from the poem might symbolize about life.

stars: ______________________

rain or fog: ______________________

pathway: ______________________

TAKE THE WORD CHALLENGE

Start

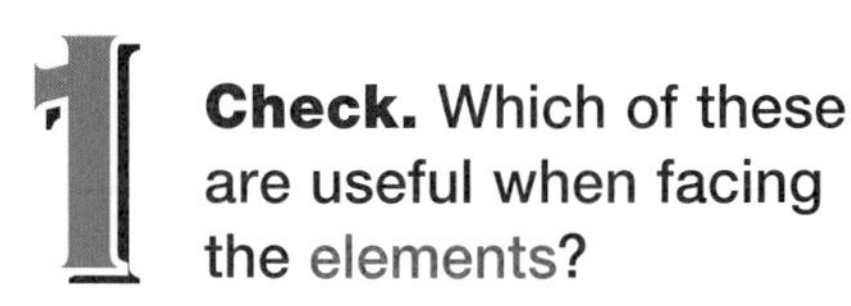

Check. Which of these are useful when facing the elements?

- ❑ a raincoat
- ❑ a compass
- ❑ a pair of hiking boots
- ❑ a water bottle
- ❑ a cell phone

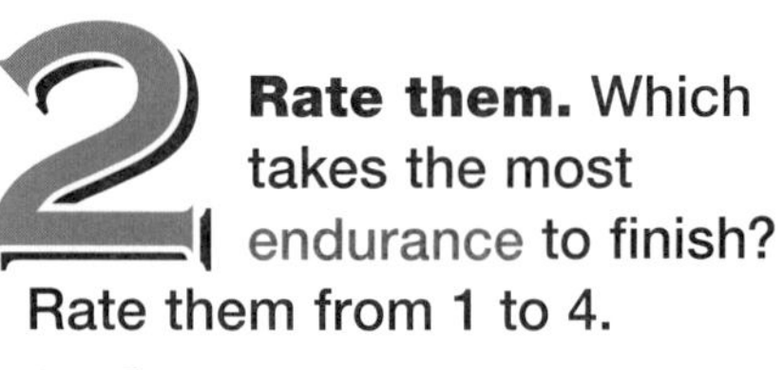

Rate them. Which takes the most endurance to finish? Rate them from 1 to 4.

1 = least endurance
4 = most endurance

_____ a long car ride

_____ a difficult hike

_____ a long book

_____ a boring movie

Synonyms

Synonyms are words that have similar meanings. Examples are *trend* and *fad* or *overwhelmed* and *stressed.*

Fill in. Match each word to its synonym below.

hostile **reaction** **sufficient**

response: ______________________________

enough: ______________________________

angry: ______________________________

4 **Describe it.** Finish the sentences.

If I smelled smoke, my instinct would be to ________

______________________________.

If I saw a snake, my instinct would be to ________________

______________________________.

If the power went out in my house, my instinct would be to

______________________________.

Think. Fill in the blanks.

A sufficient breakfast is ______________________________

______________________________.

A sufficient amount of time to study for a test is ____________

______________________________.

A sufficient amount of money to have saved is ____________

______________________________.

6 Think about it.

What can you assume about the people in this photo?

I assume that these people are at ____________________.

I assume that they have been waiting a ______________ time.

I assume that they feel

____________________.

7 Choose.

Which of these things are temporary?

- ❑ a headache
- ❑ a building
- ❑ true love
- ❑ bad weather

8 Word Families

I'm having such a strong **reaction** to this news!

I'm so excited that I don't know how to **react**!

A **word family** is a group of words that share the same base word and have related meanings, such as *react*, *reaction*, and *reacting*. To *react* is "to respond to something." A *reaction* is "a response."

Complete the sentences. Fill in each blank with the correct form of *react*.

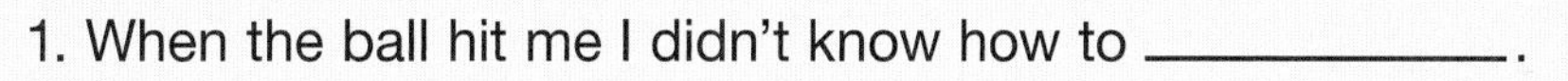

1. When the ball hit me I didn't know how to ______________.
2. Her ______________ was to jump out of the way of the speeding car.
3. She was surprised that she was ______________ so strongly to the idea.

9 Complete.

I would eventually like to ____________________

____.

It's a goal of mine because ____________________

____.

10 Fill in.

Complete these sentences with reaction or speculate.

John didn't know what Lauren's ______________ to his gift would be. He could only ______________ that she would like it.

Finish

Writing Focus

Literature Review

A **literature review** presents the reviewer's opinion of a story.

▶ **Read Daniel's literature review of "Diamond Land," the story in Workshop 3.**

Student Model

A Literature Review of "Diamond Land"

by Daniel Jackson

In my opinion, "Diamond Land" was an excellent story. To start with, I thought Ayize was a likable character. He was hard-working and brave. Also, the author wrote the story in a way that was very believable. Ayize's reaction to Nkosi's death was realistic and sad. In addition, I liked the plot of the story. When Ayize was in a hostile environment in the mines, he followed his instinct and pursued more honorable work. I recommend this story to anyone who likes stories about teens who confront obstacles.

Parts of a Literature Review

▶ **Find these parts of Daniel's literature review.**

1. Underline the sentence that clearly states the **writer's opinion** of the story.
2. Check three specific **reasons** that support the opinion.
3. Put a box around the reason you think is **strongest**.
4. Circle the **linking words** that connect the ideas.
5. Put a star by the sentence that **sums up** the writer's opinion.

Brainstorm

▶ **Read the writing prompt in the middle of the idea web. Then use the boxes to help you brainstorm your ideas.**

Setting

Characters

Writing Prompt:

Explain your opinion of "To Build a Fire." Did you think it was an excellent, average, or weak story?

Plot

Theme

Plan Your Paragraph

Writing Prompt: Explain your opinion of "To Build a Fire." Did you think it was an excellent, average, or weak story?

▶ **Use this chart to plan and organize your paragraph.**

Word Choices

____

____

____

____

____

Statement About the Story

- *In my opinion, . . .*
- *I thought . . .*
- *The story . . .*

Example or Reason 1

- *To start with, . . .*
- *First of all, . . .*
- *The first reason . . .*

Example or Reason 2

- *Also, . . .*
- *Another reason . . .*
- *Secondly, . . .*

Example or Reason 3

- *In addition, . . .*
- *Finally, . . .*
- *The third reason . . .*

Concluding Statement

- *I recommend . . .*
- *I do not recommend . . .*
- *In conclusion, . . .*

Write Your Paragraph

▶ **Use this writing frame to write a first draft of your paragraph.**

____
(title)

In my opinion, ________________________________
____
____
____

To start with, ________________________________
____
____
____

Also, ____
____
____
____

In addition, __________________________________
____
____
____

I recommend ___________________________________
____
____
____
____

Revise

▶ **Rate your paragraph. Then have a writing partner rate it.**

Scoring Guide			
weak	okay	good	strong
1	2	3	4

1. Does the beginning clearly state the **writer's opinion** of the story?

   Self 1 2 3 4

   Partner 1 2 3 4

2. Are there specific **reasons** that support the opinion?

   Self 1 2 3 4

   Partner 1 2 3 4

3. Are the reasons given **strong and convincing**?

   Self 1 2 3 4

   Partner 1 2 3 4

4. Do **linking words** connect the ideas?

   Self 1 2 3 4

   Partner 1 2 3 4

5. Does the ending **sum up** the writer's opinion?

   Self 1 2 3 4

   Partner 1 2 3 4

▶ Now revise your paragraph to make it stronger.

Grammar SUBJECT-VERB AGREEMENT

The **subject and verb** in a sentence must agree in number.

- A singular verb tells what one person, place, or thing is doing. It usually ends in *-s* or *-es*.
- A plural verb tells what more than one person, place, or thing is doing. It usually does not end in *-s* or *-es*.

Example

Singular Subject and Verb	Plural Subject and Verb
The dog follows the man.	The dogs follow the man.
The man drops the matches.	The men drop the matches.

▶ **Put an X next to the sentences that have subject-verb agreement errors.**

1. The dog sit at the man's heels. X
2. An old man gives some advice. ______
3. The man realize that it's colder than he thought. ______
4. The branches sags under the weight of the snow. ______
5. His matches burns brightly. ______
6. The dog trots back up the trail toward the camp. ______

▶ **Rewrite the following sentences with correct subject-verb agreement. (Be sure to keep all the sentences in present tense.)**

7. The man see the dark sky overhead.

______

8. The dog's eyelashes freezes in the cold air.

______

9. The dog wonder why the man hasn't built a fire.

______

10. When the matches burns out, the man begin to worry.

______

Take a close look at each of the sentences in your draft on page 159. Do the subjects and verbs all agree? If not, fix them.

Mechanics Using Possessives

A **possessive noun** shows ownership.

- Add an apostrophe (') and an *-s* to a singular noun.
- Add an apostrophe to a plural noun that ends in *-s*.

Example

Correct	Incorrect
London's story was suspenseful.	Londons story was suspenseful.
The friends' camp was set up.	The friends camp was set up.

▶ **Find and correct five errors in this paragraph.**

Student Model

I thought the story "Diamond Land" was bad. First of all, I thinks Nkosi is a hostele character. He is really mean for taking the diamonds. Secondly, I didn't believe that Ayize would get so much money for Nkosis diamonds. Finally, I didn't like reading the part where Father Thomas asumes that Ayize will have trouble in the mines. I do not recommend Williams-Garcias story to anybody.

Check and Correct

- ❑ Circle two spelling errors and correct them.
- ❑ Underline two errors with possessives and correct them.
- ❑ Correct one subject-verb agreement error.

Look at the sentences in your draft on page 159. Are all the possessive nouns formed correctly? If not, fix them.

Final Draft/Present

▶ **Write a final draft of your paragraph on paper or the computer. Check it again and correct any errors before you present it.**

Meet the Author

Jack London 1876–1916

"The proper function of man is to live, not exist. I shall not waste my days in trying to prolong them. I shall use my time."

JACK LONDON

Jack London packed a lot of adventure into his forty years of life. He sailed the world, panned for gold, and became a famous writer. However, his life wasn't always so exciting.

London was born poor in San Francisco in 1876. When he was 13, he had to leave school and work for 14 hours a day to help support his family. To escape, he first became a sailor on a seal-hunting ship; but seal hunting was too cruel for him. Next, he headed to the Alaskan wilderness to take part in the Gold Rush.

London didn't return home with gold. But he did come back with something that would make him rich and famous. It was his journal. He used it to write a story about his experiences in Alaska. After the story was published, London realized he could make a living as a writer.

During the next 18 years, London wrote dozens of books and short stories. Many of his tales of adventure have become American classics.

Famous Books:

The Call of the Wild
White Fang
The Sea-Wolf

Ask Yourself

1. **Underline** What did London do when he was thirteen years old?
2. **Circle** What did London bring back from Alaska?
3. What sort of books would you want to write?
   - ☐ adventure stories
   - ☐ history
   - ☐ romance

Real-World Skills

Comparing DVD Reviews

How can you tell if you will like a DVD? You can read a review of it. An online customer DVD review often gives a summary of the movie. It also gives the reviewer's opinion. Read these customer reviews of the movie version of Jack London's *White Fang*.

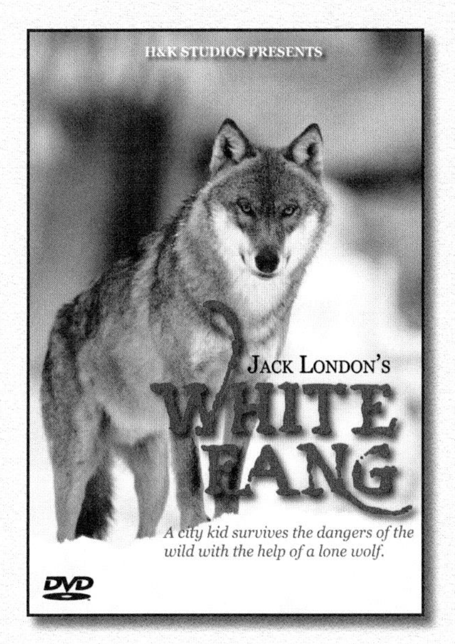

★★★ **Reviewer:** LondonFanatic, Anchorage, AK

I've always loved this story about a boy and his half-dog/half-wolf pet, so I was excited to buy this DVD. It is the best movie ever. The animals are amazing. I thought the fight between White Fang and the bear was really well done. Buy this DVD!

★☆☆ **Reviewer:** JoseMovieBuff, Los Angeles, CA

This movie was a huge disappointment. I thought the book was much better. The actors weren't believable at all. The only good thing about the movie was the Alaskan scenery. Don't waste your money.

★★☆ **Reviewer:** Raquel, Jacksonville, FL

This is one of my favorite books and movies of all times. If you like stories about the Gold Rush, you should see this film. The relationship between the boy and the dog was really believable. My only complaint is that the DVD isn't in widescreen format.

▶ **Fill in the circle next to each correct answer.**

1. What was LondonFanatic's opinion of the movie?

Ⓐ She preferred the book.
Ⓑ She thought the actors were terrible.
Ⓒ She thought it was poorly made.
Ⓓ She thought it was the best movie ever.

2. What is the movie about?

Ⓐ actors who live in Alaska
Ⓑ a boy and his dog
Ⓒ the Yukon environment
Ⓓ DVD formats

3. If the movie had been available in widescreen format, how might Raquel's opinion have been different?

Ⓐ She would have given the movie three stars.
Ⓑ She would have liked the movie less.
Ⓒ She would have given the movie one star.
Ⓓ She would have liked the dog more.

4. Who thinks the DVD is a waste of money?

Ⓐ LondonFanatic
Ⓑ JoseMovieBuff
Ⓒ Raquel
Ⓓ All three reviewers

5. Which is a reason to read customer DVD reviews?

Ⓐ to learn how the movie ends
Ⓑ to find out how much the movie costs
Ⓒ to find out showtimes
Ⓓ to see if you will like the movie

Comprehension

▶ **Fill in the circle next to the correct answer.**

1. Where does "To Build a Fire" take place?
- Ⓐ at Sulphur Creek
- Ⓑ at an old mine
- Ⓒ in the Yukon Territory
- Ⓓ on a lake

2. Which pair of words best describes the dog?
- Ⓐ loud and hyper
- Ⓑ slow and fearful
- Ⓒ wild and frightening
- Ⓓ instinctive and patient

Here's a tip.
Whenever possible, go back to the readings to find evidence to support your answer.

3. What does the man do after he runs out of matches?
- Ⓐ He tries to kill the dog.
- Ⓑ He eats his lunch.
- Ⓒ He hikes back to camp.
- Ⓓ He builds another fire.

4. Which statement is a fact about the story?
- Ⓐ The dog was the best character in the story.
- Ⓑ The man tried to hike without a trail mate.
- Ⓒ The man made poor choices.
- Ⓓ The dog should have returned to camp.

5. What is a theme of the story?
- Ⓐ Never trust an animal.
- Ⓑ Other people don't always know what's best.
- Ⓒ Always be prepared.
- Ⓓ You can make it on your own.

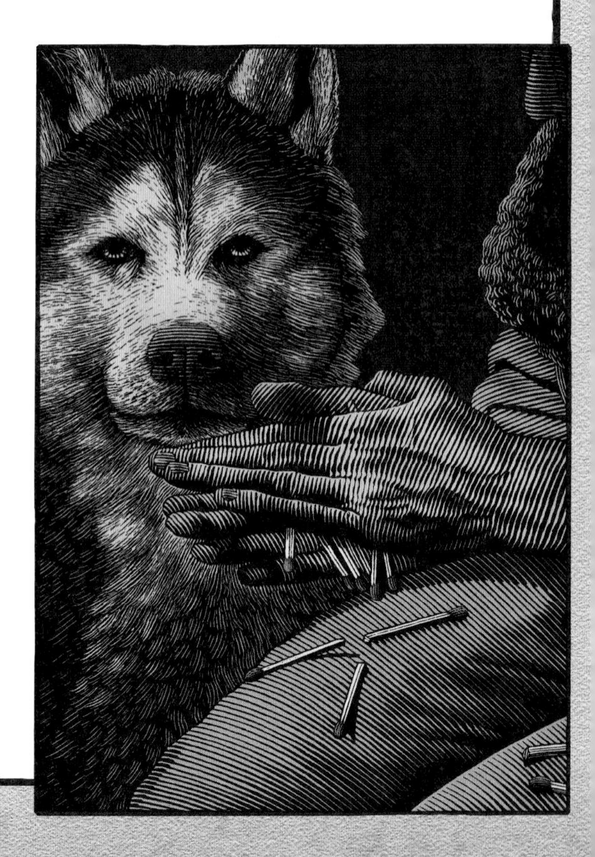

Vocabulary

▶ **Fill in the circle next to the correct definition of the underlined word.**

1. The dog became hostile when the man attacked him.
   Ⓐ quick
   Ⓑ unfriendly
   Ⓒ hungry
   Ⓓ playful

2. The dog's instinct was to turn back toward camp.
   Ⓐ lack of feeling
   Ⓑ strong fear
   Ⓒ natural tendency
   Ⓓ advice

3. It seemed like the man wasn't prepared to face the elements.
   Ⓐ animals
   Ⓑ fires
   Ⓒ weather
   Ⓓ trail

▶ **Choose the correct synonym for the underlined word.**

4. The man carried seventy matches with him. Was that sufficient?
   Ⓐ too much
   Ⓑ too bulky
   Ⓒ heavy
   Ⓓ enough

▶ **Choose the correct word to fill in the blank.**

5. The dog could tell from the man's ____________ that the situation was bad.
   Ⓐ reaction
   Ⓑ react
   Ⓒ reactionary
   Ⓓ reactive

Short Answer

▶ **Use what you've read in this Workshop to answer the question below. Check your spelling and grammar.**

Would you want to be the man's trail partner? Why or why not?

____

____

____

____

____

WORKSHOP 7

NONFICTION

Comprehension Focus
Cause and Effect

READINGS

1 ***Sea Census Under Way*** >> Science News
2 ***Dijanna Figueroa: Sea Scientist*** >> Magazine Article
3 ***Life in the Ocean Zones*** >> Science Text

Creatures of the Deep

The ocean covers 70 percent of the earth's surface. Yet it is the least explored, most mysterious place on the planet. Why?

Until recently, scientists couldn't come face to face with creatures of the deep. Now, thanks to new technology, they can dive deep, meet undersea oddballs—and much more.

At last, scientists are unlocking the secrets of the sea.

VOCABULARY BUILDER

Target Word ▶ Read the Target Words. Rate each one using the scale below.*	Meaning ▶ Read the Target Word meanings. Write in the missing ones.	Example ▶ Finish the Target Word examples below. Write in the missing ones.
adapt *a•dapt* *(verb)* ① ② ③		A time when I had to adapt was . . .
contact *con•tact* *(noun)* ① ② ③	the state of touching or connecting	
distinct *dis•tinct* *(adjective)* ① ② ③		I have a **distinct** look.
maximum *max•i•mum* *(adjective)* ① ② ③	the largest number or amount	
vast *vast* *(adjective)* ① ② ③		I have a vast collection of . . .

***Rating Scale**

① = I don't know it at all.
② = I've seen it before.
③ = I know it and use it.

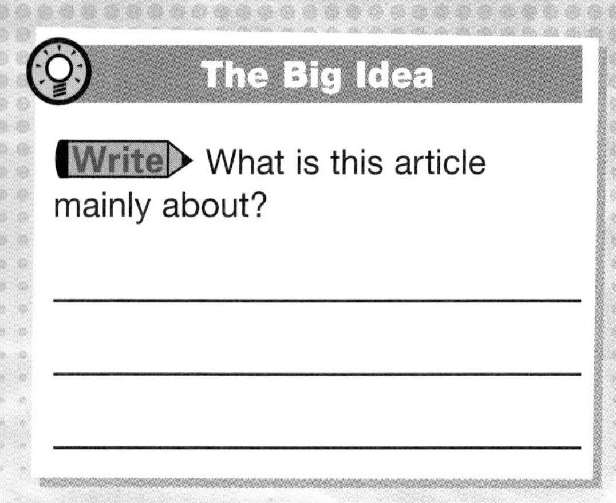

The Big Idea

Write What is this article mainly about?

____

____

____

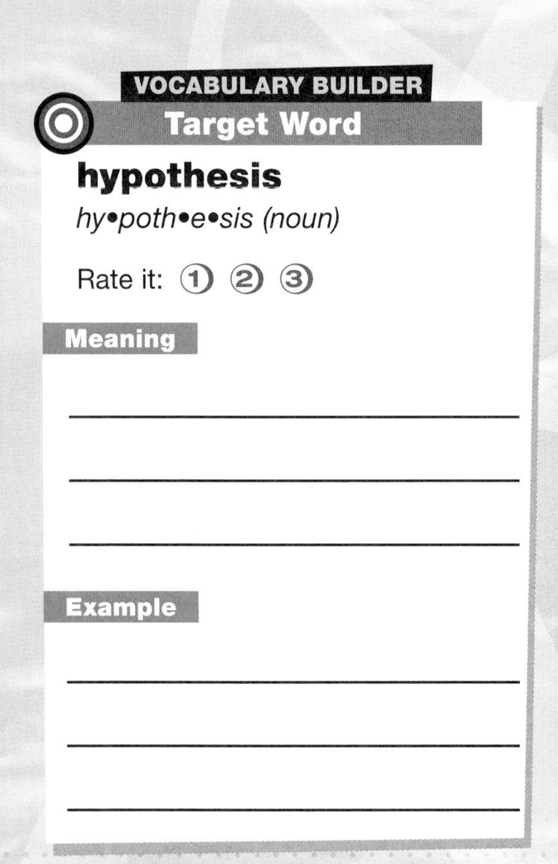

VOCABULARY BUILDER

Target Word

hypothesis

hy•poth•e•sis (noun)

Rate it: ① ② ③

Meaning

____

____

____

Example

____

____

____

React

The Census of Marine Life will take ten years and cost millions of dollars. Do you think it's worth the time and money? Why or why not?

Sea Census Under Way

The Census of Marine Life will count every creature in the sea.

How many plants and animals live in the earth's oceans? Scientists are working under the waves to find out. They are counting every sea creature—from giant whales to tiny sea slugs—for the Census of Marine Life.

Thousands of scientists from over 70 countries are working on the census. The project began in 2000. It will conclude in 2010.

Because the ocean is so vast and deep, much of it remains unexplored today. For the census, scientists are utilizing deep-sea rovers, or submersibles. Submersibles can travel to the bottom of the sea at its maximum depths.

This unique, advanced technology has helped researchers find new species at the rate of two a week. Among them are a scorpionfish and a distinct looking octopod. Scientists speculate that by 2010, they will discover two million new species!

The census has had another important effect. Scientists are discovering that some species are dying out. For example, they've learned that the number of tuna has dropped by 90% since 1950. Scientists have a **hypothesis** that tuna are disappearing as a result of overfishing and pollution.

For census scientists, the count goes on. Until the census ends in 2010, they will search the seas to discover more creatures of the deep. END

Words to Know! **census** *(n.)* an official count

Comprehension Focus

Cause and Effect

A **cause** is the reason something happens. An **effect** is the result of a cause. To find the cause and effect:

- **Ask yourself "Why did it happen?" to find the cause.**
- **Ask yourself "What happened?" to find the effect.**
- **Look for signal words or phrases such as *because*, *so*, *as a result*, *therefore*, *consequently*, and *for this reason*.**

▶ **Fill in this chart with the cause-and-effect relationships in "Sea Census Under Way."**

Cause

Effect

Much of the ocean remains unexplored today.

Cause

Effect

The Big Idea

Write What is this article mainly about?

______

______

______

VOCABULARY BUILDER

Target Word

biology

bi•ol•o•gy (noun)

Rate it: ① ② ③

Meaning

______

______

______

Example

______

______

______

React

Traveling to the ocean floor is dangerous. Why would anyone want to do it? Would you?

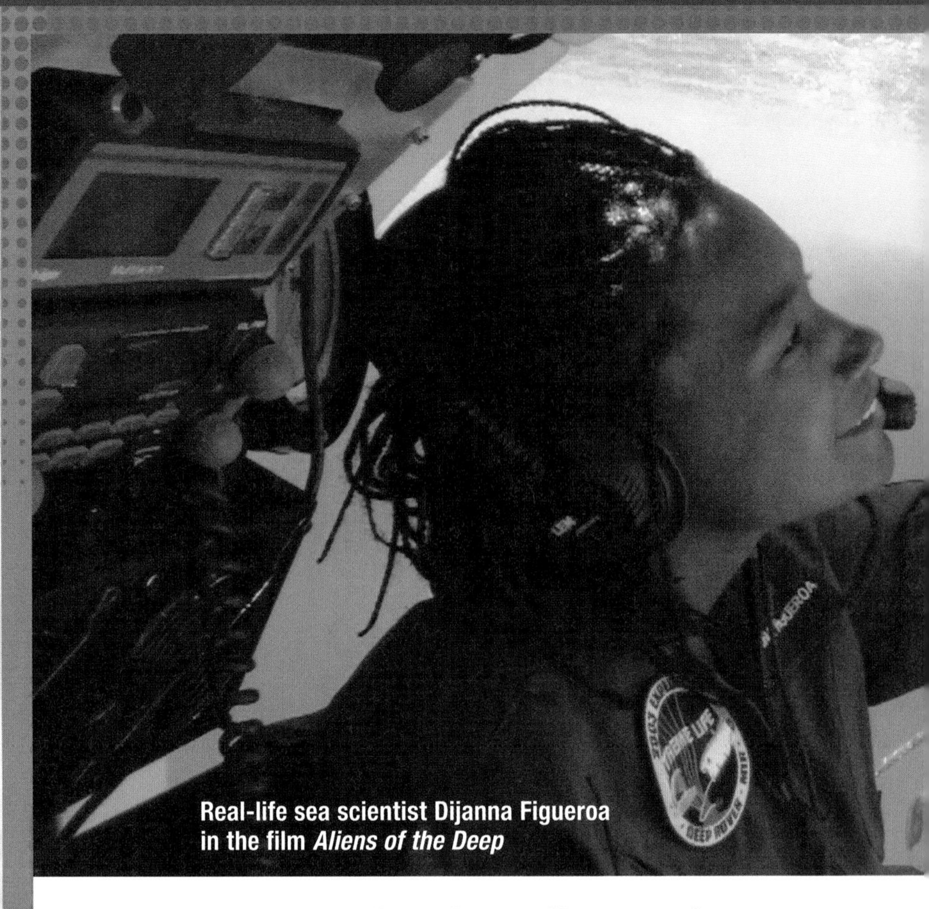

Real-life sea scientist Dijanna Figueroa in the film *Aliens of the Deep*

A marine biologist dives deep to explore life on the ocean floor.

Meet Dijanna Figueroa, a researcher in marine **biology** at the University of California, Santa Barbara. Dijanna studies sea creatures that have adapted to one of the most extreme environments on earth—the deepest parts of the ocean. "I think I have one of the coolest jobs," Dijanna says. "I get to go to the bottom of the ocean. I see distinct and amazing animals and figure out how they work."

In addition to being a marine biologist, Dijanna is also a movie star. How did she go from scientist to celebrity? It all started with a film called *Aliens of the Deep.*

Director James Cameron came to the university looking for scientists to be part of his film. Because Dijanna was an expert in creatures of the deep, she was chosen to star as one of the scientists in the movie.

Dijanna Figueroa: SEA SCIENTIST

Diving Into the Deep

With other scientists, Dijanna dived into the ocean in a special vehicle called a submersible. A submersible is like a mini submarine, but it is built to withstand incredible water pressure. Consequently, it can dive to the very bottom of the sea.

Although Dijanna had dived before, traveling in the submersible was frightening. As the sub dived deeper, it had less and less contact with sunlight. Therefore, it got darker and colder inside the sub. "Everyone put on hats and gloves," says Dijanna. "That's when I realized that we were really going down 2,500 meters to the ocean floor. I was a little afraid, but I was also excited." ➔

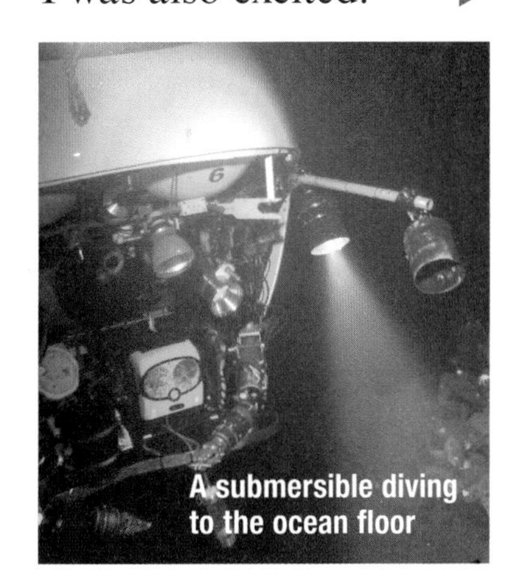
A submersible diving to the ocean floor

Words to Know! **vehicle** *(n.)* something in which people travel

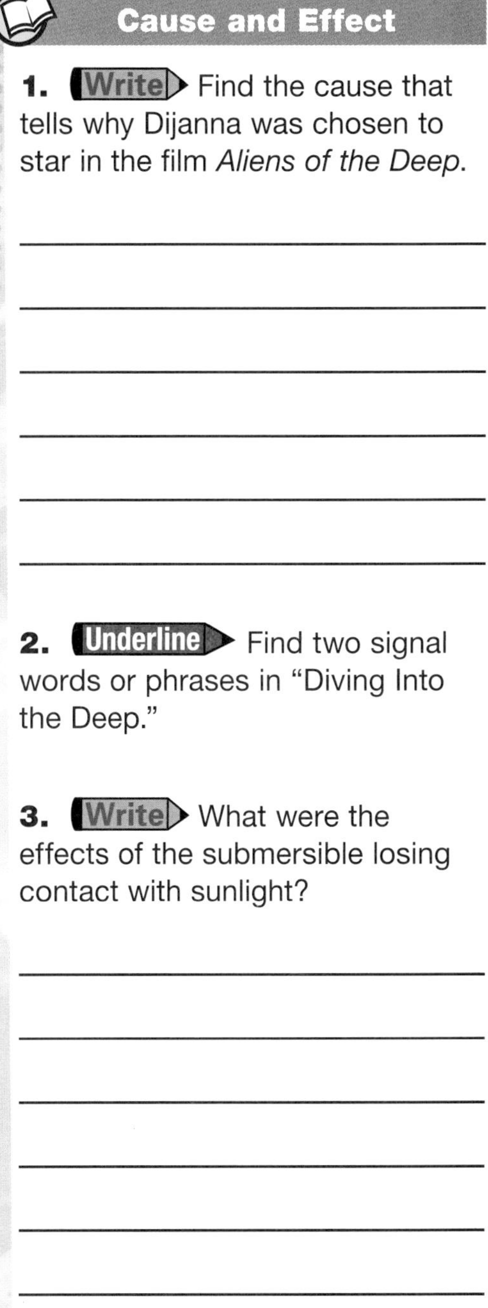

Cause and Effect

1. **Write** Find the cause that tells why Dijanna was chosen to star in the film *Aliens of the Deep*.

____

____

____

____

____

____

2. **Underline** Find two signal words or phrases in "Diving Into the Deep."

3. **Write** What were the effects of the submersible losing contact with sunlight?

____

____

____

____

____

____

Active Reading

Circle Why is the water around the hydrothermal vents so hot?

VOCABULARY BUILDER

Target Word

vary

var•y (verb)

Rate it: ① ② ③

Meaning

____

____

____

Example

____

____

____

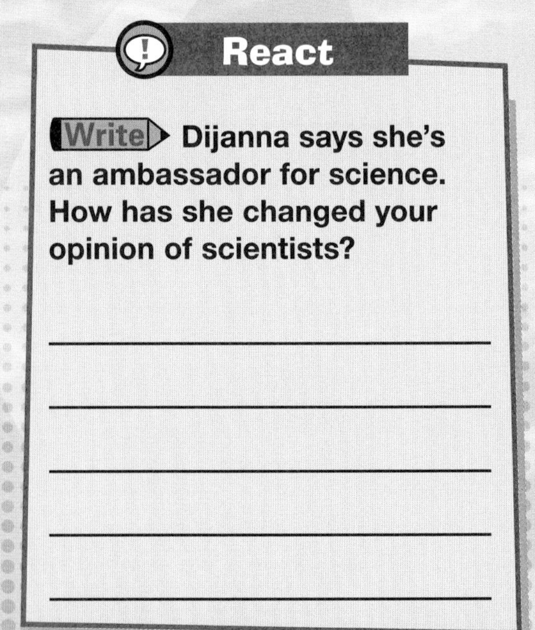

In Hot Water

During her dive, Dijanna observed hydrothermal vents. These vents are cracks in the ocean floor that are superheated by volcanic activity. As a result of the volcanic activity, the water in the vents can reach a maximum of 650 degrees.

Still, life thrives here because creatures have adapted to high temperatures—and no sunlight. "Most animals use the sun as an energy source," says Dijanna. "These animals live without sunlight, so they survive by getting energy from the chemicals and bacteria in the water."

Back to the Lab

During the dive, Dijanna collected animals from the vents to bring back to her lab. These animals have to live in a special tank that **varies** from a regular fish tank.

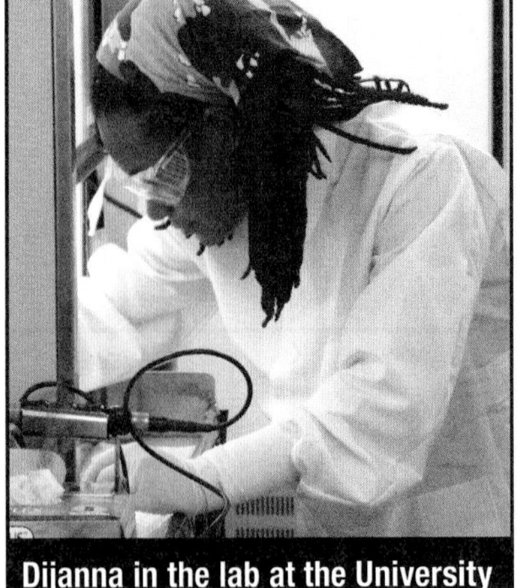

Dijanna in the lab at the University of California, Santa Barbara

The special tank is pressurized and has chemicals that recreate conditions near the vents. Because of this special tank, the creatures are able to survive in the lab.

Dijanna continues to work in the lab but her life has changed because of her movie fame. Reporters call for interviews, and people recognize her from the film. "I have become an ambassador for my science," says Dijanna.

It's a role that Dijanna is happy to play because she loves science. "Science is a great adrenaline rush," she says. END

Words to Know! **ambassador** *(n.)* one who represents something

Comprehension Focus

Cause and Effect

▶ **Fill in this chart with the cause-and-effect relationships in "In Hot Water" and "Back to the Lab."**

Cause		Effect
	→	
	→	
	→	

The Big Idea

Write What is this article mainly about?

____

____

____

VOCABULARY BUILDER

Target Word

illuminate

il•lu•mi•nate (verb)

Rate it: ① ② ③

Meaning

____

____

____

Example

____

____

____

React

How have humans had a negative effect on the ocean's environment and animals?

LIFE IN THE OCEAN ZONES

Adaptation is the key to survival

The hatchetfish uses bioluminescence to protect itself in the twilight zone.

Zones of the Ocean

The ocean is a vast body of water that occupies 70 percent of the earth's surface and, in places, is six miles deep. Scientists have divided the ocean into three major zones, according to how much light they receive. These three distinct light zones are the sunlit, twilight, and midnight zones.

The sunlit zone is closest to the surface. It is **illuminated** with sunlight. Beneath this zone is the twilight zone. Very little light reaches this zone. Below that is the midnight zone, which is completely dark.

Creatures have adapted in various ways to these unique environments, and, as a result, they have distinct characteristics that help them survive.

The Sunlit Zone

The sunlit zone is also known as the euphotic zone. It stretches from the ocean surface down to about 600 feet. Sunlight helps sustain life in this zone. As a result of the sunlight, photosynthesis occurs. Ocean plants utilize the energy of the sun to make food for themselves and to grow. These plants eventually become food sources for other creatures. The food-rich waters of the euphotic zone are home to more than 90 percent of all sea life.

Because the euphotic zone is full of light, it can be difficult for animals to hide from each other. In order to adapt to this environment, some fish camouflage themselves by changing their colors and patterns to blend into the background. The longlure frogfish, which lives on shallow coral reefs with sea sponges, can modify its color to match the color of a nearby sponge. Fish swimming by can't see the frogfish. As a result, the frogfish can catch its prey more easily. →

Words to Know! **camouflage** *(v.)* blend in with surroundings

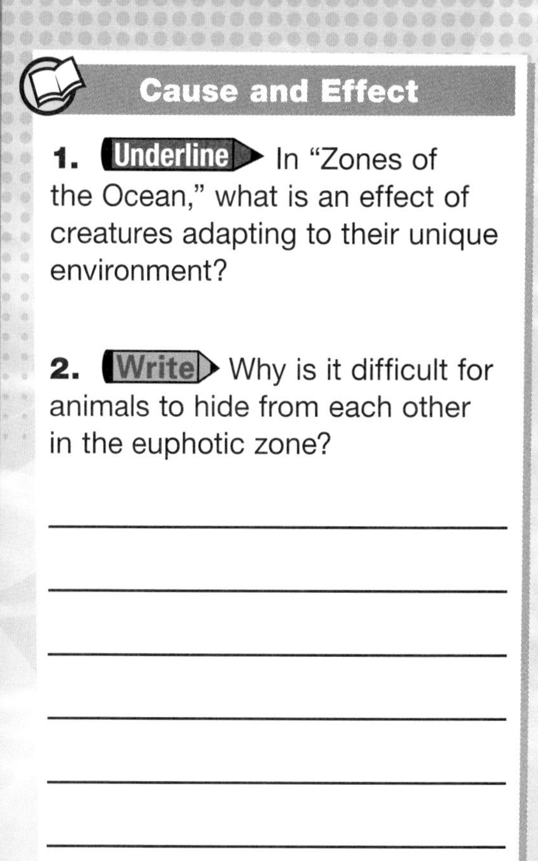

Cause and Effect

1. **Underline** In "Zones of the Ocean," what is an effect of creatures adapting to their unique environment?

2. **Write** Why is it difficult for animals to hide from each other in the euphotic zone?

____

____

____

____

____

____

Review: Summarize

Find the topic and important details in the section "The Sunlit Zone." Then, turn to a partner and summarize the section.

Active Reading

Circle Why are some animals in the twilight zone red or black?

VOCABULARY BUILDER

Target Word

factor

fac•tor (noun)

Rate it: ① ② ③

Meaning

____

____

____

Example

____

____

____

The Twilight Zone

The twilight zone, also called the disphotic zone, is the ocean layer from 600 to 3,000 feet. There is no photosynthesis in this zone because there is very little sunlight. Many animals in this zone are red or black, so they blend in with the dark water. As a result, it is harder for predators to detect them.

Some creatures in the twilight zone use special organs in their bodies to illuminate themselves, or make their own light. This adaptation is called bioluminescence.

Animals like the hatchetfish have adapted to the twilight zone by using bioluminescence to avoid contact with predators. The hatchetfish has bioluminescent organs on its stomach. These organs can change the color of the light they produce to match the light that is coming from above. Therefore, the hatchetfish is nearly invisible to predators looking up at it from below.

TEXT FEATURE **Reading a Diagram**

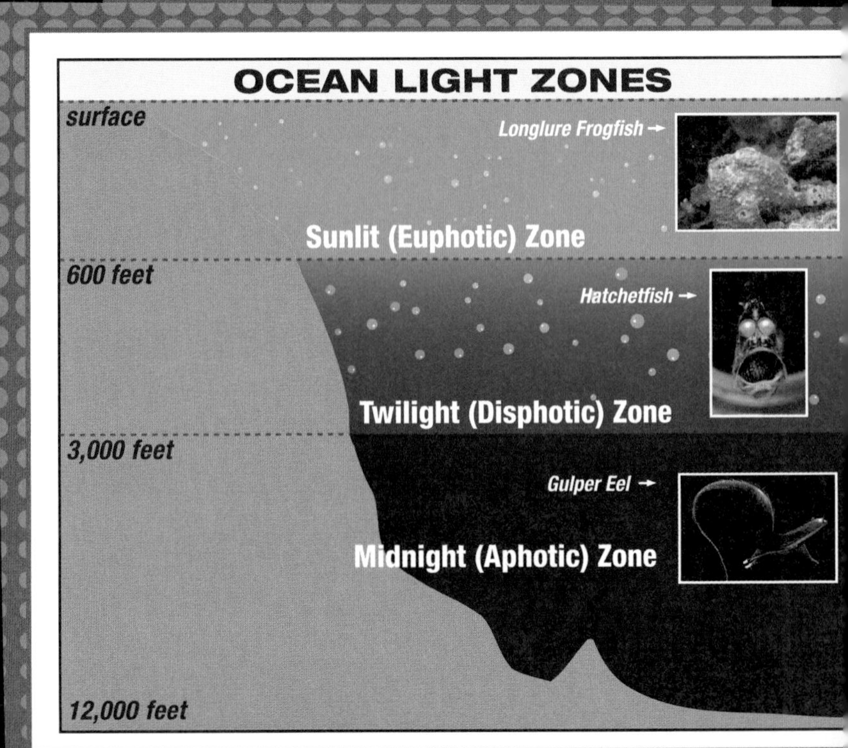

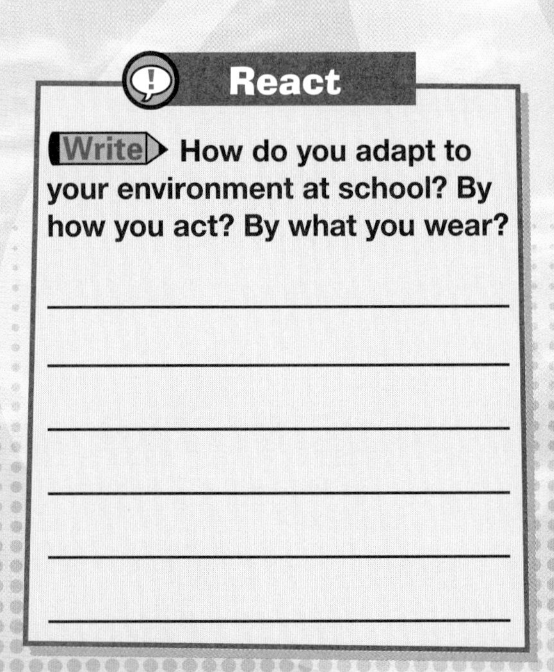

React

Write How do you adapt to your environment at school? By how you act? By what you wear?

____

____

____

____

____

____

The Midnight Zone

Fewer creatures live in the midnight, or aphotic, zone, even though it makes up 90 percent of the ocean. The water in this zone is extremely cold, and it exerts enough pressure to crush a human being. The only light in this zone comes from bioluminescent animals.

Most of the creatures in the aphotic zone live close to the toxic hydrothermal vents on the ocean floor. How do creatures survive in this hostile environment? Some animals, like tube worms, survive as a result of special bacteria in their bodies. The bacteria turns the chemicals released from the vents into food.

Another animal that lives in this zone is the gulper eel. It lives at a maximum depth of about 6,500 feet. Because of the eel's huge mouth and expandable stomach, it can eat animals larger than itself. In a zone that doesn't offer many food options, this adaptation is an important **factor** in the eel's survival.

The environments in these ocean zones are varied and extreme. Therefore, the plants and animals that live in them have had to adapt—or die. END

Words to Know! **predators** *(n.)* animals that hunt other animals

A diagram gives a detailed view of something of scientific interest.

1. The twilight zone goes from ______________
   - Ⓐ surface to 600 ft.
   - Ⓑ 600–3,000 ft.
   - Ⓒ 3,000–12,000 ft.
   - Ⓓ 600–12,000 ft.

2. What is another name for the sunlit zone?
   - Ⓐ the euphotic zone
   - Ⓑ the disphotic zone
   - Ⓒ the aphotic zone
   - Ⓓ the midnight zone

3. Which animal lives in the midnight zone?

____

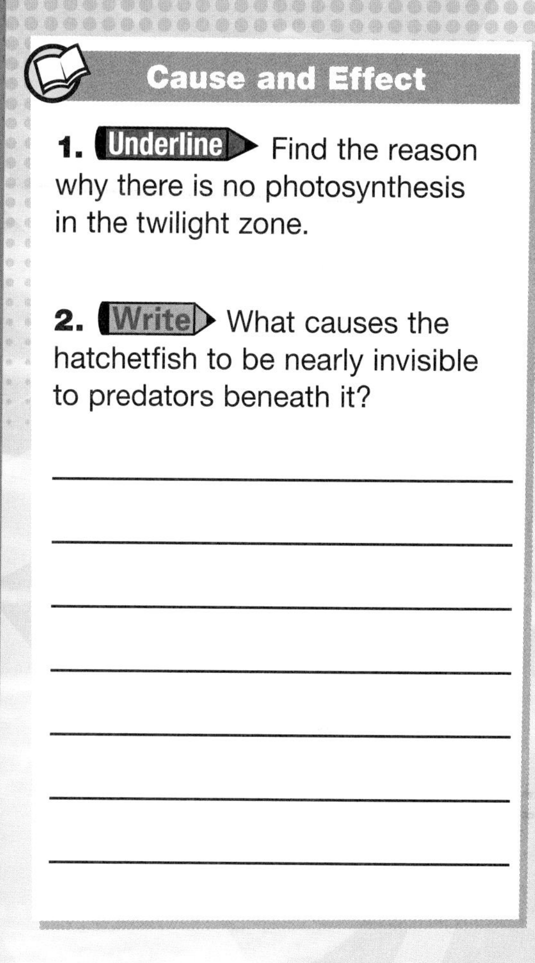

Cause and Effect

1. **Underline** Find the reason why there is no photosynthesis in the twilight zone.

2. **Write** What causes the hatchetfish to be nearly invisible to predators beneath it?

____

____

____

____

____

____

____

Skills Check

1. **Underline** Find two signal words or phrases in "The Midnight Zone."

2. **Write** For what reason can the gulper eel eat animals larger than itself?

____

____

____

____

____

TAKE THE WORD CHALLENGE

Start

1 **Decide.** Which of the following uses of the word adapt is wrong?

- ❑ It took him time to adapt to his new home.
- ❑ She decided to adapt the homeless kitten.
- ❑ It's not always easy to adapt to new surroundings.

Now cross out adapt where it's used incorrectly, and write the correct word above it.

2 **Check.** Which of the following could provide you with illumination?

- ❑ a pen
- ❑ a flashlight
- ❑ the moon
- ❑ a bicycle
- ❑ watching TV

3 **Idioms**

An **idiom** is an expression that means something different from its individual words. To "make waves" means to cause trouble.

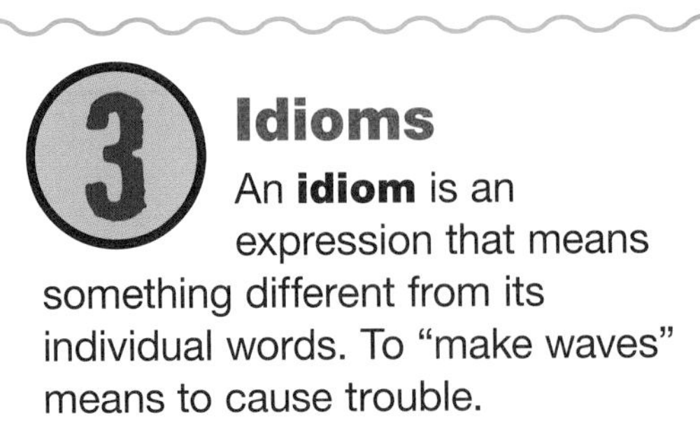

Match these idioms to their meanings.

"He put his best foot forward."	He's ready to receive his punishment.
"He's ready to face the music!"	He tried to show his best qualities.

Now, finish these sentences.

I put my best foot forward when I ______________________.

I had to face the music after I ______________________.

I made waves when I ______________________.

4 **Complete the sentences.** Fill in each blank with the correct form of distinct from below.

distinct distinctly distinction

I ____________ remember that she had very ____________ hair.

It gives her a kind of ____________.

5 **Circle one in each row.** Some things are big. Others are vast. Which one of each pair is vast?

Sahara Desert	***OR***	a sand dune
a garden	***OR***	Earth
an ocean	***OR***	a pond

6 **Fill in.** Where might you come in contact with:

mosquitos? ____________

polar bears? ____________

popcorn? ____________

a school of fish? ____________

a doctor? ____________

your classmates? ____________

7 **Tell.** If I wanted to vary my diet in order to eat better, I would:

____

____

____

____

____

8 Using a Dictionary

Look in the dictionary when you're not sure how to pronounce a word. A dictionary pronunciation guide will tell you how to say it. Check out the pronunciation of *biology* and ***biomass*** below. The two words look similar, but their pronunciations are different.

biology (bye-**ol**-uh-jee) ***noun*** The scientific study of living things.

biomass (**bye**-oh-mass) ***noun*** The amount or weight of living matter in a certain area.

Look up the pronunciation of these tricky words in the glossary. Say them to a partner. Give yourself a check when you pronounce each one correctly.

_______ epilogue   _______ trauma

_______ chronological   _______ magnitude

_______ sequel   _______ isolate

9 **Fill in.** You are visiting an aquarium. You see a sign that says "Whale Exhibit Closed from 12–1." Come up with a hypothesis about why the exhibit is closed.

I hypothesize that the whale exhibit is closed because ______

____

____

____

____

10 **Fill in.** Complete the following sentences using the words maximum and factor(s).

I had to accelerate fast in order to reach ____________ speed. There are many ____________ in winning a race. But the most important ____________ is speed.

Writing Focus

Descriptive Paragraph

A **descriptive paragraph** describes a person, place, thing, or event by using interesting and specific details.

▶ **Read Julia's descriptive paragraph about an interesting place she visited.**

Student Model

A Kayak Trip at Night

By Julia Martinez

The most interesting place I've ever visited is a small island in Puerto Rico. My grandfather and cousins took me on a kayak tour of the island at night. As we paddled along the shore, I heard the distinct calls of insects and frogs. Then I felt a cool breeze cut through the humid air, carrying with it the aroma of the rain forest plants. When we paddled into a little bay, I saw an incredible sight. The water was lit up by a vast number of tiny bioluminescent fish. We paddled our kayaks through their glowing lights. I knew that I would never forget my visit to this magical place.

Parts of a Descriptive Paragraph

▶ **Find these parts of Julia's descriptive paragraph.**

1. Underline the sentence that tells **what is being described**.
2. Check three sentences with **descriptive details**.
3. Put a box around the descriptive details you think are most **interesting**.
4. Circle the **linking words** that connect the details.
5. Put a star beside the sentence that **sums up** the description and tells the writer's **feelings** about it.

Brainstorm

▶ **Read the writing prompt in the middle of the idea web. Then use the boxes to help you brainstorm your ideas.**

Sights

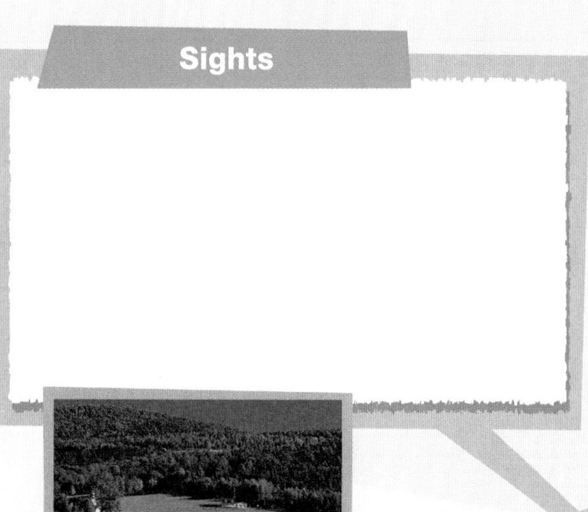

Sounds

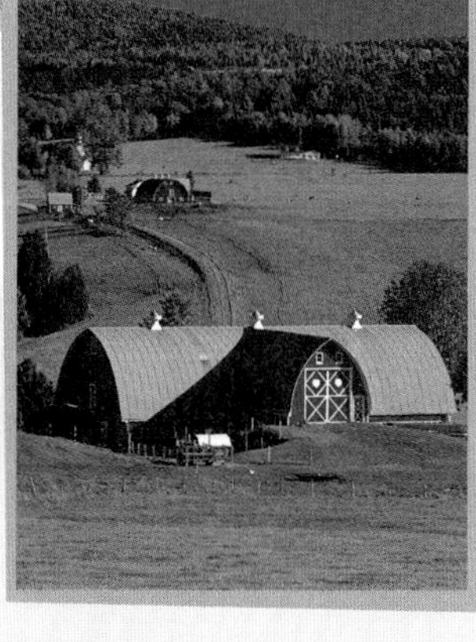

Writing Prompt:

Describe a favorite place in your neighborhood or an interesting place you have visited.

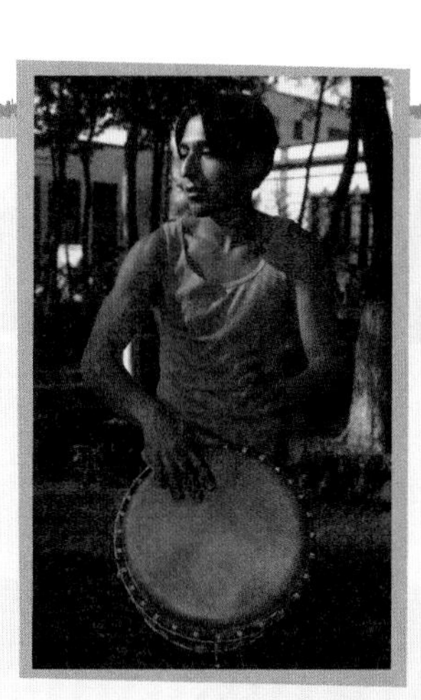

Smells

Feelings

Plan Your Paragraph

Writing Prompt: Describe a favorite place in your neighborhood or an interesting place you have visited.

▶ **Use this chart to plan and organize your paragraph.**

Word Choices

____

____

____

____

____

Topic Sentence

- *The most interesting place . . .*
- *My favorite place . . .*
- *The place I like most . . .*

Descriptive Detail

- *I heard . . .*
- *I could hear . . .*
- *The loudest sound . . .*

Descriptive Detail

- *I felt . . .*
- *I could feel . . .*
- *The smell of the . . .*

Descriptive Detail

- *I saw a(n) . . .*
- *The best sight was . . .*
- *All around me . . .*

Conclusion

- *I knew I would . . .*
- *I'm glad I went . . .*
- *All in all, . . .*

Write Your Paragraph

▶ **Use this writing frame to write a first draft of your paragraph.**

____
(title)

The most interesting place ______________________

____

____

____

I heard ___________________________

____

____

____

I felt _____________________________

____

____

____

I saw a ___________________________

____

____

____

I knew I would ______________________

____

____

____

____

Revise

▶ **Rate your paragraph. Then have a writing partner rate it.**

Scoring Guide			
weak	okay	good	strong
1	2	3	4

1. Does the beginning clearly state **what is being described**?

   Self 1 2 3 4

   Partner 1 2 3 4

2. Do the sentences contain **descriptive details**?

   Self 1 2 3 4

   Partner 1 2 3 4

3. Are the descriptive details **interesting**?

   Self 1 2 3 4

   Partner 1 2 3 4

4. Do **linking words** connect the details?

   Self 1 2 3 4

   Partner 1 2 3 4

5. Does the ending sentence **sum up** the description and tell the writer's **feelings** about it?

   Self 1 2 3 4

   Partner 1 2 3 4

▶ **Now revise your paragraph to make it stronger.**

Grammar Using Subject and Object Pronouns

A **pronoun** is a word that takes the place of a noun in a sentence.

- Use a **subject pronoun** in the subject of a sentence.
- Use an **object pronoun** after a verb or after a word such as *for* or *to*.

Example

Subject Pronoun	Object Pronoun
I visited the ocean.	The waves crashed into me.
We went snorkeling.	Fish swam around us.
She studies marine biology.	Fish fascinate her.
They live in the midnight zone.	Dijanna studies them.

▶ **Circle the correct pronoun. Write whether it is a subject or object pronoun.**

1. The director asked [she (her)] to be in the movie. ___object___
2. [She Her] went deep into the ocean in a submersible. ____________
3. [They Them] are counting the creatures in the oceans. ____________
4. The scientist took a camera with [he him]. ____________
5. The pictures showed [they them] near a vent. ____________
6. [I Me] would like to be a marine biologist. ____________

▶ **Rewrite these sentences using a pronoun for the underlined words.**

7. Dijanna studies creatures who live deep in the ocean.

____

8. The shark gave the divers a bad scare.

____

9. The man was an expert on ocean life.

____

10. The divers swam among the colorful fish.

____

Take a close look at each of the sentences in your draft on page 183. Do they all use subject and object pronouns correctly? Fix the ones that don't.

Usage Avoiding Double Negatives

Negatives are words that express *no* or *not*.

- Use only one negative word to express a single negative idea.
- It is incorrect to use two negatives to express a negative idea.

Example

Correct	Incorrect
A diver should never swim alone.	A diver shouldn't never swim alone.
The scientists didn't find anything.	The scientists didn't find nothing.

▶ **Find and correct five errors in this paragraph.**

Student Model

My favorite place is the park where I run. Every morning, I jog three miles around the lake. I can hear the sounds of the ducks and geese. Them are calling to each other. I pass a stand of pine trees that fills the air with their distinkt smell. Near the end of my run, I pass too old men fishing, even though they can't never catch anything. There's isn't nothing better than running in this park.

Check and Correct

- ☐ Circle two spelling errors and correct them.
- ☐ Underline one subject-object pronoun error and correct it.
- ☐ Correct two double-negative errors.

Look at the sentences in your own draft on page 183. Are they free of double negatives? Fix the ones that have double negatives.

Final Draft/Present

▶ **Write a final draft of your paragraph on paper or on the computer. Check it again and correct any errors before you present it.**

Careers

Aquarist

Stephen Brorsen is a senior aquarist at the Monterey Bay Aquarium in California. Aquarists get to toss fish to hungry sea lions—but that's just one small part of Stephen's job. He also goes into the wild to capture new animals for the exhibits. When necessary, he removes injured animals so they can be treated. "Every day is a new day. I love caring for sea animals," says Stephen.

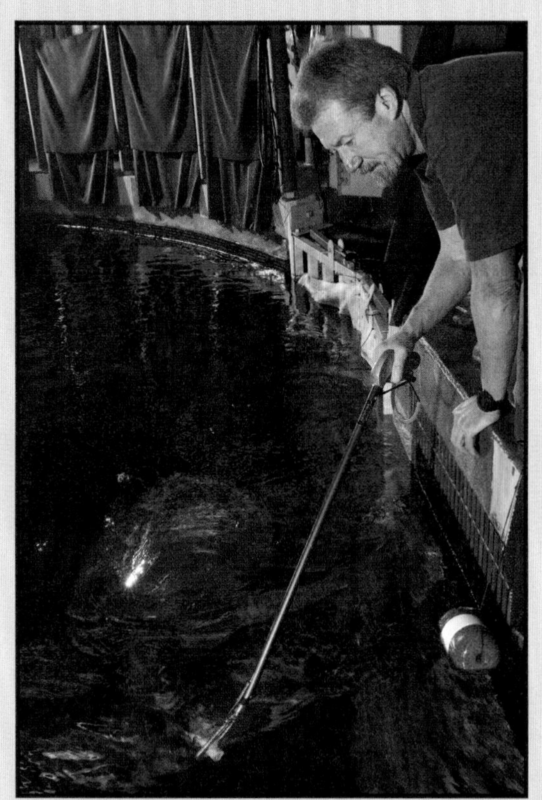

Stephen Brorsen feeds a sea turtle at the Monterey Bay Aquarium.

Name: Stephen Brorsen

Hometown: Pacific Grove, California

Job: Senior Aquarist, Monterey Bay Aquarium

Duties:
- prepare and clean animal exhibits
- feed animals
- capture animals for exhibit

Skills:
- swimming
- scuba diving
- lifting heavy objects (like sand bags and water buckets)
- wrangling 300-pound sea turtles

Similar Jobs:
- marine biologist
- marine animal rescuer

Pay: $35,000–$60,000 per year

Education: Bachelor's or Master's Degree in Marine Science

Ask Yourself

1. **Underline** Mark the skills you think you already have.
2. **Circle** Mark where Stephen works.
3. Would you want this job?
   - ❑ I don't want it.
   - ❑ I might want it.
   - ❑ I really want it.

Real-World Skills

Following Instructions

Stephen cares for sea animals at the Monterey Bay Aquarium. One of his jobs is feeding the aquarium's two sea turtles. Read the feeding instructions. Then answer the questions.

FEEDING INSTRUCTIONS FOR SEA TURTLES

Feed Sea Turtles Twice Daily

1. In the food room, grab one food tray for each turtle.
2. On each tray, measure out ½ pound each of:
   - squid
   - romaine lettuce
   - bell peppers
3. Prepare "seafood tacos." Roll up one piece of squid and one slice of bell pepper in each romaine lettuce leaf.
4. Every other day, give each turtle one vitamin tab by slipping it into a taco during the first feeding of the day.
5. Carry the trays to the turtle feeding area.
6. Use the poles in the turtle feeding area to lure each turtle to its own feeding station. (This keeps the turtles from trying to eat each other's food.)
   - Turtle A will go to its station when you hold up the red pole.
   - Turtle B will go to its station when you hold up the yellow pole.
7. Feed one tray of tacos to each turtle, using long-handled tongs.

▶ **Fill in the circle next to the correct answer.**

1. What is the purpose of this document?
Ⓐ to tell visitors what turtles eat
Ⓑ to explain how to feed the turtles
Ⓒ to provide a recipe for seafood tacos
Ⓓ to explain how to capture a turtle

2. How many meals does each turtle eat in one week?
Ⓐ 2
Ⓑ 28
Ⓒ 7
Ⓓ 14

3. In what do you wrap a seafood taco?
Ⓐ romaine lettuce leaves
Ⓑ squid
Ⓒ tortillas
Ⓓ turtle shells

4. How many pounds of food does each turtle eat at one feeding?
Ⓐ 1
Ⓑ 3
Ⓒ 1½
Ⓓ ½

5. How often do the turtles get a vitamin?
Ⓐ once a day
Ⓑ twice a day
Ⓒ once every other day
Ⓓ twice a week

Comprehension

▶ **Fill in the circle next to the correct answer.**

1. Which sentence gives the best summary of "Sea Census Under Way"?
Ⓐ Scientists are counting the people who live near the ocean.
Ⓑ The census is a ten-year project dedicated to recording all the plants and animals living in the oceans of the world.
Ⓒ So far, the census has not found any new species of marine life.
Ⓓ Scientists hope that the census will encourage people to protect the ocean.

Here's a tip.
Look for words like *cause*, *effect*, *fact*, and *opinion* in questions. These cue words can help you figure out what kind of answer is expected.

2. Which of the following statements is an opinion?
Ⓐ The ocean covers 70 percent of the earth's surface.
Ⓑ The sunlit zone is also called the euphotic zone.
Ⓒ Many creatures in the twilight zone look weird.
Ⓓ Bioluminescence is the production of light by living things.

3. Hydrothermal vents are hot because of ________________.
Ⓐ volcanic activity under the ocean floor
Ⓑ the concentrated amount of sunshine they get
Ⓒ the vast number of fish swimming around them
Ⓓ the hot water that surrounds them

4. Little sunlight illuminates the twilight zone of the ocean. One effect of this is that ________________.
Ⓐ the zone is rich in plant life
Ⓑ fish gather around hydrothermal vents
Ⓒ predators can see their prey easily
Ⓓ no plants grow there

5. The creatures in the different ocean zones demonstrate how ________________.
Ⓐ fish are very similar to land animals
Ⓑ living things adapt to their environments
Ⓒ light is necessary for things to survive
Ⓓ scientists know very little about life in the oceans

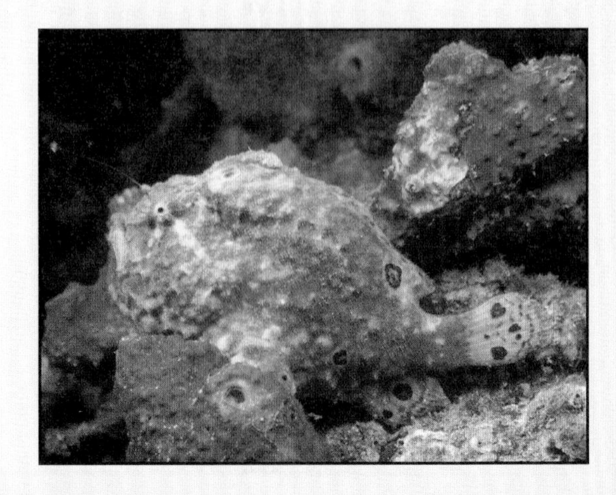

Vocabulary

▶ **Fill in the circle next to the correct definitions of the underlined words.**

1. Scientists are recording the <u>maximum</u> number of fish in the <u>vast</u> oceans.

   Ⓐ smallest, great
   Ⓑ warmest, whole
   Ⓒ largest, huge
   Ⓓ most unusual, changing

2. The diver was careful not to come in <u>contact</u> with the poisonous fish.

   Ⓐ danger
   Ⓑ distance
   Ⓒ connection
   Ⓓ conflict

3. The fish <u>adapted</u> to its environment by developing a <u>distinct</u> pattern of stripes.

   Ⓐ adjusted, different
   Ⓑ touched, similar
   Ⓒ swam, unattractive
   Ⓓ discovered, marine

▶ **Fill in the circle next to the best answer.**

4. What does the idiom "making waves" mean in this sentence?

   Jamal was making waves when he said that his dog ate his homework.

   Ⓐ helping out
   Ⓑ telling the truth
   Ⓒ causing trouble
   Ⓓ daydreaming

▶ **How would the pronunciation guide in a dictionary show the underlined word?**

5. Bioluminescence is one <u>adaptation</u> fish have made to the twilight zone.

   Ⓐ **ad**-apt-ay-sheen
   Ⓑ ad-a-ptay-**shuhn**
   Ⓒ ad-ap-**tay**-shuhn
   Ⓓ ad-ap-**tay**-sheen

Short Answer

▶ **Use what you've read in this Workshop to answer the question below. Check your spelling and grammar.**

Why are the oceans the most unexplored part of our planet?

____

____

____

____

WORKSHOP 8

NONFICTION

Comprehension Focus
Compare and Contrast

READINGS

1 ***How Globalization Is Shrinking the World*** >> News Report
2 ***Outsource It*** >> Magazine Article
3 ***Exploding Economies*** >> Social Studies Text

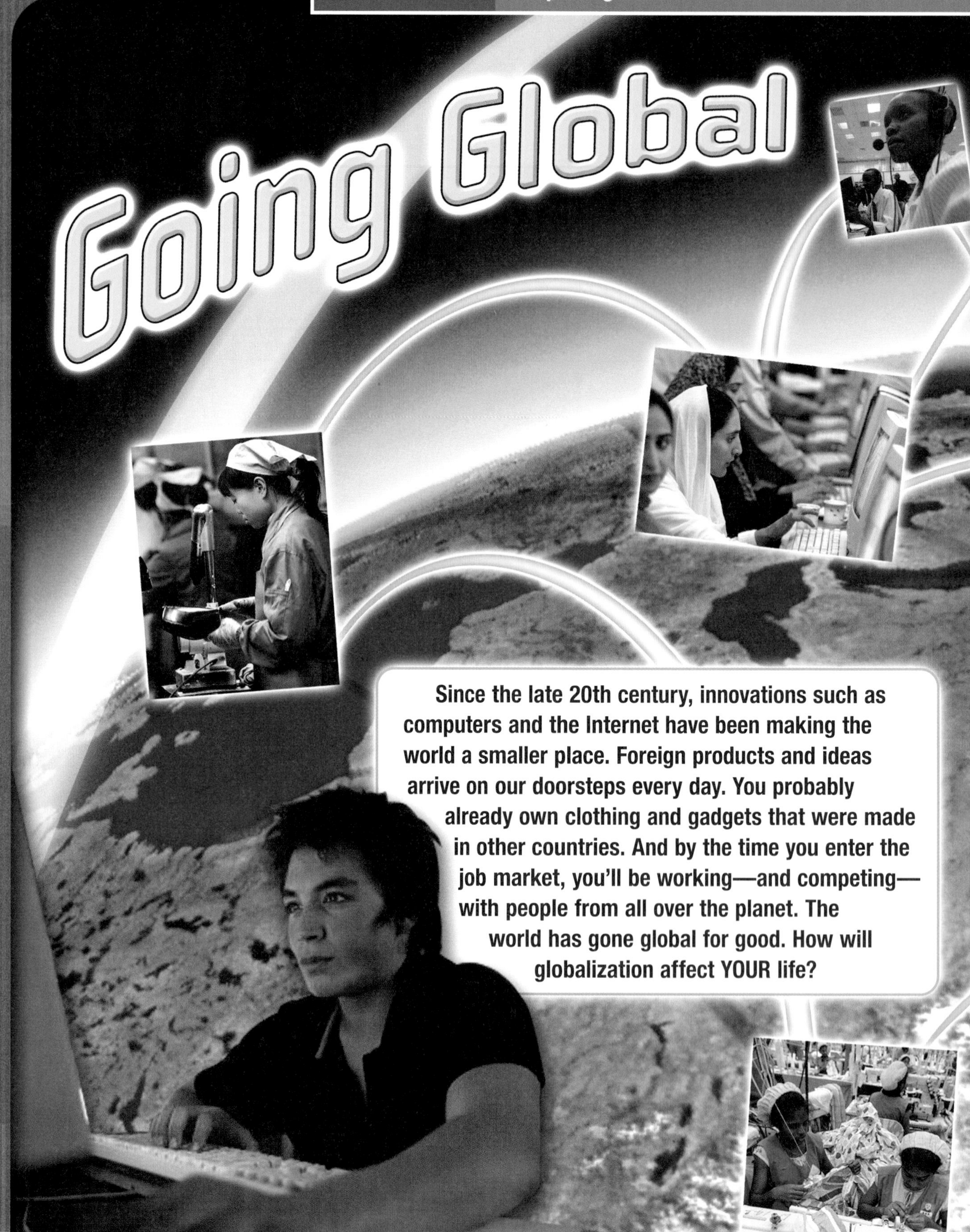

Going Global

Since the late 20th century, innovations such as computers and the Internet have been making the world a smaller place. Foreign products and ideas arrive on our doorsteps every day. You probably already own clothing and gadgets that were made in other countries. And by the time you enter the job market, you'll be working—and competing—with people from all over the planet. The world has gone global for good. How will globalization affect YOUR life?

VOCABULARY BUILDER

Target Word ▶ Read the Target Words. Rate each one using the scale below.*	Meaning ▶ Read the Target Word meaning. Write in the missing ones.	Example ▶ Finish the Target Word examples below. Write in the missing ones.
coordinate *co•or•di•nate* *(verb)* ① ② ③		Two parts of my outfit that I like to coordinate are . . .
domestic *do•mes•tic* *(adjective)* ① ② ③	from or of one's own country; not involving other countries	
infrastructure *in•fra•struc•ture* *(noun)* ① ② ③		Faster buses would improve this town's **infrastructure**.
innovation *in•no•va•tion* *(noun)* ① ② ③	a new invention, method, or idea	
trend *(noun)* ① ② ③		A new trend I'd like to start is . . .

*Rating Scale

① = I don't know it at all.
② = I've seen it before.
③ = I know it and use it.

The Big Idea

Write What is this article mainly about?

___

___

___

VOCABULARY BUILDER

Target Word

isolated

i•so•lat•ed (adj)

Rate it: ① ② ③

Meaning

___

___

___

Example

___

___

___

React

What do you use or wear that was made in another country? What American-made products might be sold all over the world?

How Globalization Is Shrinking the World

In the past, far-apart countries were **isolated** by distance. Around the year 2000, the world began to shrink. Its physical size didn't change. But once-isolated countries were brought together by innovations of the late 1900s. By 2000, the whole world was sharing products, ideas, and even people.

This phenomenon—called globalization—was sparked by a revolution in telecommunications. Before globalization, contacting other countries meant using the mail or the phone.

But by the late 1980s, desktop computers were becoming trendy. Email was catching on. In 1993, the first user-friendly Web browser was launched, and soon, millions around the globe were accessing the Internet. U.S. companies began to invest billions in building global computer networks. Now, people everywhere could exchange information cheaply and instantly.

Within a few years, companies were doing business in new ways. Products once made and sold domestically could be made in other countries and sold worldwide. U.S. firms that once hired employees domestically could now hire workers in Latin America and Asia. And businesses around the world could form partnerships with each other. Globalization had become a booming trend.

So far, it is a trend that shows no signs of slowing down or fading away. END

Words to Know! **telecommunications** *(n)* electronic systems for communicating at a distance

Comprehension Focus

Compare and Contrast

When you **compare**, you tell how two things are the same. When you **contrast**, you tell how they are different. To compare and contrast:

- **Ask yourself how two things are the same. Look for signal words such as *also*, *still*, and *too*.**
- **Ask yourself how two things are different. Look for signal words such as *but* and *however*. Look also for words such as *once*, *before*, *now*, and *then*, which signal that things have changed over time.**

▶ **Fill in this chart to compare and contrast the world before and after globalization.**

Before Globalization

Different

1. Global Communication

- Far-apart countries were isolated by distance.
-

2. Global Business

-
-

Same

1. Global Communication

- The physical size of the world didn't change.
- People communicate with people in other countries.

2. Global Business

- Companies make and sell products.
- Companies hire people to work for them.

After Globalization

Different

1. Global Communication

- Once-isolated countries were brought together by innovations.
-

2. Global Business

-
-

The Big Idea

Write What is this article mainly about?

____

____

____

VOCABULARY BUILDER

Target Word

contract

con•tract (verb)

Rate it: ① ② ③

Meaning

____

____

____

Example

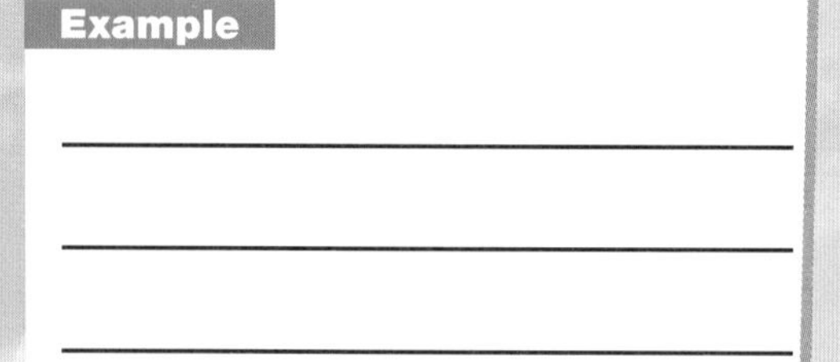

____

____

____

React

If you wanted to hire an online tutor, would you hire someone local or someone from another country? Does it matter? How would you decide?

Outsource It

Americans are creating millions of jobs—elsewhere. Sending work outside the U.S. is a growing trend.

Worldwide Service

Having trouble with algebra? Get help over the Internet from a tutor in India. Bored with your favorite online game? Hire a kid in China to play the easy levels. Birthday package arrive damaged? That voice on the phone that helps you exchange your gift may be coming to you from the other side of the earth!

What's all this about? Offshore tutors, gamers for hire, and customer service from around the world are just three examples of a fast-growing trend in business: outsourcing. Increasingly, American companies and people are **contracting** with workers from other countries to provide products and services that were once provided by American workers.

Global Workplace

Before globalization, most American companies were staffed mainly by Americans. But in the era of globalization, millions of jobs that were once accomplished domestically are now performed in other countries, by foreign employees.

One Texas-based computer company, for example, employed only local workers back in 1984. By 2005, it had hired thousands of workers in India and the Philippines to do everything from helping customers to developing software and testing products. In 2006, the company announced plans to increase its workforce in India by 50 percent.

What's happened there is typical: Surveys show that about 70 percent of U.S. technology companies outsource jobs in information technology. →

Words to Know! **offshore** *(adj)* located in a foreign country

Compare and Contrast

1. **Circle** Find a sentence in "Worldwide Service" that describes a change in the way American people and companies do business.

2. **Write** In "Global Workplace," find the following:

- one way that American companies were different before globalization

____

____

____

____

____

____

- one way that American companies were different after globalization

____

____

____

____

____

____

____

Active Reading

Circle ▶ Why do American companies outsource jobs?

VOCABULARY BUILDER

Target Word

valid

val•id (adjective)

Rate it: ① ② ③

Meaning

____

____

____

Example

____

____

____

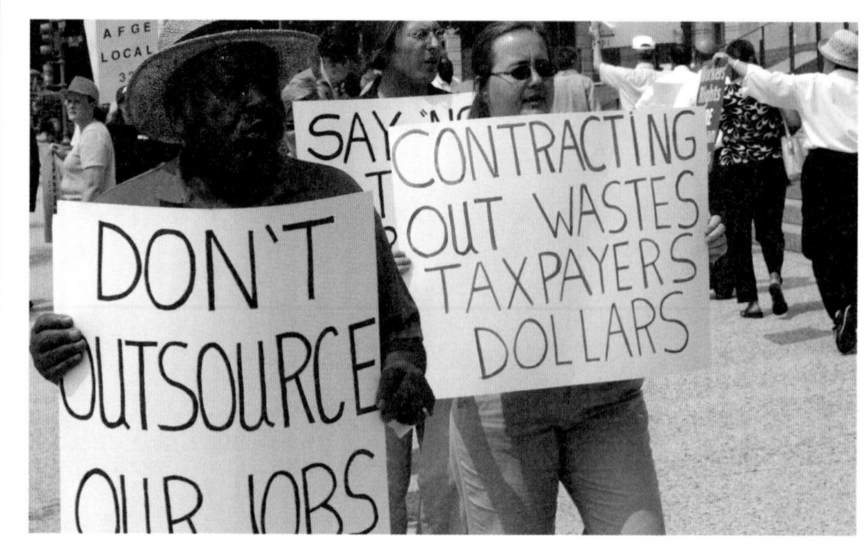

Cheap Labor

What's behind the outsourcing boom? The dollar is the driving force. Many jobs can be handled more cheaply outside the U.S.

Domestic customer service jobs pay about $28,000 a year, compared with $5,000 a year in India. The average Chinese factory worker makes only 64 cents an hour, while American workers make *at least* the federal minimum wage of $5.15 an hour. What about tutors in India? They average $20 an hour, compared with an American tutor, who averages $50 an hour.

Good or Bad?

What does outsourcing mean for Americans? There are **valid** arguments for and against it. On the one hand, it means lower prices on goods made cheaply overseas.

On the other hand, cheap labor is often exploited labor. Who wants to stitch sneakers for $2 a day—like some factory workers in Asia and Latin America?

Then there are the jobs lost to outsourcing. In Bangalore, India, alone, about 160,000 people have jobs providing services to U.S. clients—which means 160,000 fewer jobs for American workers. END

Words to Know! **federal** *(adj)* related to the central government

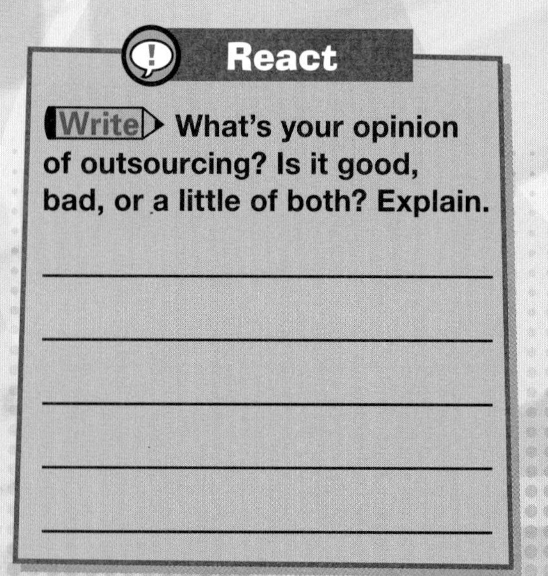

React

Write ▶ **What's your opinion of outsourcing? Is it good, bad, or a little of both? Explain.**

____

____

____

____

____

Comprehension Focus

Compare and Contrast

▶ Fill in this chart to compare and contrast information in "Cheap Labor" about workers in the U.S. versus workers in other countries.

Within the U.S.		Outside the U.S.
Different	**Same**	**Different**
1. Customer Service Jobs	**1.** Customer Service Jobs Help customers with problems	**1.** Customer Service Jobs
2. American Workers	**2.** Factory Workers Make Products	**2.** Chinese Workers
3. American Tutors	**3.** Tutors Help students	**3.** Indian Tutors

The Big Idea

Write What is this article mainly about?

____

____

____

VOCABULARY BUILDER

Target Word

usage

us•age (noun)

Rate it: ① ② ③

Meaning

____

____

____

Example

____

____

____

React

Many people in India speak three or more languages. Could knowing another language help you on the job? Explain.

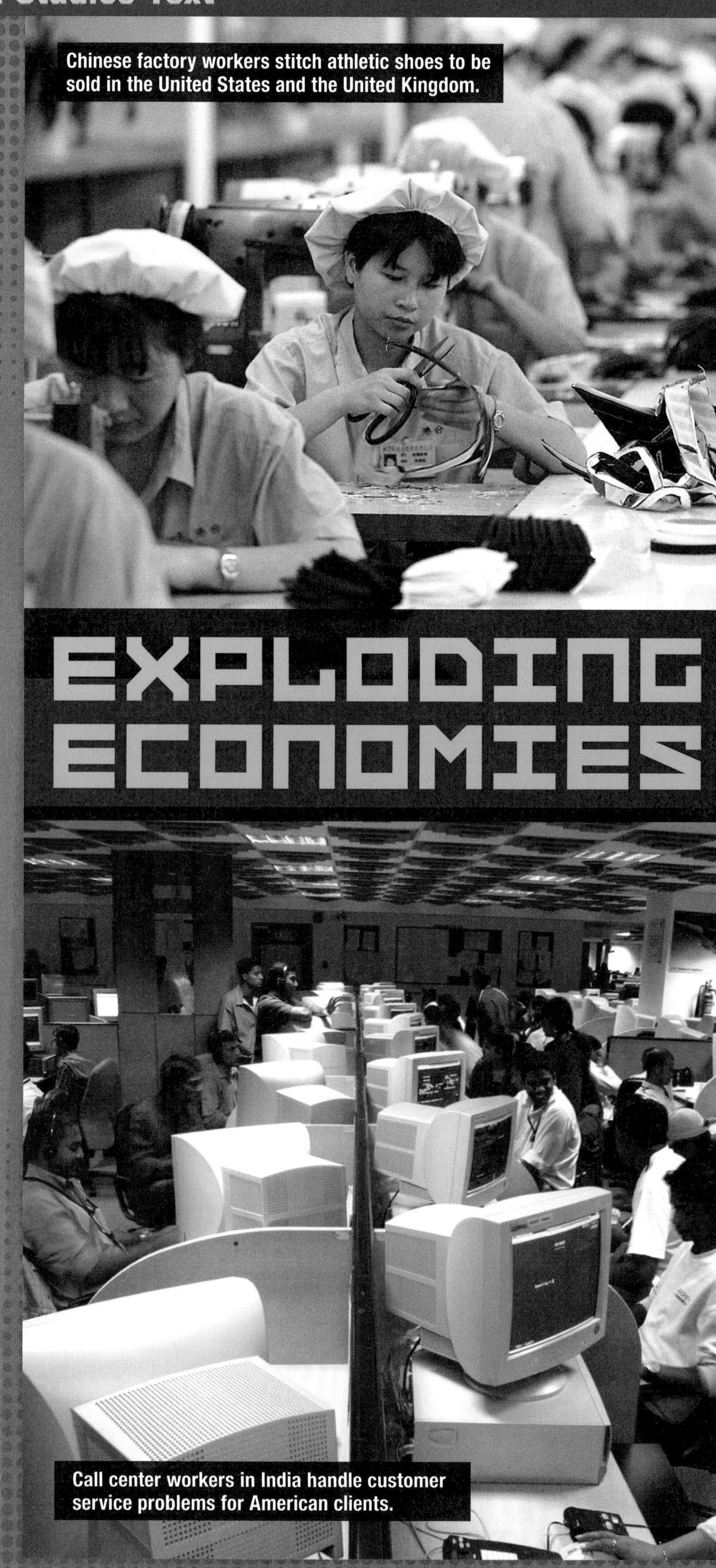

Chinese factory workers stitch athletic shoes to be sold in the United States and the United Kingdom.

EXPLODING ECONOMIES

Call center workers in India handle customer service problems for American clients.

Decade of Change

The 1990s was a decade of innovations in technology. But email, Internet **usage**, and other technologies weren't the only forces that were changing the world.

During the 1990s, 3 billion new people became participants in the global economy. They came from places like China, India, Russia, Eastern Europe, and Latin America.

Many of these areas had long been isolated from the world economy by restrictive governments and economic systems. Now, slowly, those systems were loosening up, allowing individuals and companies more freedom to do business.

India Plugs In

Probably no country has benefited more from these changes than India. With its traditionally strong emphasis on education, India graduates about 3 million college students each year. One third of them are fluent in three or more languages.

But India had always lacked the infrastructure to support big businesses and institutions. Explains Indian-American executive Dinakar Singh, "For decades, you had to leave India to be a professional."

Then the Internet arrived. Large numbers of Indians still go to college. But now, they need not move to pursue careers. As Singh explains, the Internet allows Indians to "plug into the world from India."

Today, India accounts for 44 percent of the world's outsourcing. High-tech workers in booming Bangalore aren't just answering calls. They are computer chip designers, software developers, and video game entrepreneurs. Trend watchers predict the next great innovation may come from a place such as Bangalore. →

Words to Know! **restrictive** *(adj)* limiting

Compare and Contrast

1. Write ▸ How was the global economy different during the 1990s than before the 1990s?

____

____

____

____

2. Circle ▸ Find a sentence that tells how India was the same after the arrival of the Internet.

3. Underline ▸ Find a sentence that tells how India was different after the arrival of the Internet.

Review: Cause and Effect

Write ▸ What is an effect of the Internet arriving in India?

____

____

____

____

Active Reading

Circle ▶ How large is China's economy, compared with the rest of the world?

VOCABULARY BUILDER

Target Word

efficient

ef•fi•cient (adjective)

Rate it: ① ② ③

Meaning

____

____

____

Example

____

____

____

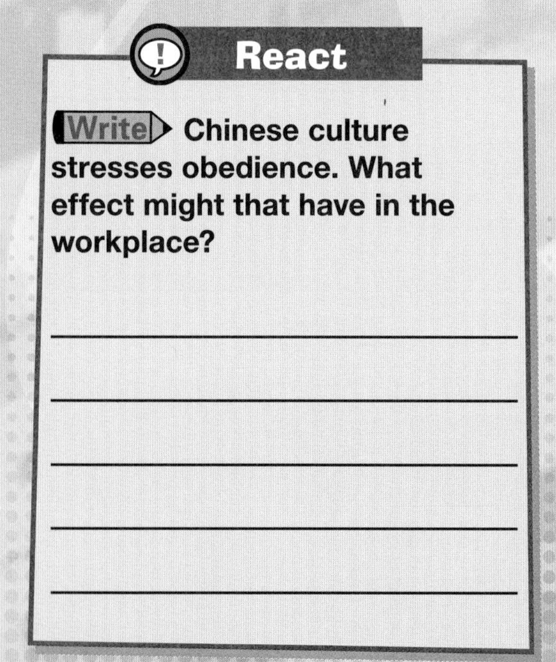

React

Write ▶ **Chinese culture stresses obedience. What effect might that have in the workplace?**

____

____

____

____

____

China on the Rise

In the era of globalization, no country has become an economic powerhouse faster than China. Since former leader Deng Xiao Peng began a program of economic reforms in 1978, China's gross domestic product (GDP)—the total value of all goods and services produced in a year—has quadrupled. Once plagued by poverty and starvation, China now has the world's sixth-largest economy. Some experts say it is poised to overtake the U.S. as number one.

How did the Chinese economy expand so rapidly? With almost 1.5 billion people, China has the world's largest workforce. And the nation is experiencing the largest human migration in history, with hundreds of millions of rural peasants moving to cities to work.

Over the past decade, Chinese factories have become **efficient** and well-coordinated, producing masses of goods at low costs. An automotive factory near Shanghai produces 60,000 luxury vehicles yearly. The vehicles resemble American luxury SUVs, but sell for less than a third of the price.

Chinese factories keep labor costs down by using low-paid workers to perform tasks that are done by costly machines in the United States. Management costs are low, too. Chinese culture stresses obedience; employees require minimal supervision.

Made in China

Because of its reliable workforce and ability to deliver goods cheaply, China has become the world's factory floor. It manufactures more toys, clothes, shoes, and electronics than any other nation. China supplies 70 percent of the goods sold in one major U.S. chain store.

What does the future hold? Like India, China emphasizes education. The country currently has 17 million post-secondary students. In 2004, China graduated 325,000 engineers—five times as many as the U.S.

With a growing army of educated workers, China hopes that future products will not only be "made in China" but designed there. END

Words to Know! **minimal** *(adj)* extremely little

TEXT FEATURE Analyzing an Editorial Cartoon

In an editorial cartoon, the cartoonist comments on an issue. This cartoon is about the United States and China.

1. Who is pictured in the cartoon?

Ⓐ American graduates Ⓒ factory workers
Ⓑ teachers Ⓓ Chinese engineers

2. What comment is the cartoon making?

Ⓐ Chinese-made graduation caps are unattractive.
Ⓑ Americans should stop buying goods made in China.
Ⓒ Chinese-made products are popping up everywhere.

3. Why do you think the artist set this cartoon at a graduation ceremony?

____

____

Compare and Contrast

1. **Circle** How does the price of a Chinese luxury vehicle compare to that of an American luxury SUV?

2. **Write** Find one way that Chinese factories are different from factories in the U.S.

____

____

____

____

Skills Check

1. **Underline** How are China and India alike?

2. **Write** In what way does China hope its products will be different in the future?

____

____

____

____

VOCABULARY

TAKE THE WORD CHALLENGE

Start

Think about it. List the following things.

A fashion trend you like:

____

A fashion trend you hate:

____

A trendy item you want to own:

____

2 **Evaluate.** Write ***V*** next to each valid excuse for not doing your homework. Write ***NV*** next to each excuse that is not valid.

_____ I was too tired.

_____ I went out with my friends instead.

_____ I was sick with the flu.

_____ There was a really good show on TV.

_____ I had a family emergency.

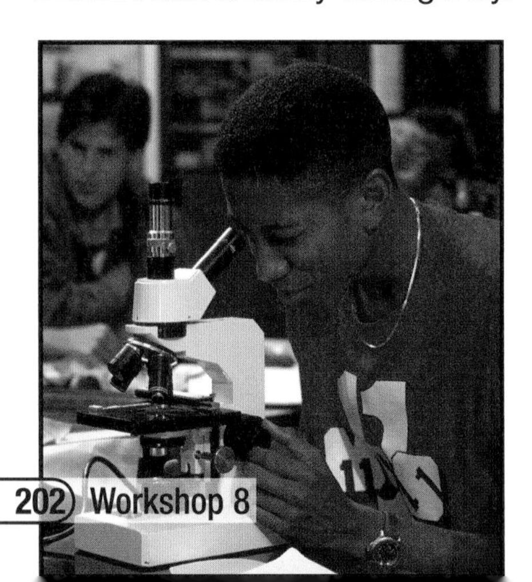

3 Context Clues

Sometimes you'll see a word you don't know in a sentence. One way to figure out what it means is to look at the words around it. These words are the "context" for the word. They can give you "context clues."

What do you think *coordinate* means? Study the context, and make a guess. Check the glossary to see whether you got it right.

- ❑ destroy
- ❑ organize
- ❑ admire
- ❑ hide

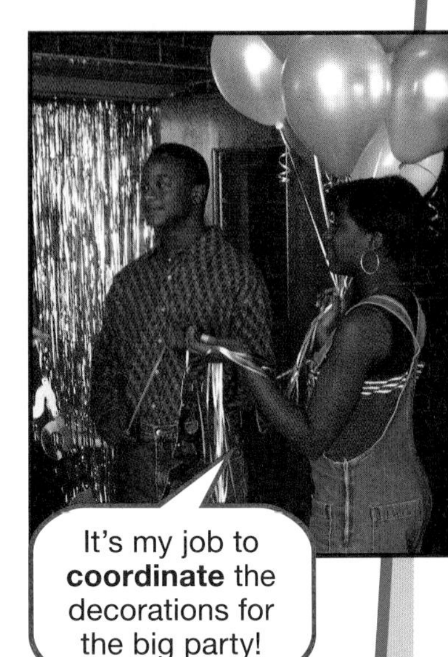

4 **Decide.** To fly to these places, would you take a domestic or international flight? Write ***D*** for domestic or ***I*** for international.

_____ Seattle, Washington	_____ Cancún, Mexico
_____ Beijing, China	_____ Albany, New York
_____ Paris, France	_____ Bangalore, India
_____ Austin, Texas	_____ Phoenix, Arizona
_____ Milwaukee, Wisconsin	_____ Miami, Florida

5 **Complete the sentences.** Fill in each blank with the correct form of isolate from below.

isolate   **isolation**   **isolating**

The scientist was trying to ____________ germs in a lab. Because the germs were dangerous, the scientist had to work in ____________. I think I would find working all alone very ____________.

6 **Evaluate.** Which is the correct usage of the word infrastructure?

- ☐ This city's infrastructure is in really bad shape.
- ☐ My infrastructure is really sore today from playing ball last night.

7 **Check them.** Which of these activities make you a consumer? Check all that apply.

- ☐ eating something
- ☐ selling something
- ☐ buying something
- ☐ using something

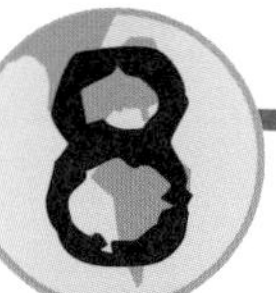

These bracelets are a fashion **trend** at my school. I'm always on top of the latest **trends**.

8 Noun Endings

To show more than one person, place, or thing, add an –*s* to most nouns.

- If a noun ends in *ss*, *s*, *x*, *ch*, or *sh*, add –*es* to make it plural, as in *buses* or *dresses*.
- If a noun ends in a consonant and *y*, change the *y* to *i* and add –*es* to make it plural, as in *spies*.
- Plus, watch out for irregular plurals like *mice*, the plural of *mouse*. These don't follow the rules!

Write the plural of each word below.

Singular	Plural
beach	____________
trend	____________
city	____________
goose	____________
tax	____________

9 **Fill in.** Complete these sentences with either contract or consumer.

The ____________ is planning to ____________ for cell phone service with a new company that offers low rates. As a thrifty ____________ I'd be happy to sign a ____________ for such inexpensive phone service.

10 **Complete the sentences.** Fill in each blank with the correct form of innovate from below.

innovative **innovation** **innovator**

My brother is an amazing ____________. When it's his turn to make dinner, he always does something ____________. His latest ____________ was fried macaroni and cheese with pickles.

Finish

Writing Focus

Persuasive Paragraph

A **persuasive paragraph** tries to convince the reader to share the writer's opinions.

▶ **Read Corinne's persuasive paragraph about outsourcing.**

Student Model

Stop Outsourcing Jobs!

By Corinne Smith

I strongly believe that the United States should not outsource jobs to other countries. One reason is that Americans need those jobs. My mom lost her factory job when the work was outsourced to China. A second reason is that it seems weird to get services over the Internet. When I need help with homework, I like to talk to someone in person. Finally, workers in other countries are often exploited. Chinese factory workers earn less in one year than my mom made in a month! Outsourcing is unfair to everyone. For these reasons, I believe that outsourcing should stop.

Parts of a Persuasive Paragraph

▶ **Find these parts of Corinne's persuasive paragraph.**

1. Underline the sentence that states the writer's **opinion**.
2. Check three **reasons** that support the opinion.
3. Put a box around the reason you think is **strongest**.
4. Circle the **linking words** that connect the ideas.
5. Put a star beside the sentence that **restates** the writer's opinion.

Brainstorm

▶ **Read the writing prompt in the middle of the idea web. Then use the boxes to help you brainstorm your ideas.**

Cheap Labor

Low Prices

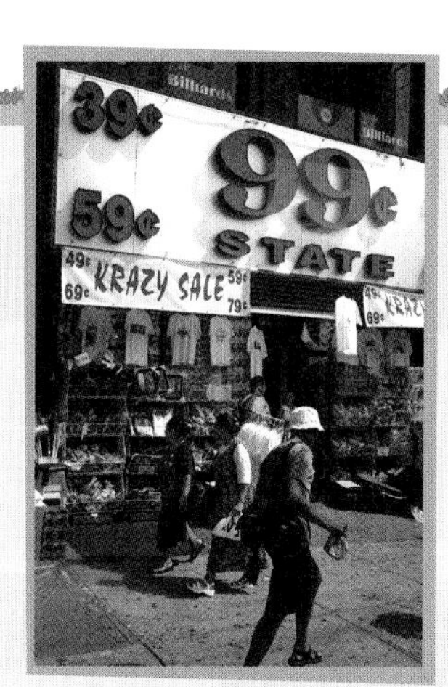

Writing Prompt:
Write a persuasive paragraph for or against outsourcing.

Worldwide Service

Loss of Domestic Jobs

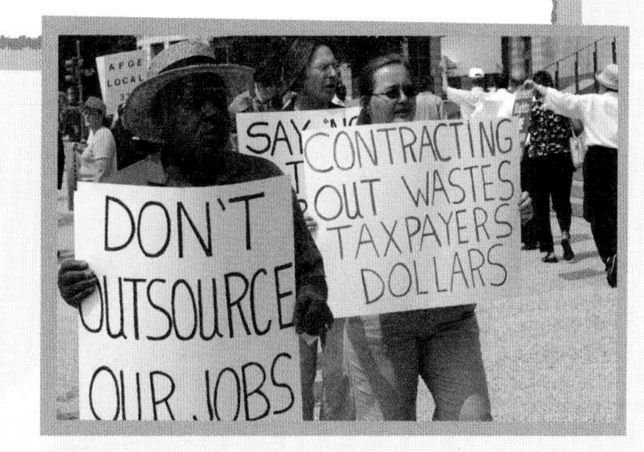

Plan Your Paragraph

Writing Prompt: Is outsourcing good or bad for Americans? Write a persuasive paragraph for or against outsourcing.

▶ Use this chart to plan and organize your paragraph.

Word Choices

____

____

____

____

____

Topic/Opinion Sentence

- *I strongly believe that . . .*
- *Outsourcing jobs can . . .*
- *Americans need . . .*

Reason 1

- *One reason is that . . .*
- *First of all, . . .*
- *A good thing to remember . . .*

Reason 2

- *A second reason is that . . .*
- *Also, . . .*
- *Another important point . . .*

Reason 3

- *Most important, . . .*
- *It's also important . . .*
- *Finally, . . .*

Conclusion

- *For these reasons, . . .*
- *In conclusion, . . .*
- *Overall, . . .*

Write Your Paragraph

▶ **Use this writing frame to write a first draft of your paragraph.**

____
(title)

I strongly believe that ______________________________
____
____
____

One reason is that ______________________________
____
____
____

A second reason is that ______________________________
____
____
____

Most important, ______________________________
____
____
____

For these reasons, ______________________________
____
____
____
____

Revise

▶ **Rate your paragraph. Then have a writing partner rate it.**

Scoring Guide			
weak	okay	good	strong
1	2	3	4

1. Does the first sentence clearly state the writer's **opinion**?

Self	1	2	3	4
Partner	1	2	3	4

2. Is the opinion supported by several **reasons**?

Self	1	2	3	4
Partner	1	2	3	4

3. Are the reasons given **strong** and **convincing**?

Self	1	2	3	4
Partner	1	2	3	4

4. Do **linking words** connect the ideas?

Self	1	2	3	4
Partner	1	2	3	4

5. Does the concluding sentence **restate** the writer's opinion?

Self	1	2	3	4
Partner	1	2	3	4

▶ Now revise your paragraph to make it stronger.

Grammar Using Adjectives That Compare

An adjective is a word that tells about or describes a noun. Adjectives can compare two or more people, places, or things.

- To use an adjective to **compare two things**, add *-er* to the adjective or use the word *more*.
- To use an adjective to **compare three or more things**, add *-est* to the adjective or use the word *most*.

Example

Adjective Comparing Two Things	Adjective Comparing Three or More Things
China is richer than it was 10 years ago.	He is the richest person in the country.
Outsourcing is more popular now than before the 1990s.	She is the most popular actress in the world.

▶ **Circle the correct comparing word in the sentences below.**

1. Communication is [(faster) fastest] now than in the past.
2. Email is [quicker quickest] than postal mail.
3. China has the [more most] efficient factories in Asia.
4. The United States outsources [more most] jobs than ever before.
5. India gets the [bigger biggest] share of outsourced jobs in the world.
6. China has [more most] people than any other country in the world.

▶ **Rewrite the sentences to compare three or more things correctly.**

7. China now graduates the <u>more</u> engineers in the world.

   ____

8. India has the <u>larger</u> call centers in the world.

   ____

9. The 1990s was the decade with the <u>more</u> innovations in recent history.

   ____

10. American workers may soon be facing the <u>bigger</u> job shortage ever.

   ____

Take a close look at each of the sentences in your draft on page 207. Do they use adjectives that compare correctly? Fix the ones that don't.

Mechanics USING QUOTATION MARKS

Quotation marks show the exact words of a speaker.

- The first word of a quotation is capitalized.
- Punctuation usually goes inside the ending quotation mark.

Example

Correct	Incorrect
Katie said, "Way to go!"	Katie said, "way to go!"
Alex yelled, "You did it!"	Alex yelled, "You did it"!

▶ **Find and correct five errors in this paragraph.**

Student Model

One reason I'm in favor of outsourcing is that it means lower prices for Americans. My family's flat-screen TV was made in China. We couldn't afford a more ixpensive one. Also, when I needed help with homework, Mom ofered to hire me a tutor. I thought it would cost too much. But Mom heard about this tutoring service in India that was cheapest than tutors here. "Great, I told her, Let's try it!"

Check and Correct

- ❑ Circle two spelling errors and correct them.
- ❑ Insert two missing quotation marks.
- ❑ Correct one error with a comparison.

Look at the sentences in your own draft on page 207. Do they all use quotation marks correctly? Fix the ones that don't.

Final Draft/Present

▶ **Write a final draft of your paragraph on paper or the computer. Check it again and correct any errors before you present it**

Careers

Industrial Technician

Industrial Technicians operate telecommunications networks that keep employees connected and companies running smoothly. Carl Williams manages a team of computer technicians at a multinational manufacturing firm. He has colleagues in many different cities and countries. "The best part of my job is interacting with people from different cultures," Carl says. "That, and I get to keep up with the latest technologies."

Name: Carl Williams

Hometown: Leonia, NJ

Job: Vice President, Information Services

Duties:
- Manages a staff of workers
- Monitors the network infrastructure for any problems that may occur
- Installs and repairs computer hardware and software

Skills:
- Ability to learn new things quickly
- Excellent oral and written communication skills
- Ability to work as part of a team

Similar Jobs:
- Data Center Managers
- Systems Administrators

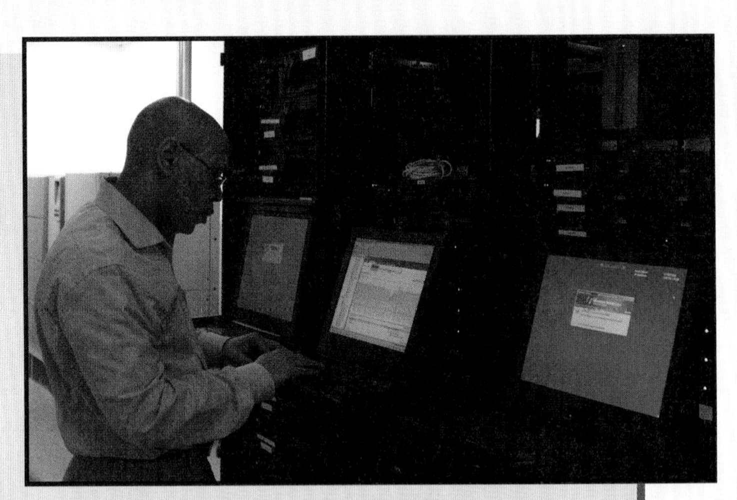

In his company's data center, Carl monitors the company computer network to make sure everything is running smoothly.

Pay: $80,000–$100,000 per year

Education: Bachelor's degree in computer science or management information systems

Ask Yourself

1. **Underline** Mark the skills you think you already have.
2. **Circle** Mark how much this job pays.
3. Would you want this job?
   - ❑ I don't want it.
   - ❑ I might want it.
   - ❑ I really want it.

Real-World Skills

Using a Request Form

When employees at a large company like Carl's need their computer equipment replaced, repaired, or upgraded, they fill out a request form and submit it to the computer technician team. Take a look at the request form below. Then answer the questions on the right.

Computer Equipment Request Form

Section One

REQUEST FOR COMPUTER EQUIPMENT

Employee requesting equipment: ______________

Department: ______________

Building address: ______________

Phone number: ______________

Section Two

NOTEBOOK COMPUTERS

❑ Standard notebook computer

❑ Vinyl carrying case

❑ Keyboard and mouse

MONITORS

❑ 17-inch

❑ 19-inch

❑ 20-inch

PRINTERS

❑ Black and White

❑ Color

SOFTWARE

❑ Graphic design

❑ Illustration

❑ Internet browsing

❑ Word processing

❑ Video editing/recording

Section Three

SIGNATURES REQUIRED FOR APPROVAL

Employee's Manager: ______________

Head of Department: ______________

Finance Manager: ______________

▶ **Fill in the circle next to the correct answer.**

1. What is the purpose of this document?

Ⓐ to report a broken printer
Ⓑ to request a computer repair
Ⓒ to request new computer equipment
Ⓓ to request help using new software

2. In which section would you write your work address and phone number?

Ⓐ Section One
Ⓑ Section Two
Ⓒ Section Three
Ⓓ None of the above

3. In Section Two, under which heading can you request a carrying case for your computer?

Ⓐ Software
Ⓑ Printers
Ⓒ Notebook Computers
Ⓓ Monitors

4. What is the largest size monitor an employee can request?

Ⓐ 20-inch
Ⓑ 17-inch
Ⓒ 25-inch
Ⓓ That information is not given on the form.

5. How many people must approve an employee's request for equipment?

Ⓐ 2
Ⓑ 3
Ⓒ 10
Ⓓ None

Comprehension

▶ **Fill in the circle next to the correct answer.**

1. Which statement below is an opinion?

Ⓐ Email is faster than postal mail.

Ⓑ A new Web browser was launched in 1993.

Ⓒ The Internet is the greatest innovation of the late 20th century.

Ⓓ Personal computers were in use by the late 1980s.

Here's a tip.

Read over your answers carefully. Double-check that you filled in the answers in the correct places.

2. Many U.S. companies outsource factory jobs because ________________.

Ⓐ foreign factories are cleaner than American factories

Ⓑ factory labor is cheaper in other countries

Ⓒ it's against the law to build factories in the U.S.

Ⓓ the company owners enjoy visiting other countries

3. How are customer service jobs different in India than in the U.S.?

Ⓐ Customers are nicer to service people in India.

Ⓑ Customer service jobs pay less in the U.S.

Ⓒ Customer service jobs pay less in India.

Ⓓ There are no differences.

4. How is China different now than it was 10 years ago?

Ⓐ Its economy is much smaller.

Ⓑ It has replaced most factory workers with expensive machines.

Ⓒ Most of its factories have closed down.

Ⓓ Millions of rural Chinese have moved to big cities.

5. In the future, what is a likely result of globalization?

Ⓐ Countries will become more isolated from each other.

Ⓑ The latest innovations in technology will come from all over the world.

Ⓒ Companies will build thousands of factories in the U.S.

Ⓓ None of the above.

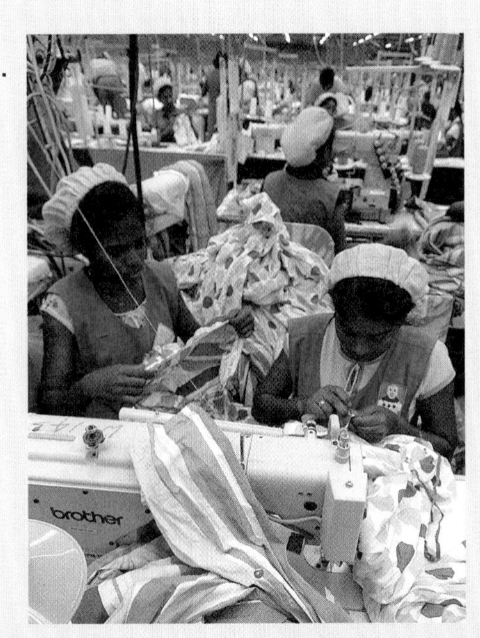

Vocabulary

▶ **Fill in the circle next to the correct definitions of the underlined words.**

1. Cell phones are my favorite <u>innovation</u> of the last 10 years.
   Ⓐ new thing
   Ⓑ activity
   Ⓒ cell phone use
   Ⓓ method of communication

2. Those sneakers are the latest <u>trend</u> at my school.
   Ⓐ footwear
   Ⓑ outdated product
   Ⓒ current style
   Ⓓ increase

3. A country with a strong <u>infrastructure</u> can support big <u>domestic</u> businesses.
   Ⓐ Internet, electronic
   Ⓑ foundation, native
   Ⓒ building, homemade
   Ⓓ economy, foreign

▶ **Choose the word with the correct noun ending to complete this sentence.**

4. Those two cities have solid ________________.
   Ⓐ infrastructuries
   Ⓑ infrastructure
   Ⓒ infrastructureses
   Ⓓ infrastructures

▶ **Choose the correct definition of the underlined word using context clues.**

5. My dad is against outsourcing, but his opinion is far from <u>universal</u>. Many people in my town support outsourcing.
   Ⓐ ridiculous
   Ⓑ alone in the world
   Ⓒ belonging to everyone
   Ⓓ expressing anger

Short Answer

▶ **Use what you've read in this Workshop to answer the question below. Check your spelling and grammar.**

Do you think globalization will have an impact on your future? Explain.

____

____

____

____

____

Comprehension Focus
Make Inferences

READINGS

The Art of the Memoir

The Writing of

Francisco Jiménez

Backbreaking labor. Constant fear. No money. Rundown shacks. These were the conditions that the Jiménez family faced when they came to America. So why did they do it? For the promise of a life that was better than the one they left behind.

Francisco Jiménez overcame countless obstacles and today is a celebrated author and teacher. In this workshop, you'll meet him and hear his story in his very own words.

VOCABULARY BUILDER

Target Word ▶ Read the Target Words. Rate each one using the scale below.*	Meaning ▶ Read the Target Word meanings. Write in the missing ones.	Example ▶ Finish the Target Word examples below. Write in the missing ones.
autobiographical *au•to•bi•o•graph•i•cal* *(adjective)* ① ② ③		In my autobiographical account, I'd tell about . . .
chronological *chron•o•log•i•cal* *(adjective)* ① ② ③	arranged according to when something happened	
documentation *doc•u•men•ta•tion* *(noun)* ① ② ③		This **documentation** shows that we are American citizens.
migrant *mi•grant* *(noun)* ① ② ③	a person who regularly moves from one area or country to another	
obstacle *ob•sta•cle* *(noun)* ① ② ③		An obstacle I overcame this year was . . .

***Rating Scale**

① = I don't know it at all.
② = I've seen it before.
③ = I know it and use it.

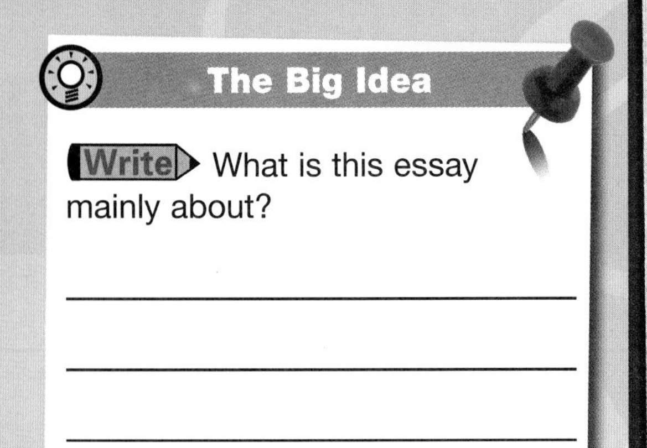

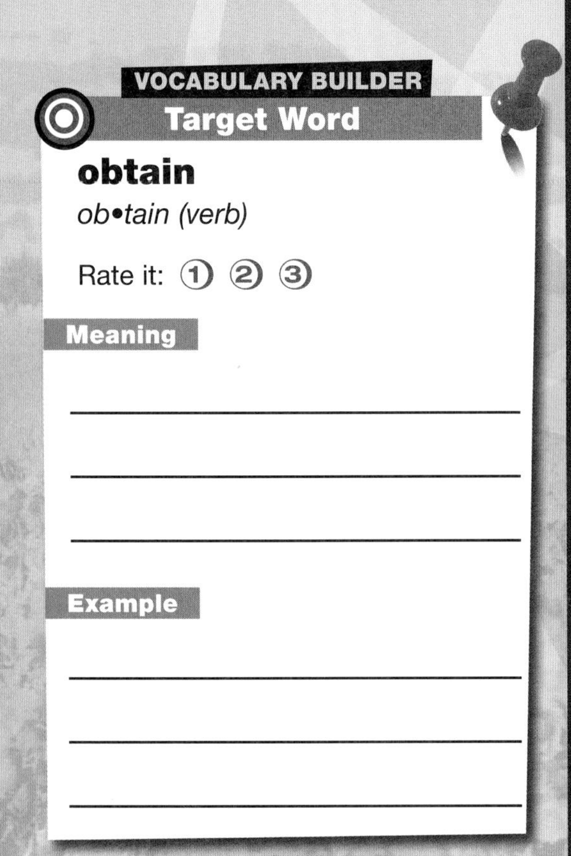

Writing a Memoir:

A Note From Francisco Jiménez

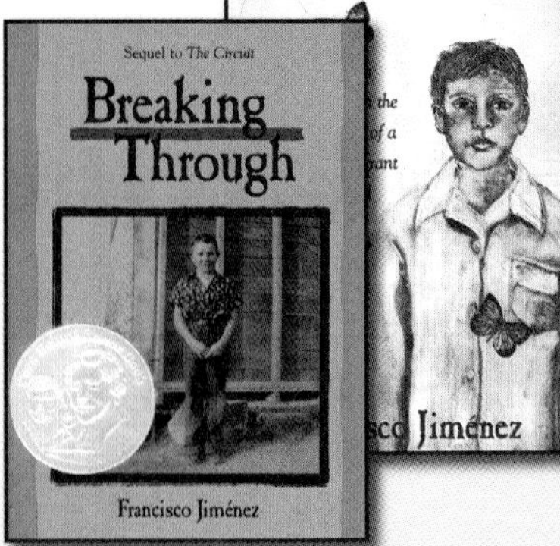

Breaking Through, the sequel to *The Circuit*, is autobiographical. It spans crucial years of my young adult life, beginning with the deportation of my family and me back to Mexico. Relying heavily on memory, I selected meaningful events and experiences in my life. I recounted them in chronological order from the perspective of the teenager I was then. I made use of my powers of imagination and invention to fill in small details that I have forgotten with the passage of time. For example, when I could not remember exact words of some conversations, I created dialogue, and I added description to capture my impressions and reactions to particular events and experiences.

In addition to relying on the power of memory, I used other valuable resources to write my book. I interviewed family members and looked through family photographs and documents, including deportation papers, which I **obtained** through the Freedom of Information Act. I also made use of my junior high and high school records and read through *The Breeze*, the Santa Maria High School student newspaper, and the *Santa Maria Times*. I also visited the Santa Maria Historical Museum.

I wrote this memoir to pay tribute to my family and teachers and to document part of my own history, but, more importantly, to voice the experiences of many children and young adults who confront numerous obstacles in their efforts to "break through [their cocoons] . . . and become butterflies." How they manage to break through depends as much on their courage, hope, and God-given talents as it does on the loving, compassionate, and generous people who commit themselves to making a difference in the lives of children and young adults. END

Words to Know! **sequel** *(n.)* a book or movie that continues the story of an earlier one

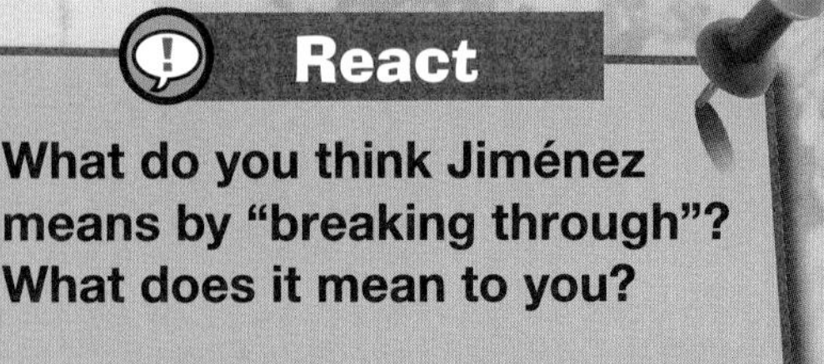

Comprehension Focus

Make Inferences

When you **make inferences**, you form ideas about things that are not directly stated in the text. To make inferences:

- **Look for a situation in the text in which the author gives clues but doesn't state exactly what is happening.**
- **Think about what you already know about the topic.**
- **Combine the text clues with your own experiences or knowledge to make an inference.**

▶ **Fill in this chart to make an inference about "Writing a Memoir."**

What I Learned From Reading

Jiménez read through the Santa Maria High School newspaper and the Santa Maria Times as resources for his book. He also visited the Santa Maria Historical Museum.

What I Already Know

My Inference

The Big Idea

Write What is this memoir mainly about?

____

____

____

from

Breaking Through

by Francisco Jiménez

Francisco Jiménez and his family moved from Mexico to the United States. They were barely getting by as migrant workers. In this excerpt from his memoir, the family faces big—and frightening—changes.

React

Write Francisco Jiménez says he lived in constant fear for many years of his childhood. Do you think it was right or wrong for his family to come to the U.S.?

____

____

____

____

I lived in constant fear for ten long years, from the time I was four until I was fourteen years old.

It all started back in the late 1940s when Papá, Mamá, my older brother, Roberto, and I left El Rancho Blanco, a small village nestled on barren, dry hills several miles north of Guadalajara, Jalisco, Mexico, and headed to California, hoping to leave our life of poverty behind. I remember how excited I was making the trip on a second-class train traveling north from Guadalajara to Mexicali. We traveled for two days and nights. When we arrived at the United States–Mexico border, Papá told us that we had to cross the barbed-wire fence without being seen by *la migra,* the immigration officers dressed in green uniforms. During the night we dug a hole underneath the wire wall and wiggled like snakes under it to the other side. "If anyone asks you where you were born," Papá said firmly, "tell them Colton, California. If *la migra* catches you, they'll send you back to Mexico." We were picked up by a woman whom Papá had contacted in Mexicali. She drove us, for a fee, to a tent labor camp on the outskirts of Guadalupe, a small town on the coast. From that day on, for the next ten years, while we traveled from place to place throughout California, following the crops and living in migrant labor camps, I feared being caught by the Border Patrol.

As I got older, my fear of being deported grew. I did not want to return to Mexico because I liked going to school, even though it was difficult for me, especially English class. I enjoyed learning, and I knew there was no school in El Rancho Blanco. Every year Roberto and I missed months of school to help Papá and Mamá work in the fields. We struggled to make ends meet, especially during the winter, when work was scarce. Things got worse when Papá began to have back problems and had trouble picking crops. Luckily, in the winter of 1957, Roberto found a part-time job working year-round as a janitor at Main Street Elementary School in Santa Maria, California.

Words to Know!	**deported** *(v.)* forced to return to the country that a person came from

Make Inferences

What I Learned From Reading

1. Underline ▶ Find a detail that tells what Papá says about crossing the barbed-wire fence.

What I Already Know

2. Write ▶ Why would a person want to do something without being seen?

____

____

____

____

____

____

My Inference

3. Write ▶ What can you infer about the legality of what the Jiménez family is doing?

____

____

____

____

____

____

Active Reading

Star What is Francisco's job after school and on weekends?

I was getting ready to recite the preamble to the Declaration of Independence, which our class had to memorize.

We settled in Bonetti Ranch, where we had lived in army barracks off and on for the past few years. My brother's job and mine—thinning lettuce and picking carrots after school and on weekends—helped support our family. I was excited because we had finally settled in one place. We no longer had to move to Fresno at the end of every summer and miss school for two and a half months to pick grapes and cotton and live in army tents or old garages.

But what I feared most happened that same year. I was in my eighth-grade social studies class at El Camino Junior High School in Santa Maria. I was getting ready to recite the preamble to the Declaration of Independence, which our class had to memorize. I had worked hard at memorizing it and felt confident. While I waited for class to start, I sat at my desk and recited it silently one last time:

We hold these truths to be self-evident: that all men are created equal; that they are endowed by their creator with certain unalienable rights; that among these are life, liberty, and the pursuit of happiness . . .

I was ready.

After the bell rang, Miss Ehlis, my English and social studies teacher, began to take roll. She was interrupted by a knock on the door. When she opened it, I saw the school principal and a man behind him. As soon as I saw the green uniform, I panicked. I felt like running, but my legs would not move. I trembled and could feel my heart pounding against my chest as though it too wanted to escape. My eyes blurred. Miss Ehlis and the officer walked up to me. "This is him," she said softly, placing her right hand on my shoulder.

React

Write **When Francisco sees the uniform, he panics. What would you have been thinking if you were in his situation?**

____

____

____

____

____

Words to Know!	**barracks** *(n.)* a group of buildings in which soldiers live

Comprehension Focus

Make Inferences

▶ Fill in this chart to make inferences about pages 218–220 of "Breaking Through."

What I Learned From Reading

The teacher spoke softly and placed her hand on Francisco's shoulder.

My Inference

What I Already Know

Active Reading

Write Who does the immigration officer pick up after Francisco?

___

___

___

VOCABULARY BUILDER

Target Word

administration

ad•min•is•tra•tion (noun)

Rate it: ① ② ③

Meaning

___

___

___

Example

___

___

___

React

Do you think Francisco's teacher should have done anything differently? Should she have tried to protect him? Should she have said something to him? Explain.

"Are you Francisco Jiménez?" he asked firmly. His deep voice echoed in my ears.

"Yes," I responded, wiping my tears and looking down at his large, black shiny boots. At that point I wished I were someone else, someone with a different name. My teacher had a sad and pained look in her eyes. I followed the immigration officer out of the classroom and into his car marked BORDER PATROL. I climbed in the front seat, and we drove down Broadway to Santa Maria High School to pick up Roberto, who was in his sophomore year. As cars passed by, I slid lower in the seat and kept my head down. The officer parked the car in front of the school and asked me to wait for him while he went inside the **administration** building.

A few minutes later, the officer returned with Roberto following him. My brother's face was as white as a sheet. The officer asked me to climb into the back seat with Roberto. *"Nos agarraron, hermanito,"* Roberto said, quivering and putting his arm around my shoulder.

"Yes, they caught us," I repeated. I had never seen my brother so sad. Angry, I added in a whisper, "But it took them ten years." Roberto quickly directed my attention to the officer with a shift of his eyes and put his index finger to his lips, hushing me. The officer turned right on Main Street and headed toward Bonetti Ranch, passing familiar sites I figured I would never see again: Main Street Elementary School; Kress, the five-and-dime store; the Texaco gas station where we got our drinking water. I wondered if my friends at El Camino Junior High would miss me as much as I would miss them.

"Do you know who turned you in?" the officer asked, interrupting my thoughts.

"No," Roberto answered.

"It was one of your people," he said, chuckling.

I could not imagine whom it could have been. We never told anyone we were here illegally, not even our best friends. I looked at Roberto, hoping he knew the answer. My brother shrugged his shoulders. "Ask him who it was," I whispered.

"No, you ask him," he responded.

The officer, who wore large, dark green sunglasses, must have heard us, because he glanced at us through the rear-view mirror and said, "Sorry, can't tell you his name."

When we arrived at Bonetti Ranch, a Border Patrol van was parked in front of our house, which was one of many dilapidated army barracks that Bonetti, the owner of the ranch, bought after the Second World War and rented to farm workers. My whole family was outside, standing by the patrol car. Mamá was sobbing and caressing Rubén, my youngest brother, and Rorra, my little sister. They hung on to Mamá's legs like two children who had just been found after being lost. Papá stood between my two younger brothers, Trampita and Torito. Both cried silently as Papá braced himself on their shoulders, trying to ease his back pain. Roberto and I climbed out of the car and joined them. The immigration officers, who towered over everyone, searched the ranch for other undocumented residents, but found none. →

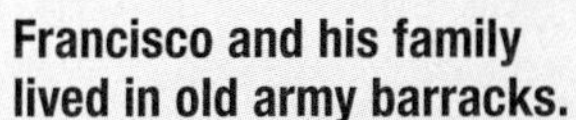

Francisco and his family lived in old army barracks.

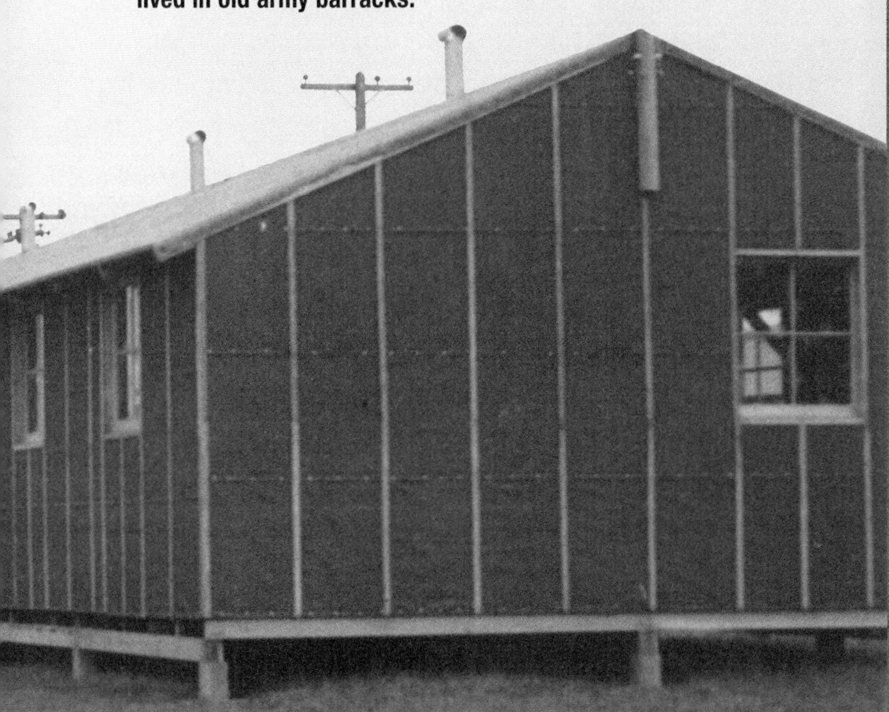

Words to Know! **dilapidated** *(adj.)* old and in very bad condition

Make Inferences

What I Learned From Reading

1. Underline Find a detail about what Francisco does as he is in the car on the way to pick up Roberto.

What I Already Know

2. Write Why might someone try to hide?

____

____

____

____

____

____

My Inference

3. Write How does Francisco feel about riding in the car with the officer?

____

____

____

____

____

____

Active Reading

Star ▶ Why did Franciso's parents decide to cross the border in Nogales?

VOCABULARY BUILDER

Target Word

voluntary

vol•un•tar•y (adjective)

Rate it: ① ② ③

Meaning

____

____

____

Example

____

____

____

React

Do you think Francisco's family was treated fairly by the immigration officials? Why or why not?

We were hauled into the Border Patrol van and driven to San Luis Obispo, the immigration headquarters. There we were asked endless questions and given papers to sign. Since Papá did not know English and Mamá understood only a little, Roberto translated for them. Papá showed them his green card, which Ito, the Japanese sharecropper for whom we picked strawberries, had helped him get years before. Mamá showed birth certificates for Trampita, Torito, Rorra, and Rubén, who were born in the United States. Mamá, Roberto, and I did not have documentation; we were the only ones being forced to leave. Mamá and Papá did not want to separate our family. They pleaded with the immigration officer in charge to allow us to stay a few more days so that we could leave the country together. The officer finally agreed and told us we could leave on a **voluntary** basis. He gave us three days to report to the U.S. immigration office at the border in Nogales, Arizona.

The next morning as we were getting ready for our trip back to Mexico, I went outside and watched the school bus pick up kids from the ranch. As it drove away, I felt empty inside and had a pain in my chest. I went back inside to help pack. Papá and Mamá were sitting at the kitchen table surrounded by my brothers and sister, who listened quietly as my parents discussed our trip. Papá took out the metal box in which he kept our savings and counted it. "We don't have much, but we'll have to live on the other side of the border with the little we have. Maybe it'll last us until we fix our papers and come back legally," he said.

"And with God's help, we will!" Mamá said. "There's no doubt."

The city of Nogales is at the Arizona/Mexico border.

"I am not that sure, but we'll try," Papá responded.

I was happy to hear Papá and Mamá say this. I relished the thought of returning to Santa Maria, going back to school, and not fearing *la migra* anymore. I knew Roberto felt the same. He had a sparkle in his eyes and a big smile.

Papá and Mamá decided to cross the border in Nogales because they had heard that the immigration office there was not as busy as the one in Tijuana or Mexicali. We packed a few belongings, stored the rest in our barrack, and left our *Carcachita*, our old jalopy, locked and parked in front. Joe and Espy, our next-door neighbors, drove us to the Greyhound bus station on North Broadway in Santa Maria. We bought our tickets to Nogales and boarded.

After traveling for about twenty hours, we arrived, exhausted, at the Nogales, Arizona, bus station in the morning. We picked up our belongings and headed to the immigration and customs office, where we reported in. We had made the deadline. We were then escorted on foot across the border to the Mexican side of Nogales. The twin cities were separated by a tall chain-link fence. Grassland, mesquite, scattered low shrubs, and bare rocky soil surrounded both sides of the border. The sky was cloudless and the streets were bone-dry. We walked the unpaved streets along the fence, looking for a place to stay. We ran into barefoot children in tattered clothes rummaging through waste bins. I felt a knot in my throat. They reminded me of when we were living in Corcoran and would go into town in the evenings looking for food in the trash behind grocery stores.

Words to Know!	**rummaging** *(v.)* searching for something by moving things around

Draw Conclusions

Write Reread the description of Nogales in the last paragraph on this page. What conclusion can you draw about what people's lives were like there?

____

____

____

____

____

____

____

Review: Compare and Contrast

1. **Write** Which family members had legal documentation to stay in the United States?

____

____

____

2. **Write** Which family members were being forced to leave?

____

____

____

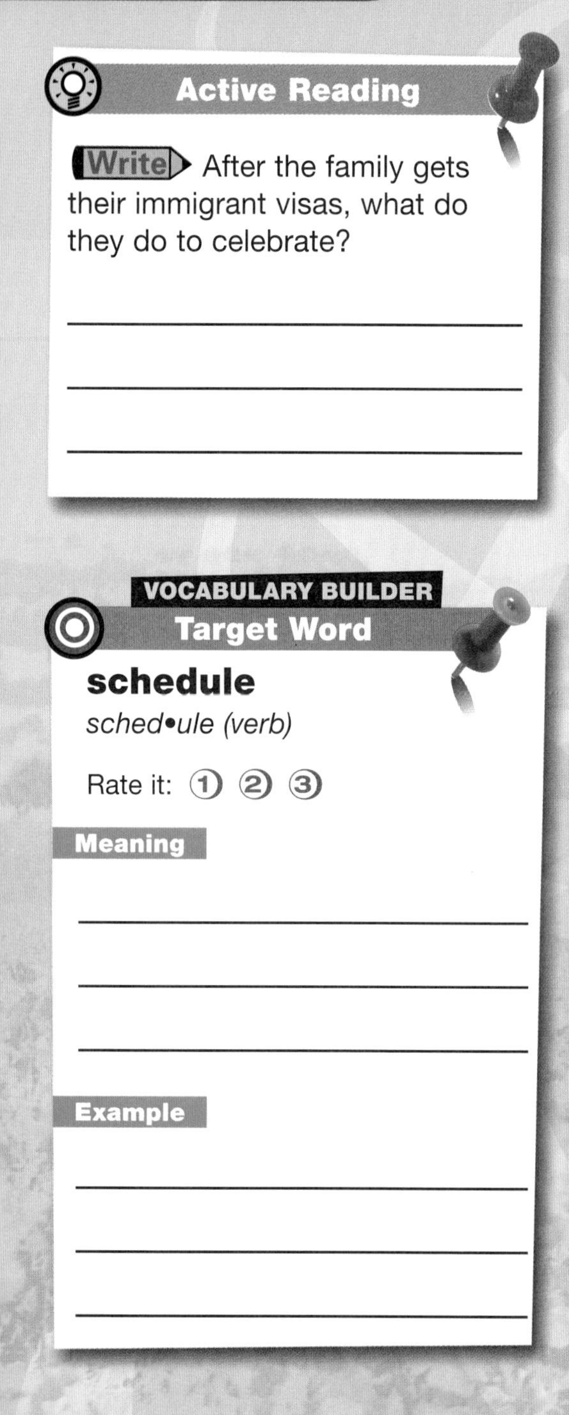

We finally found a cheap, rundown motel on Campillo Street, a few blocks from the border. As Papá and Mamá checked in, I looked around the cramped office. Through the dirty window, I could see part of the overpass bridging the two Nogaleses and the chain-link fence separating the two cities. On the corner of the dark yellow counter, which came up to my chin, was a pile of discolored motel brochures held in place by three small rocks. The shape and color of the stones fascinated me. They looked like gold nuggets. I picked one of them up to examine it closely, but Mamá slapped my hand and told me to put it back. When no one was looking, I snatched one and put it in my pocket.

The motel room was small, like the cabins we lived in at the cotton labor camps. We took the sagging mattress off the bed and placed it on the worn yellow linoleum floor so Papá and Mamá could sleep on it. The rest of us went to bed on the box spring. That night I felt listless and had a hard time sleeping. I kept thinking about what I had done. The following morning, I went outside, holding the rock in my fist and wondering what to do. I thought of throwing it underneath the overpass, but I felt guilty and scared. I went back to the office and, pretending I was getting a brochure, put it back.

Every day after Mamá bought food for us from street vendors for our meals, she and Papá went to the immigration office to check on our petition for visas. Each time they went they were asked for more information. Papá sent a telegram to Fito, my cousin in Guadalajara, asking him to secure our birth certificates and to send them to us by mail. Four days after they arrived, we were **scheduled** to take a medical examination. We were issued a one-day pass to cross the U.S. border and take the examination at St. Joseph's Hospital, which was located a few blocks from the U.S. customs office. We checked in at the front desk and sat in the waiting room to be called. The room's walls were light green and the white floors were spotless, just like the uniforms worn by the nurses and doctors.

Words to Know!	**listless** *(adj.)* feeling tired and uninterested in doing things

The receptionist came out and handed us a Foreign Service/U.S. Medical Examination of Visa Applicants form. Roberto helped Mamá read the form's long list of diseases and check yes or no.

After waiting for several days, we were notified that our petition for an immigrant visa had been approved. Papá, Mamá, Roberto, and I were beside ourselves when we got the news. We could not stop smiling. My younger brothers and sisters did not understand what it all meant, but they jumped up and down on the stained mattress like grasshoppers. "This calls for a special meal," Mamá said. That evening she went out and bought enchiladas, rice, and beans.

After supper, Papá lay on the bed to rest his back. "I've been thinking about where we go from here," he said. *Back to Santa Maria, of course. Where else?* I thought. Papá bit his lower lip and continued. "It's the rainy season; there's little work in the fields during this time, and my back is getting worse." He paused, and went on, "The only sure thing is Roberto's janitorial job. What if he goes back to Santa Maria and the rest of us go to Guadalajara and stay with my sister Chana? It'll give me a chance to see a *curandera* about my back. In the spring, when I am cured, we can go back to Santa Maria and I can work in the fields again." My heart fell to my stomach. I did not want to miss more school. I wanted to tell Papá that I did not like his idea, but I did not say anything. Papá never allowed us to disagree with him. He said it was disrespectful. →

Francisco, Trampita, and Roberto as young children in Tent City, Santa Maria, California. Conditions were hard for them in America, but full of promise.

Make Inferences

What I Learned From Reading

1. **Underline** What does Francisco pretend he is doing when he puts the rock back?

What I Already Know

2. **Write** Why might someone pretend to do one thing when they are doing something else?

____

____

____

____

____

____

My Inference

3. **Write** Why does Francisco pretend he is getting a brochure?

____

____

____

____

____

____

Active Reading

Star What does Roberto say he will do when he gets paid?

"What if Panchito goes back with Roberto?" Mamá said. "That way he can help him at work and both can attend school." I knew Mamá had read my mind. She winked at me when she saw me smile.

"You're a grown man, a real *macho*," Papá said, directing his attention to my brother. "You can take care of Panchito. *Verdad, mijo*." My brother grinned and nodded.

The thought of being apart from Papá, Mamá, and my brothers and sister saddened me, but the idea of missing school and not being with Roberto pained me even more.

"I'll go back with him, but I'll miss you," I said, holding back my tears.

"We'll miss you too," Mamá said, wiping her eyes.

"I'll send you money every month when I get paid," Roberto said proudly.

"You're a good son," Papá said, motioning for Roberto to sit by his side on the bed.

"They're all a blessing," Mamá added, smiling at Roberto and me and hugging Rorra, Torito, and Trampita.

We decided to leave the hotel that evening to avoid paying for another night. I went with Mamá to the office to check out. I wanted to look at the rocks one more time. The clerk caught my eye and said, "Those are copper pyrite rocks."

"They look like gold," I replied.

"It's fool's gold." He picked up the rock I had taken before and handed it to me. "Here, you can have this one. It'll bring you good luck."

React

Write **Do you think that Francisco should have gone with Roberto or with his parents? Explain.**

____

____

____

____

____

The hotel clerk gave Francisco a copper pyrite rock.

I glanced at Mamá. She smiled and nodded. "Thanks," I said, taking the rock and placing it in my pocket. *I am glad I returned it and didn't throw it away,* I thought.

We finished packing and headed to the bus station on foot. It was starting to rain, so we hurried. Roberto, Papá, Trampita, and I carried the cardboard boxes. Mamá held Rorra by the hand. Torito and Rubén ran behind us, trying to keep up. "Not so fast!" they cried out. "Wait for us!" Armed guards stopped us at the border gate and asked us for documentation. Their green uniforms gave me the chills. Papá showed them our papers, and they let us cross to Nogales, Arizona.

We were dripping wet by the time we arrived at the bus station. Mamá went up to the counter and bought two one-way tickets to Santa Maria for Roberto and me and five tickets to Guadalajara for the rest of the family. We went to the restroom and dried ourselves with paper towels, then sat in silence on a wooden bench, waiting for the bus. Torito and Trampita were fidgety. They jumped off the bench, ran to the pinball machine, and pushed each other, trying to pull on the handle. Papá made a sharp hissing sound like a rattlesnake to get their attention. He made this noise whenever he was annoyed with something we were doing. They did not hear him, so he hissed louder, but the loudspeaker announcing the departures and arrivals drowned it out. With a slight tilt of his head toward the pinball machine, Papá motioned for me to get Trampita and Torito. Papá gave them a stern look and told them to sit and be quiet. I sat between Trampita and Torito and placed my arms around them. I felt sad, thinking how much I was going to miss them.

I glanced at the clock on the wall and went outside to get fresh air. It was pouring rain. Looking up at the dark sky, I wished we were all going back to Santa Maria together. I heard an announcement over the loudspeaker, but I did not pay attention. "Our bus is here, Panchito," Roberto said, as he and the rest of my family approached me from behind. Roberto and I hugged Papá and Mamá and kissed our brothers and sister.

→

Make Inferences

What I Learned From Reading

1. **Underline** Francisco smiles when Mamá suggests that he go with Roberto. Find what Mamá does when she sees him smile.

What I Already Know

2. **Write** What is one reason why people wink at each other?

___

___

___

___

___

___

My Inference

3. **Write** Why does Mamá suggest that Francisco go with Roberto?

___

___

___

___

___

___

Active Reading

Star When Francisco and Roberto arrive at Bonetti Ranch, what are they welcomed by?

"Que Dios los bendiga," Mamá said, giving us her blessing. Tears came to her eyes as she forced a smile. Roberto and I climbed onto the bus. We took our seat, wiped the fog off the window, and waved. The rain pelted the bus with full force as it pulled away.

Across the aisle, a little boy played horse on his father's lap. He jumped up and down and repeatedly smacked the side of his legs, shouting, "Faster, faster!" I turned away, closed my eyes, and leaned on Roberto's shoulder. I wept silently until I fell asleep.

When I woke up, the rain had disappeared. A strong wind whipped up dust, debris, and gravel and forced the bus to slow down to a snail's pace. Once the wind died down, the bus pulled over at a rest stop next to an old gas station and market. Roberto and I climbed down to stretch our legs. On the side of the station was a makeshift open stand braced by four posts. Hanging from one of the upper-right posts was a crate with a wooden crucifix on it. Roberto and I made the sign of the cross and bowed our heads. I prayed silently that my family would arrive safely in Guadalajara. We climbed back on the bus and continued our journey.

We finally arrived in Santa Maria in the early evening of the next day. We took a cab to Bonetti Ranch, where we were welcomed by a torrential downpour and a pack of bony stray dogs. The cab drove slowly, bumping up and down and swaying from side to side as it hit potholes full of water. It felt as though we were in a ship in the middle of a stormy sea. Our barrack was cold and lifeless. We placed our boxes on the floor and turned on the kitchen light. "Well, here we are, Panchito," Roberto said sadly. When he saw me choke up, he added, "Time will go by fast, you'll see."

"Not fast enough," I said. We unpacked our boxes and went to bed. Neither one of us slept well that night. END

React

Write **The story ends at this point in Francisco's life. Do you want to read the rest of his autobiography? Explain.**

____

____

____

____

____

____

____

____

____

Words to Know! **makeshift** *(adj.)* made for temporary use

 TEXT FEATURE **Reading a Map**

FRANCISCO JIMÉNEZ'S JOURNEY

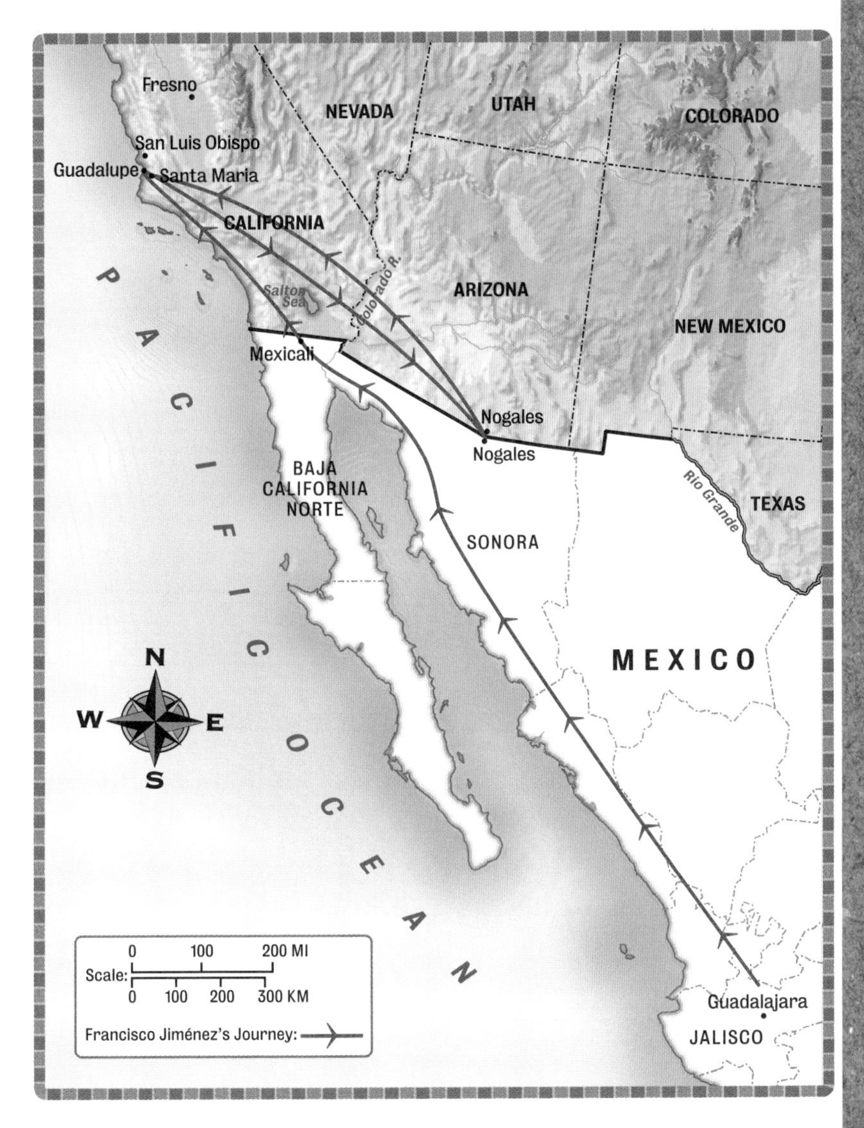

This map shows cities, states, and countries.

1. What information about Jiménez does this map show?

Ⓐ where he traveled
Ⓑ where his parents live
Ⓒ where he went to college
Ⓓ where he got married

2. Which city is closest to Santa Maria?

Ⓐ Mexicali
Ⓑ Guadalupe
Ⓒ Nogales
Ⓓ San Luis Obispo

3. What is the distance between Santa Maria and Nogales?

____

Draw Conclusions

Write What is more important to Francisco: being in the U.S. or being together with his family?

____

Skills Check

1. **Underline** How does Francisco react when he sees the little boy playing with his father?

2. **Write** How does it feel to be separated from people you love?

____

3. **Write** Why does seeing the boy and his father make Francisco upset?

____

Active Reading

Star Why couldn't Jiménez put down *The Grapes of Wrath*?

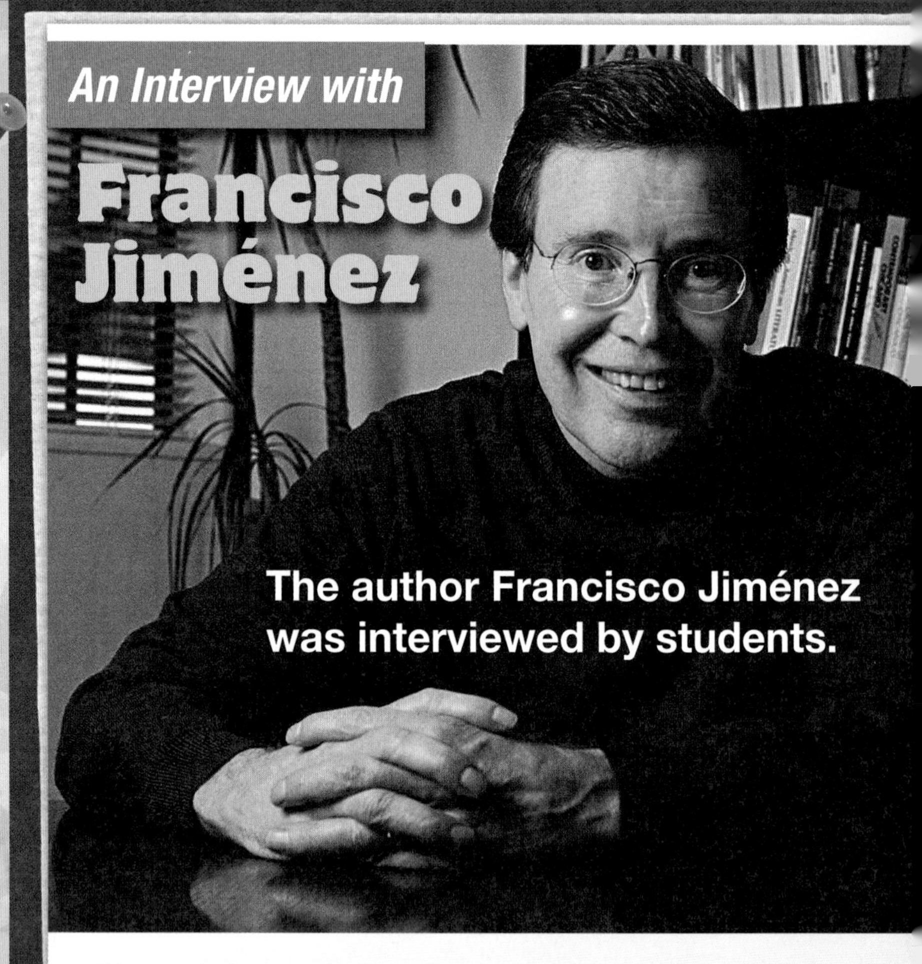

An Interview with Francisco Jiménez

The author Francisco Jiménez was interviewed by students.

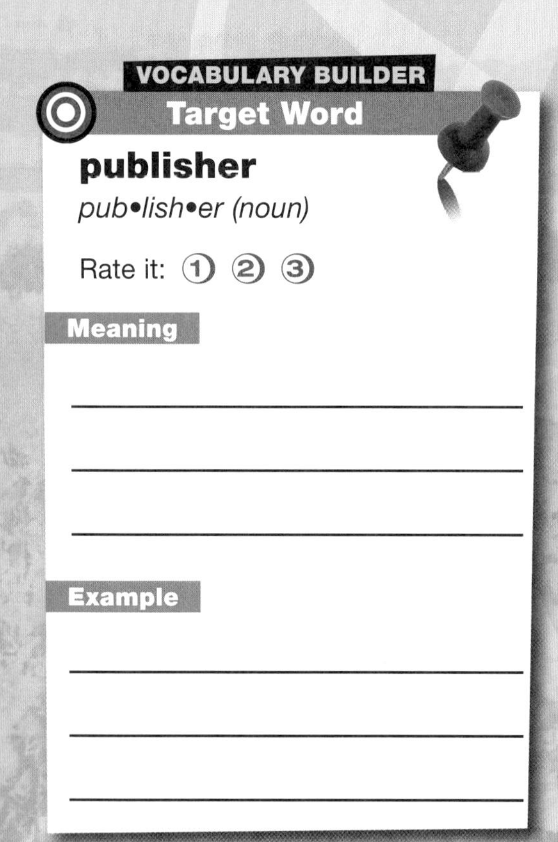

VOCABULARY BUILDER

Target Word

publisher

pub•lish•er (noun)

Rate it: ① ② ③

Meaning

____

____

____

Example

____

____

____

How did you get started writing? Was it difficult?

I started writing when I was a sophomore in high school. My English teacher assigned essays that were based on personal experiences. I began to write about the experiences I had as a child growing up in a family of Mexican migrant workers. Mrs. Bell felt that I had writing talent, even though I had difficulty with the English language. Her words were very encouraging. She had me read *The Grapes of Wrath*, and although the novel was difficult to read, I could not put it down because I could relate to what I was reading. For the first time I realized the power of language to move hearts and minds.

How long did it take you to "succeed"?

The manuscript for *The Circuit* was turned down by a major **publisher**. I then sent it to the University of New Mexico Press, and they published it. The success of *The Circuit* made it easier for me to get a contract from Houghton Mifflin to write the sequel. So I feel blessed that my work has not been rejected too often, except for that one time.

React

What question would you like to ask Francisco Jiménez?

Have any of the people in your books read your books? What did they say about them?

All the characters in *The Circuit* are members of my family. Most of the characters in *Breaking Through* are also members of my family. All of them appreciated my writing their story because they felt that their story was the story of many, many families who experienced the migrant way of life and many families who are experiencing that same life today.

Do you have any advice to help us write?

My advice is to read a lot and of course to write a lot, because the more you write, the more your skills in writing improve. And reading does help a lot in writing. Writing is not an easy task. It requires a lot of practice. For example, I usually do nine drafts for every story I write. Don't get discouraged; just keep writing.

If you are interested in writing your own experiences, start by doing research by interviewing your parents and other relatives. Look through photographs and family documents. You can also listen to music that was popular when you were growing up. Music will take you back in time to those experiences that you had at the time those songs were popular. The material that you have gathered after your research will help you to recall past experiences.

Is there anything else you would like to share?

I think it's important [to realize] that there are many people that have never had the opportunity to read or write and who are very intelligent. I get the question, "Why do I write these stories?" I wrote *The Circuit* and *Breaking Through* to chronicle part of my family's history, but more importantly to voice the experiences of an important sector of our society that has been largely ignored. Through my writing, I hope to give readers an insight into the lives of migrant farm worker families and their children, whose back-breaking labor (picking fruit and vegetables) puts food on our tables. Their courage, struggles, and hopes and dreams for a better life for their children and their children's children give meaning to the term "the American Dream." Their story is the American story. END

Theme

1. **Write** What do you think Francisco Jiménez means by "the American Dream"?

____

____

____

____

____

2. **Write** How would you define the American Dream?

____

____

____

____

____

3. **Write** Do you think Francisco Jiménez fulfilled the American Dream? Explain.

____

____

____

____

____

TAKE THE WORD CHALLENGE

It's not **fair**! I got sunburned at the **fair** because my skin is so **fair**.

Start

1

Think. What kind of documentation do you need for each of these activities?

____
Driving a car

____
Traveling to another country

____
Taking out a library book

____
Proving where you were born

3

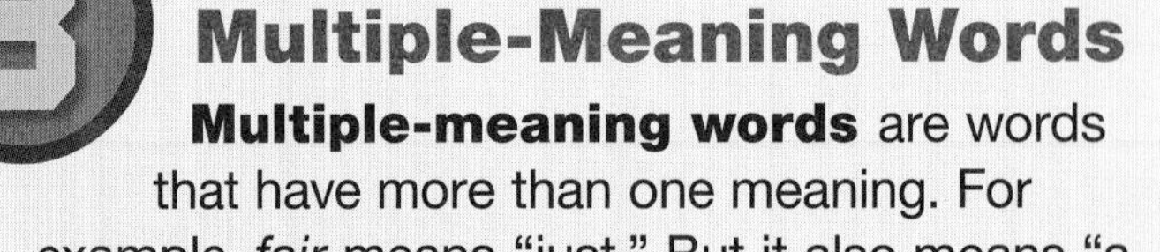

Multiple-Meaning Words

Multiple-meaning words are words that have more than one meaning. For example, *fair* means "just." But it also means "a carnival or celebration." And it also means "pale."

Fill in these sentences with *light*, *draft*, or *train*.

1. Please turn off the ____________ when you go.
2. Can you close the window? I feel a ____________ coming in.
3. I can carry this box by myself. It's ____________.
4. Did you take the bus or the ____________ to your aunt's house?
5. I'm working on my third ____________ of this essay.
6. My coach is going to ____________ me for the track meet.

2

Plan it. You have multiple events scheduled for the same time. **Write *E* if the event is easy to reschedule. Write *H* if it's hard to reschedule.**

_____ eating dinner with your family

_____ playing in your team's playoff baseball game

_____ going to the movies with a friend

_____ going on a job interview

4

Name it. Write the name of a member of the administration of:

your school: ______________________________

your town: ______________________________

the United States: ______________________________

5

Decide. How easy is it to obtain each of the following?

1 = easy to obtain
2 = hard to obtain

_____ sold-out concert tickets

_____ a job

_____ a newly released DVD

_____ your favorite meal

6

Rate it. Which of these obstacles do you face?

1 = not a big obstacle
2 = sort-of a big obstacle
3 = a big obstacle

_____ getting up in the morning

_____ keeping track of homework assignments

_____ managing your time

_____ getting along with your siblings

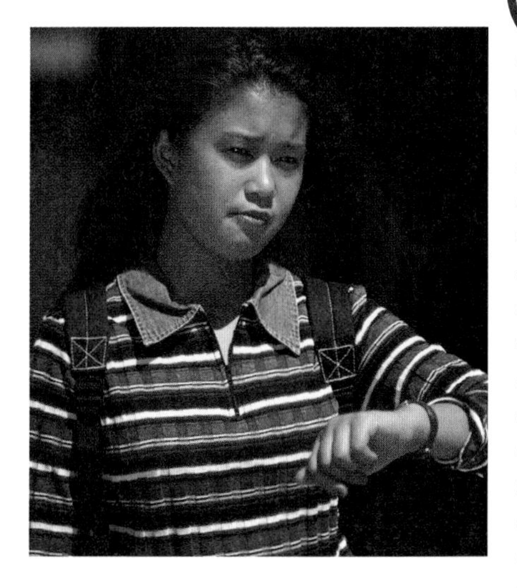

7

Order it. Read these events in the life of a migrant worker. Put them in chronological order.

1 = happened first

4 = happened last

_____ He finds a job working on a vegetable farm.

_____ A worker comes to the United States.

_____ The vegetable crop is harvested. The work for the season is over.

_____ The worker moves to another farm, where there is more work.

8

After I write my **autobiography**, people will **automatically** ask me for my **autograph**!

Greek Roots

A **root** is a word or word part from another language that is the basis of an English word. The word *autobiography* comes from the Greek root *auto*, which means "self."

Fill in these sentences with *automobile*, *automatically*, or *autograph*.

1. After the game I ran over to get the pitcher's ____________.
2. Does that ____________ still run? It sure looks old!
3. I used to have to download my email every day, but now my computer does it ____________.

9

Evaluate. Are the following chores voluntary or required in your house? Write ***V*** if it's voluntary. Write ***R*** if it's required.

_____ washing dishes

_____ cleaning your room

_____ doing laundry

_____ vacuuming

_____ cleaning the bathroom

10

Complete the sentences. Fill in each blank with the correct form of *publish* below.

publish **publisher** **publishing**

My uncle is looking for a ____________ to ____________ a book he has written. I told him if he could wait a few years I'll be able to help him. I plan to get a job in ____________ when I graduate.

Finish

Writing Focus

Personal Narrative

A **personal narrative** tells about an event in the writer's life.

▶ **Read Elliot's personal narrative about a challenge that his family faced.**

Student Model

My Brother's Illness

by Elliot Chang

When I was 12, my younger brother Jacob was diagnosed with leukemia. It all started when he began getting frequent nosebleeds. Then, my parents heard that it could be a sign of something serious, so they took him to the doctor. The doctor ran tests, and soon we obtained the results. Jacob had leukemia. He was scheduled to start treatment right away. One obstacle was that the treatment made him feel awful. In the end, he was cured of his illness. Looking back now, I can see how the experience brought our family closer together. We're all so grateful that my brother is healthy again.

Parts of a Personal Narrative

▶ **Find these parts of Elliot's personal narrative.**

1. Underline the sentence that tells about the **event**.
2. Check three important **details** that tell about the event.
3. Number these details in the **time order** they happened.
4. Circle the **linking words** that connect the details.
5. Put a star before the sentence that **sums up** the event and tells the writer's **feelings** about it.

Brainstorm

▶ **Read the writing prompt in the middle of the idea web. Then use the boxes to help you brainstorm your ideas.**

Family Challenges

Health Challenges

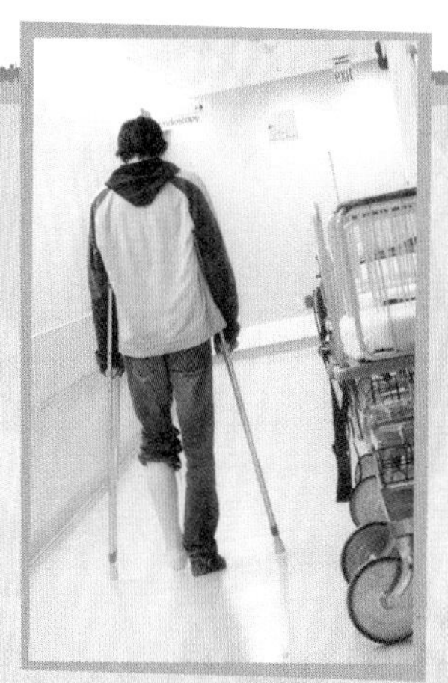

Writing Prompt:

Tell about a challenging situation that you or your family faced.

Challenging Events

Challenging Changes

Plan Your Paragraph

Writing Prompt: Tell about a challenging situation that you or your family faced.

▶ **Use this chart to plan and organize your paragraph.**

Word Choices

____

____

____

____

____

Event

- *When I was . . .*
- *Once . . .*
- *One memory I have is . . .*

Detail 1

- *It all started when . . .*
- *First, . . .*
- *To start with, . . .*

Detail 2

- *Then, . . .*
- *Next, . . .*
- *After that, . . .*

Detail 3

- *In the end, . . .*
- *Finally, . . .*
- *Then, . . .*

Ending

- *Looking back now, . . .*
- *I'll never forget . . .*
- *This is a memory that . . .*

Write Your Paragraph

▶ **Use this writing frame to write a first draft of your paragraph.**

____
(title)

When I was ______________________________
____
____
____

It all started when ______________________________
____
____
____

Then, ______________________________
____
____
____

In the end, ______________________________
____
____
____

Looking back now, ______________________________
____
____
____
____

Revise

▶ **Rate your paragraph. Then have a writing partner rate it.**

Scoring Guide			
weak	okay	good	strong
1	2	3	4

1. Does the beginning clearly state the **event**?
   - **Self** 1 2 3 4
   - **Partner** 1 2 3 4
2. Are there **details** that tell about the event?
   - **Self** 1 2 3 4
   - **Partner** 1 2 3 4
3. Are the details arranged in the **time order** they happened?
   - **Self** 1 2 3 4
   - **Partner** 1 2 3 4
4. Do **linking words** connect the details?
   - **Self** 1 2 3 4
   - **Partner** 1 2 3 4
5. Does the ending **sum up** the event and tell the writer's **feelings** about it?
   - **Self** 1 2 3 4
   - **Partner** 1 2 3 4

▶ Now revise your paragraph to make it stronger.

Grammar Using Adverbs

An adjective describes a person, place, or thing. An adverb describes a verb, an adjective, or another adverb. Many adverbs end in *-ly*.

- Use adverbs to make your writing more precise.

Example

Adjective	Adverb
His teacher was a kind person.	His teacher kindly looked at him.
The family packed at a quick pace.	The family packed quickly.
Francisco was sad on the bus.	He looked sadly out the window.

▶ **Circle the adverbs in the sentences below.**

1. Francisco was [**real** **really**] afraid of being deported.
2. In the winter, it was [**extremely** **extreme**] hard to find work.
3. Francisco [**true** **truly**] loved going to school.
4. The family had to leave the country [**immediately** **immediate**].
5. Everyone waited [**patiently** **patient**] for news about their visas.
6. [**Final** **Finally**] they were able to return to the United States.

▶ **Rewrite the sentences using the correct form of the adverb.**

7. Mrs. Bell saw that Francisco was incredible talented.

____

8. Francisco got his second book published more easy than his first book.

____

9. His family members thought he recounted their story very accurate.

____

10. Francisco Jiménez wrote about migrant families who work tireless.

____

Take a close look at each of the sentences in your draft on page 239. Do they use adverbs correctly? If not, fix them.

Usage CORRECTING SENTENCE FRAGMENTS

Each **sentence** must state a complete idea.

- You can often add a subject or a verb to a sentence fragment to form a complete sentence.

Example

Correct	Incorrect
Francisco Jiménez wrote an autobiographical account.	An autobiographical account.

▶ **Find and correct five errors in this paragraph.**

Student Model

Once, my family faced a big challenge. A hurricane was schedooled to hit our town. First, the mayor asked people to evacuate on a volunteery basis. Packed up and left immediate. After the storm was over, we returned to our home. Much of our house was destroyed, and so were some of our belongings. Were all safe. This is a memory that will never go away.

Check and Correct

- ❑ Circle two spelling errors and correct them.
- ❑ Underline one incorrectly formed adverb and correct it.
- ❑ Correct two sentence fragments.

Look at the sentences in your own draft on page 239. Do they all contain a subject and a verb? If not, fix them.

Final Draft/Present

▶ **Write a final draft of your paragraph on paper or the computer. Check it again and correct any errors before you present it.**

Meet the Author

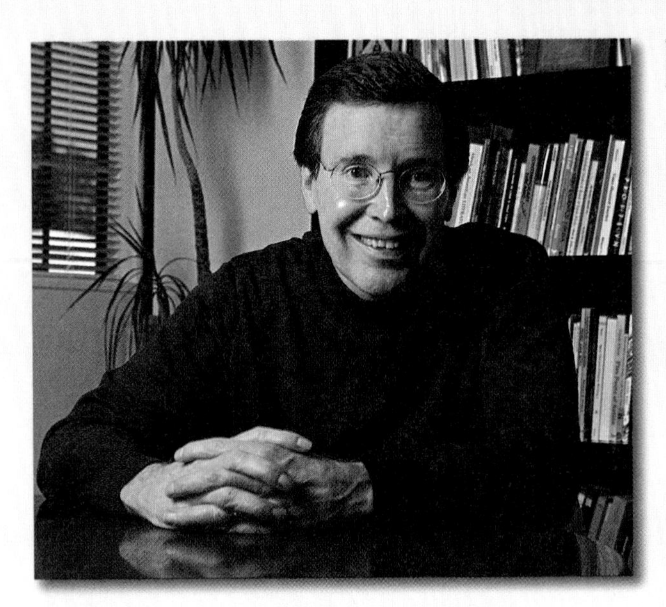

Francisco Jiménez

Francisco Jiménez was born in Tlaquepaque, Mexico, in 1943. His family moved to California when he was a young child, and he grew up picking fruit and vegetables in the fields. Since his family moved from place to place in search of work, Jiménez had no permanent home or consistent schooling.

When Jiménez was fourteen, his family was deported to Mexico. They obtained the documentation they needed and returned to the United States. Jiménez finished middle school at his school in California, graduated from Santa Maria High School, and attended the University of Santa Clara. He went on to earn advanced degrees from Columbia University.

Today, Francisco Jiménez is a college professor at Santa Clara University. His award-winning books, *The Circuit* and *Breaking Through*, document an important part of the American experience.

> "When I write, I don't have a particular audience in mind. I simply write from the point of view of the child or the young adult that I once was."

Books:

The Circuit
Breaking Through
La Mariposa (picture book)
The Christmas Gift (picture book)

Ask Yourself

1. Underline ▶ Where did Jiménez graduate from high school?
2. Circle ▶ Where does Jiménez work today?
3. What kind of book do you prefer to read?
   - ❑ nonfiction
   - ❑ short stories
   - ❑ biographies and autobiographies

Explain. ____

____

Real-World Skills

Reading Flight Schedules

When Francisco Jiménez comes out with a new book, he travels around the country to talk to readers and bookstore owners. Reading the flight schedules in airports is critical to him arriving at his appointments on time. Look at the flight schedule below. Then answer the questions.

DEPARTURES

Departing from	Departing to	Airline	Flight #	Gate	Time	Remarks
San Jose, CA	Denver, CO	Skylight	217	B17	10:15 A.M.	canceled
San Jose, CA	Miami, FL	Air USA	73	A2	11:05 A.M.	on time
San Jose, CA	Miami, FL	Air USA	74	A2	12:05 P.M.	on time
San Jose, CA	Dallas, TX	Western Air	16	D12	12:55 P.M.	delayed 1 hour
San Jose, CA	Chicago, IL	Cruisin' Airways	2	C9	1:20 P.M.	on time

▶ **Fill in the circle next to each correct answer.**

1. From which gate will Flight 16 to Dallas depart?

Ⓐ gate D11
Ⓑ gate B17
Ⓒ gate A2
Ⓓ gate D12

2. At 10:15 A.M., what are passengers from Flight 217 to Denver likely to be doing?

Ⓐ trying to get onto a different flight to Denver
Ⓑ preparing for the airplane to take off
Ⓒ landing in Denver
Ⓓ going to the airport to catch their flight

3. Where should you go to catch Flight 2 to Chicago?

Ⓐ to gate A2
Ⓑ to gate D12
Ⓒ to gate C9
Ⓓ Go to a customer service counter. Your flight has been canceled.

4. Which airline flies to Dallas, TX?

Ⓐ Cruisin' Airways
Ⓑ Western Air
Ⓒ Air USA
Ⓓ Skylight

5. You are running late and will miss Flight 73 to Miami. What should you do?

Ⓐ Rent a car and start driving.
Ⓑ Try to take Flight 16 to Dallas instead.
Ⓒ Try to get a ticket for Flight 74 to Miami.
Ⓓ Go home. There are no more flights to Miami today.

Comprehension

▶ **Fill in the circle next to the correct answer.**

1. Which of these did Francisco Jiménez do first?
Ⓐ ride on a bus to the United States/Mexican border
Ⓑ celebrate by eating a special meal
Ⓒ prepare to recite part of the Declaration of Independence
Ⓓ write his autobiography

2. What happened when the immigration officer came to Francisco's classroom?
Ⓐ Francisco had to leave school.
Ⓑ Francisco decided he didn't like school anymore.
Ⓒ Roberto began working at an elementary school.
Ⓓ Francisco recited the Declaration of Independence.

Here's a tip.
Check your work against the reading you're being tested on. Make sure your answer agrees with what's in the reading.

3. How are Francisco and Roberto similar?
Ⓐ They both stole rocks from the motel.
Ⓑ Both were unwilling to get jobs to help their family.
Ⓒ They both disliked school.
Ⓓ They were both upset about being separated from their family.

4. Which of these will most likely happen in the future?
Ⓐ Francisco Jiménez will move back to the barracks.
Ⓑ People will continue to read Francisco Jiménez's books.
Ⓒ Francisco Jiménez will stop writing.
Ⓓ People will stop writing memoirs.

5. The author probably wrote his memoir to
Ⓐ forget everything that ever happened to his family.
Ⓑ impress his high school teacher, Mrs. Bell.
Ⓒ help people understand the struggles of migrant workers.
Ⓓ write a book that's similar to *The Grapes of Wrath*.

Vocabulary

▶ **Fill in the circle next to the correct definition of the underlined word.**

1. *Breaking Through* is about the <u>obstacles</u> that a <u>migrant</u> family faces.

Ⓐ difficulties, traveling
Ⓑ distractions, unhappy
Ⓒ memories, scattered
Ⓓ successes, famous

2. The Jiménez family needed to show <u>documentation</u> to the authorities.

Ⓐ old letters
Ⓑ receipts
Ⓒ money
Ⓓ official papers

3. Francisco Jiménez organized his book in <u>chronological</u> order.

Ⓐ memoir
Ⓑ old-fashioned
Ⓒ time
Ⓓ confusing

▶ **Choose the correct definition for the underlined multiple-meaning word.**

4. It's typical to write more than one <u>draft</u> of a story.

Ⓐ current of air
Ⓑ way to pick college athletes for pro teams
Ⓒ piece of writing that's not finished
Ⓓ system where people must fight in war

▶ **Choose the correct word to fill in the blank.**

5. Francisco Jiménez's ____________________ account tells his family's story.

Ⓐ biography
Ⓑ biology
Ⓒ automatic
Ⓓ autobiographical

Short Answer

▶ **Use what you've read in this Workshop to answer the question below. Check your spelling and grammar.**

How does Francisco Jiménez's experience inspire you to face obstacles in your own life?

____

____

____

Glossary

A glossary is a useful tool found at the back of many books. It contains information about key words in the text. Look at the sample glossary entry below.

This is an **entry word**—the word you look up. It is divided into syllables.

The **pronunciation** comes after the entry word. Letters and letter combinations stand for different sounds. The accented syllable is marked in boldfaced letters.

This tells you what **part of speech** the entry word is.

con•flict

1. (**kon**-flict) *noun* A battle or disagreement. *Leo and his brother had a conflict over who had to walk the dog.*
2. (kuhn-**flict**) *verb* To clash, disagree, or not match up. *Your plans to use the car tonight conflict with my plans to go to the mall.*

A **number** appears at the beginning of each meaning when more than one meaning is given for the entry word.

Look here to find the **meaning** of the entry word.

conflict

ac•cel•er•ate
(ak-**sel**-uh-rate) *verb*
1. To increase. *Sarah's progress as a writer accelerated after she took a writing class.*
2. To get faster. *Dan's bike accelerated when he went down the hill.*

ac•cess
(**ak**-sess) *noun*
1. The ability, chance, or right to do or use something. *Do you have access to the storage room?*
2. A way to enter a building or get into a place. *The only access to the theater was the side door.*

ac•com•plish
(uh-**kom**-plish) *verb*
To do something successfully. *We accomplished our goal of raising $10,000 for the charity.*

ac•cu•mu•late
(uh-**kyoo**-myuh-late) *verb*
To gather or collect things or let them pile up. *Erica lets papers accumulate in her locker.*

accumulate

ac•cu•rate
(**ak**-yuh-ruht) *adjective*
Exactly correct. *Double check your answers to make sure they are accurate.*

a•dapt
(uh-**dapt**) *verb*
1. To change something to suit a new purpose. *We need to adapt the recipe to fit his dietary needs.*
2. To change your ideas or behavior to fit a new situation. *The students will have to adapt to the new teacher's methods.*

ad•e•quate
(**ad**-uh-kwit) *adjective*
Good enough. *If my grades are adequate, I will get into college next year.*

ad•min•is•tra•tion
(ad-**min**-uh-stray-shuhn) *noun*
The management of a school, company, or government. *The school's administration decided to crack down on bullying.*

a•gent
(**ay**-juhnt) *noun*
Someone who arranges things for other people. *The baseball player's agent makes sure the player is well paid.*

al•ter•ca•tion
(awl-tur-**kay**-shuhn) *noun*
A fight or quarrel. *The sisters had an altercation over who got to play the video game.*

am•bas•sa•dor
(am-**bass**-uh-dur) *noun*
Someone who represents something. *Alisa is our class ambassador to the student government.*

a•nal•y•sis
(uh-**nal**-uh-siss) *noun*
The careful examination of something in order to better understand it or something related to it. *Analysis of the evidence proved that the suspect was innocent.*

ap•pro•pri•ate
(uh-**proh**-pree-uht) *adjective*
Suitable or right for a particular person, place, or purpose. *I need to find an appropriate birthday card for my grandfather.*

Prefixes

Inappropriate **begins with the prefix *in-*, meaning "not." A prefix is a letter or group of letters added to the beginning of a word. A prefix changes the meaning of a word. *Inappropriate* means "not appropriate."**

as•pect
(**ass**-pekt) *noun*
One feature or characteristic of something. *The happy ending was my favorite aspect of the romance novel.*

as•sume
(uh-**soom**) *verb*
To suppose that something is true, without checking it. *I assume that Derrick is meeting me at the library this afternoon as usual.*

au•to•bi•o•graph•i•cal
(*aw*-toh-**bye**-ah-graf-uh-kuhl) *adjective*
About the person who wrote the book. *The next book will be autobiographical and tell about the writer's childhood in Chicago.*

bar•racks
(**ba**-rhks) *noun*
A group of buildings in which soldiers live. *The soldiers must clean the barracks before breakfast.*

be•lov•ed
(bi-**luhv**-id) *adjective*
Loved very much. *I gave a gift to a beloved friend.*

bi•as
(**bye**-uhss) *noun*
Prejudice. *The fans on that side of the arena are biased against the home team.*

bi•ol•o•gy
(bye-**ol**-uh-jee) *noun*
The scientific study of living things. *We study frogs in biology.*

brief
(**breef**) *adjective*
Short. *Donna had a brief visit with her aunt.*

cam•ou•flage
(**kam**-uh-flahzh)
1. *verb* To blend in with the surroundings. *The rabbit's white fur camouflages it in the snow.*
2. *noun* Covering that makes animals, people, and objects look like their surroundings. *The soldier put on camouflage before going out on the mission.*

ca•pa•ble
(**kay**-puh-buhl) *adjective*
Having the power, skill, or other qualities to do something, especially something difficult. *After taking many lessons, Sasha is capable of flying a plane.*

ca•tas•tro•phe
(kuh-**tass**-truh-fee) *noun*
A disaster. *The hurricane was a catastrophe that ruined many homes.*

cen•sus
(**sen**-suhss) *noun*
An official count. *The census shows that 40,000 people live in our city.*

chron•o•log•i•cal
(*kron*-uh-**loj**-uh-kuhl) *adjective*
Arranged according to when something happened. *We put the events in chronological order on a time line.*

com•pli•cate
(**kom**-pli-kate) *verb*
To make something more difficult. *Don't complicate the directions by adding more steps.*

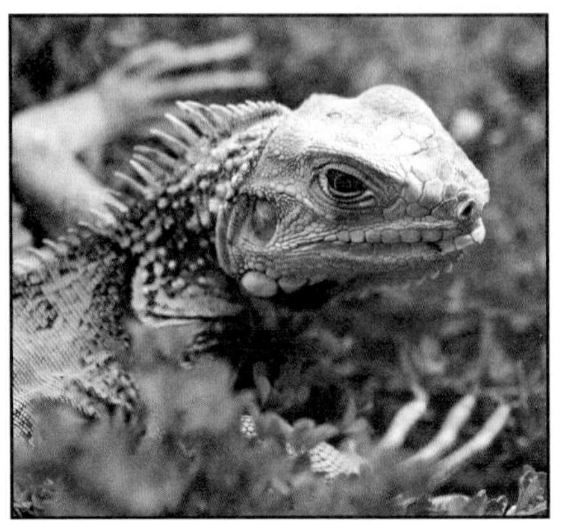
camouflage

con•clude
(kuhn-**klood**) *verb*
1. To decide something after considering all the information you have. *After hanging out with the new kid, I conclude that he is really funny!*
2. To complete something that you have been doing. *Let's conclude this meeting in five minutes.*

Verb Ending

The past-tense of *conclude* is *concluded*. The present-tense form is *conclude*. Verb endings show when an action takes place. To show an action in the past, you often can add *-ed*. If a verb ends with the letter *e*, it is usually dropped before adding *–ed* or *–ing*.

con•flict
1. (**kon**-flict) *noun*
A battle or disagreement. *Leo and his brother had a conflict over who had to walk the dog.*
2. (kuhn-**flict**) *verb*
To clash, disagree, or not match up. *Your plans to use the car tonight conflict with my plans to go to the mall.*

con•se•quence
(**con**-se-quence) *noun*
The result of an action. *Bad grades can be a consequence of skipping your homework.*

con•sist
(kuhn-**sist**) *verb*
To be made of or contain a number of different things. *The final exam consists of multiple choice and essay questions.*

con•tact
(**kon**-takt)
1. *noun* The state of touching or connecting. *Our shoulders made contact when we passed each other in the hallway.*
2. *verb* To communicate with a person, organization, or country. *The baby-sitter tried to contact the child's parents.*

con•tract
1. (**kon**-trakt) *noun* A legal written agreement between two people or companies that says what each side must do for the other. *The singer signed a contract with a record label.*
2. (kuhn-**trakt**) *verb* To enter into or make an agreement. *I contracted for service with the new phone company.*

co•or•di•nate
(koh-**or**-duh-*nate*) *verb*
To organize people or things so that they work or go well together. *As manager, it's my job to coordinate the staff.*

cri•sis
(**krye**-siss) *noun*
A big problem or an emergency. *We faced a major crisis when the tornado hit our town.*

crit•ic
(**krit**-ik) *noun*
1. Someone who judges something harshly. *My sister is such a critic when it comes to my cooking.*
2. Someone whose job is to judge something. *The critic gave the movie a good review.*

de•com•pose
(dee-kuhm-**pose**) *verb*
To decay. *By spring, the fallen leaves had decomposed.*

ded•i•cate
(**ded**-uh-kate) *verb*
1. To commit time and energy to a goal. *Joelle dedicates two hours each afternoon to practicing the piano.*
2. To say or write that something, such as a book, movie, or song, etc. has been written, made, or sung in honor of someone. *I dedicate this song to my mother.*

Multiple-Meaning Words

Dedicate **means "to spend time and energy on something." It also means "to say that something, such as a book, has been written in honor of someone." Multiple-meaning words are words that have more than one meaning.**

de•fine
(di-**fine**) *verb*
To explain or describe something exactly. *Every year, our teachers define what they expect from us.*

de•mean•or
(de-mean-er) *noun*
The way in which a person or animal behaves. *The smiling toddler had a joyful demeanor.*

de•port
(di-**port**) *verb*
To force a person to return to the country that the person came from. *The tourist was deported when his visa expired.*

de•tect
(di-**tekt**) *verb*
To notice or discover something. *I detect a bad odor in the room.*

de•vise
(di-**vize**) *verb*
To plan. *Let's devise a way to fix the broken bike.*

di•lap•i•dat•ed
(duh-**lap**-uh-day-tid) *adjective*
Old and in very bad condition. *The dilapidated building is about to fall down.*

dilapidated

dis•rupt
(diss-**ruhpt**) *verb*
To stop or break up. *My brother's loud music disrupts my concentration.*

dis•tinct
(diss-**tingkt**) *adjective*
Clearly different. *The coconut flavor makes these chocolate cookies distinct.*

dis•tress
(diss-**stess**) *noun*
The need for help. *The trapped animal was in distress.*

dis•trib•ute
(diss-**trib**-yoot) *verb*
To give things out. *Please distribute the worksheet to the class.*

Suffixes

***Distribution* ends with the suffix *–ion.* A suffix is a letter or group of letters added to the end of a word. The suffix *–ion* changes distribute from a verb to a noun.**

doc•u•men•ta•tion
(dok-yuh-men-**tay**-shuhn) *noun*
Official papers that prove that something is in order or correct. *The tourists had documentation to show that they were U.S. citizens.*

do•mes•tic
(duh-**mess**-tik) *adjective*
1. In or from your own country; not involving any other countries. *I took a domestic flight from New York to Florida.*
2. Relating to family relationships and life at home. *My brother likes to do domestic chores like taking out the garbage.*

ef•fi•cient
(uh-**fish**-uhnt) *adjective*
Working well, quickly, and without wasting time or energy. *The efficient students finished their project early.*

el•e•ments
(**el**-uh-muhnts) *noun*
Weather, especially bad weather. *Dress warmly to protect yourself from the elements.*

em•pha•size
(**em**-fuh-size) *verb*
To show that an opinion, idea, quality, etc. is important. *His speech emphasized the need for healthier school lunches.*

en•dur•ance
(en-**dur**-uhnce) *noun*
The ability to remain strong and patient even though you feel pain or have problems. *Lea has the endurance to run a marathon.*

Synonyms

***Endurance* is "the ability to remain strong and patient" and *energy* is "the strength to do active things." These words are synonyms, words that have similar meanings.**

ep•i•logue
(**ep**-uh-log) *noun*
A speech or piece of writing added to the end of a play, story, or poem. *The epilogue explained what happened to the characters after the story ended.*

es•ti•mate
(**ess**-ti-mate) *verb*
To make an educated guess. *Laura estimated how much her school supplies would cost.*

e•ven•tu•al•ly
(i-**ven**-choo-uh-lee) *adverb*
After a long time. *Eventually, the baby fell asleep.*

ev•i•dence
(**ev**-uh-duhnss) *noun*
Information and facts that help prove something or make you believe that something is true. *The evidence proved that the suspect was guilty.*

ex•ert
(eg-**zurt**) *verb*
To put to use; put forth. *I must exert all my strength to lift the heavy box.*

exert

ex•on•er•ate
(eg-**zon**-uh-rate) *verb*
To free from blame. *Kyle was exonerated after Julie admitted she took the stereo.*

ex•ploit
(ek-**sploit**) *verb*
1. To treat someone unfairly in order to gain what you want. *No one wants to work there because the bosses exploit the workers.*
2. To use effectively and completely. *Let's exploit our basketball skills to crush the other team.*

ex•tract
(ek-**strakt**) *verb*
To take or pull something out. *The dentist had to extract two of my teeth.*

fac•tor
(**fak**-tor) *noun*
One of the things that helps produce a result. *The bad weather was a factor in our decision to cancel our trip.*

fed•er•al
(**fed**-ur-uhl) *adjective*
Related to the central government of a country. *I have to pay both state and federal taxes.*

hem•i•sphere
(**hem**-uhss-fihr) *noun*
One of the halves of the earth, especially the northern or southern parts above and below the equator. *We're traveling to the Southern Hemisphere for our vacation this year.*

home•land
(**home**-land) *noun*
The country where you were born. *Mexico is my grandmother's homeland.*

Compound Words

Homeland **is a compound word. A compound word is made up of two smaller words, like *home+land*.**

hos•tile
(**hoss**-tuhl) *adjective*
Very unfriendly. *The dog was hostile to the stranger.*

hy•poth•e•sis
(hye-**poth**-uh-siss) *noun*
An explanation of something that has not yet been proven to be true. *The scientist spent hours in the lab trying to prove her hypothesis.*

illuminate

il•lu•mi•nate
(i-**loo**-muh-nate) *verb*
1. To make a light shine on something. *The neon sign illuminates the exit.*
2. To make something clearer and easier to understand. *He illuminates his theories by giving specific examples of how they could work.*

im•mense
(i-**menss**) *adjective*
Extremely large. *My father had a hard time lifting the immense pumpkin.*

im•pair
(im-**pair**) *verb*
To damage or make less good. *The constant loud music impaired the boy's hearing.*

im•pres•sion•a•ble
(im-**presh**-uhn-nuh-buhl) *adjective*
Easily influenced. *Your little brother is impressionable, so try to set a good example for him.*

in•di•vid•u•al
(*in*-duh-**vij**-oo-uhl)
1. *noun* A person. *Each individual needs paper and a pencil.*
2. *adjective* Separate. *The model train set includes six individual cars.*

in•fra•struc•ture
(in-frah-**struhk**-chur) *noun*
The basic foundation a company, city, state, or country needs in order to function well. *The fire department is part of the city's infrastructure.*

in•gen•ious
(in-**jeen**-yuhss) *adjective*
Inventive and original. *Ashley came up with an ingenious plan to raise money for the class trip.*

Root Words

The word *ingenious* comes from the Latin root *ingenium* which means "born talented." A root is a word or word part from another language that is the basis of an English word.

in•no•va•tion
(in-uh-**vay**-shuhn) *noun*
A new invention, method, or idea. *The button was an early innovation in fashion.*

in•stinct
(**in**-stingkt) *noun*
Behavior that is natural rather than learned. *Ducks swim by instinct.*

in•ter•nal
(in-**tur**-nuhl) *adjective*
Happening or existing inside someone or something. *The heart is an internal organ.*

Antonyms

Internal means "on the inside." External means "on the outside." These words are antonyms, words that have opposite meanings.

in•vest
(in-**vest**) *verb*
1. To give time, effort, or money, to make something succeed. *We invested lots of time in growing our garden.*
2. To give or lend money to something, such as a company, in the belief that you will get more money back in the future. *Is it smart to invest your money in lottery tickets?*

i•so•lat•ed
(**eye**-suh-late-id) *adjective*
Far away from other people or places. *We camped in an isolated area of the woods.*

lim•i•ta•tion
(lim-u-**te**-shuhn) *noun*
Something that blocks one from success. *My lack of money put limitations on what I could buy at the mall.*

list•less
(**list**-luhs) *adjective*
Feeling tired and uninterested in doing things. *When I had the flu, I felt listless.*

lurch
(**lurch**) *verb*
To move in an unsteady way. *The new driver hit the brakes and the car lurched forward.*

mag•ni•tude
(**mag**-nuh-tood) *noun*
Size or importance. *A tornado of great magnitude wiped out the little town.*

make•shift
(**make**-shift) *adjective*
Made for temporary use. *The kids sold lemonade from a makeshift booth on the sidewalk.*

ma•nip•u•late
(muh-**nip**-yuh-late) *verb*
To make someone do what you want by deceiving or influencing him or her. *Nathan manipulated his little sister into doing his chores.*

max•i•mum
(**mak**-suh-muhm) *adjective*
The largest number or amount. *The maximum number of books you can check out is ten.*

mi•grant
(**mye**-gruhnt) *noun*
A person who regularly moves from one area or country to another. *The migrants traveled through several states looking for work.*

min•i•mal
(**min**-uh-muhl) *adjective*
Extremely little. *Jake likes minimal noise when reading.*

min•i•mum
(**min**-uh-mum) *adjective*
The smallest possible number or amount. *What's the minimum price for a new cell phone?*

mod•i•fy
(**mod**-uh-fye) *verb*
To change or alter. *I need to modify my study habits to get better grades.*

neg•a•tive
(**neg**-uh-tiv) *adjective*
Having a bad or harmful effect. *Too much sun can have a negative effect on your skin.*

ob•sta•cle
(**ob**-stuh-kuhl) *noun*
Something that gets in your way or prevents you from doing something. *My sore ankle was an obstacle on the basketball court.*

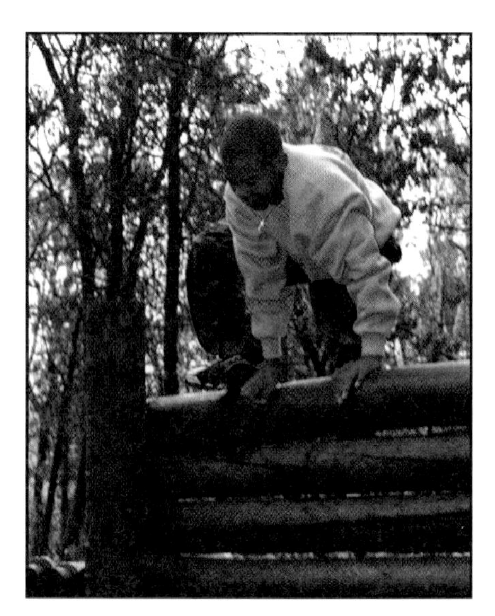

obstacle

ob•tain
(uhb-**tayn**) *verb*
To get or be given something. *I need to obtain some money for new sneakers.*

off•shore
(**of-shor**) *adjective*
1. Located in a foreign country. *The company has a factory offshore, in China.*
2. Located a distance from the shore. *They're drilling for oil offshore.*

per•pe•tra•tor
(**pur**-puh-tray-ter) *noun*
Someone who has done wrong. *The perpetrator went to jail for two years.*

per•pet•u•ate
(pur-**pech**-oo-ate) *verb*
To make something last for a long time. *Don't perpetuate the rumor by repeating it.*

phase
(**faze**)
1. *noun* One part or stage of something. *During the last phase of the contest, we will pick a winner.*
2. *verb* To introduce something gradually. *The clothing store will phase in some new styles over the summer.*

plunge
(**pluhnje**) *verb*
To move through with force. *Tracy plunged into the water, making a big splash.*

Idioms

Someone who starts something new is said to be "taking the plunge." "Take the plunge" is an idiom, an expression that means something different from the separate words.

pre•cise
(pri-**sisse**) *adjective*
Exact and correct in every detail. *Use the precise amount of each ingredient, or the recipe will not turn out well.*

pred•a•tor
(**pred**-uh-tur) *noun*
An animal that hunts other animals. *The snake is a predator of mice.*

proc•ess
(**pross**-ess) *noun*
A series of actions that produce a result. *Building my Web site was a long process.*

pro•por•tion
(pruh-**por**-shuhn) *noun*
1. A part or share of a larger number or amount. *A large proportion of the class voted.*
2. The relationship between the amounts, sizes, or numbers of related things. *The proportion of cats to dogs on our block is two to one.*

pro•voke
(pruh-**voke**) *verb*
To make a person or an animal angry. *Janelle provokes her sister by teasing her.*

prox•im•i•ty
(prok-**sim**-uh-tee) *noun*
Nearness. *I love the proximity of my house to the park.*

pub•lish•er
(**puhb**-lish-ur) *noun*
A person who produces and distributes an article, book, magazine, newspaper, or any other printed material so that people can read or buy it. *The publisher came out with seven new books this month.*

pur•sue
(pur-**soo**) *verb*
1. To continue doing an activity or trying to achieve something over a long time. *Ashley will pursue a college degree while working part time.*
2. To follow or chase someone in order to catch him or her. *The police had to pursue the thieves for ten blocks before catching them.*

rand
(**rand**) *noun*
A unit of money in South Africa. *Brianna paid fifty rand for a bracelet while she was on a vacation in South Africa.*

re•act•ion
(ree-**ak**-shuhn) *noun*
An action in response to something. *Juan let out a scream in reaction to the hairy spider.*

reaction

re•cede
(ri-**seede**) *verb*
To move back. *The water rushed onto the beach and then receded into the ocean.*

re•solve
(ri-**zolv**) *verb*
1. To decide that you will try hard to do something. *I resolve to finish all my homework before dinner.*
2. To deal with a problem or difficulty successfully. *Let's resolve our argument right now.*

re•strict
(ri-**strikt**) *verb*
To keep within limits. *My mother restricts us to one hour of TV a day.*

re•veal
(ri-**veel**) *verb*
To show or tell something that was previously hidden or not talked about. *Please reveal how you did the magic trick.*

rum•mage
(**ruhm**-ig) *verb*
To search for something by moving things around. *Justin rummaged through his locker to find his homework.*

rummage

rur•al
(**rur**-uhl) *adjective*
Having to do with the countryside or farming. *My dad grew up in a rural area.*

sched•ule
(**skej**-ool)
1. *verb* To plan something for a specific time. *Let's schedule practice for Tuesday night.*
2. *noun* A plan or timetable. *The bus schedule changes on the weekend.*

se•quel
(**see**-kwuhl) *noun*
A book or movie that continues the story of an earlier one. *I hope my favorite book will have a sequel.*

si•mul•ta•ne•ous•ly
(sye-muhl-**tay**-nee-uhss-lee) *adverb*
At the same time. *My two favorite shows air simultaneously.*

spec•u•late
(**spek**-yuh-late) *verb*
To guess why something happened or what will happen next without knowing all the facts. *Everybody at school loves to speculate about who will win the big contest.*

spur
(**spur**) *verb*
To encourage or prompt. *Jasmine spurred her friend to try out for soccer.*

ster•i•lize
(**ster**-uh-lize) *verb*
To be made clean and free from germs. *The doctors sterilized their hands by scrubbing them with soap and hot water.*

suf•fi•cient
(suh-**fish**-uhnt) *adjective*
Enough or an adequate amount. *We left sufficient food for the cats while we were away.*

su•per•fi•cial
(soo-pur-**fish**-uhl) *adjective*
1. Affecting only the surface of your skin or the outside part of something. *The accident caused only superficial damage to the car.*
2. Based only on the first things you notice, not on complete knowledge. *At a superficial glance, this game seems easy.*

tech•nique
(tek-**neek**) *noun*
A special method or way of doing something. *The doctor invented a new technique for heart surgery.*

Noun Endings

To make a noun plural, most nouns just need an *s*, like *techniques.* But nouns that already end in an *s* need *–es*, like *buses*. Nouns that end in *y* need *–ies*, like *policies*.

tech•nol•o•gy
(tek-**nol**-uh-jee) *noun*
Electronic or digital products or systems. *Video games are my favorite form of technology.*

tel•e•com•mu•ni•ca•tions
(tel-uh-kuh-myoo-nuh-**kay**-shuhns) *noun*
Electronic systems for communicating at a distance. *This new type of telecommunications lets me talk to all my friends at one time.*

tem•po•rar•y
(**tem**-puh-*rer*-ee) *adjective*
Lasting for only a short time. *The shot hurt a little, but the pain was only temporary.*

the•o•ry
(**thee**-ur-ee) *noun*
An explanation for something that may be reasonable, but has not yet been proven true. *The police have a theory about who did the crime.*

trau•ma
(**trah**-muh) *noun*
A severe injury. *I bumped my head, but not hard enough to cause trauma.*

trend
(**trend**) *noun*
1. The way a system is generally developing or changing. *Recently, there has been a trend toward smaller cars.*
2. Current style. *Baggy pants are a trend in many schools.*

un•der•take
(*uhn*-dur-**take**) *verb*
To try or attempt. *Josh will undertake the written part of our group project.*

us•age
(**yoo**-sij) *noun*
The act, way, or amount of using. *The group took a survey on Internet usage in schools.*

u•til•ize
(**yoo**-tuh-lize) *verb*
To use something effectively. *Let's utilize all our skills to finish this project.*

val•id
(**val**-id) *adjective*
1. Sound; based on strong reasons or facts. *Dana had a valid excuse for being late.*
2. Able to be used for legal or official reasons. *If your driver's license expires, it is no longer valid.*

Homophones

Vary **means "to differ from something of the same type" and *very* means "to a great extent." These are homophones, words that sound alike but have different spellings and meanings.**

var•y
(**vair**-ee) *verb*
1. To differ from something of the same type. *Styles vary from one shoe store to the next.*
2. To change often. *You need to vary your exercise routine to stay in good shape.*

vast
(**vast**) *adjective*
Extremely large. *An ocean is a vast body of water.*

ve•hi•cle
(**vee**-uh-kuhl) *noun*
Something in which people travel. *Will you go by plane, train, or some other vehicle?*

ver•i•fy
(**ver**-uh-fye) *verb*
To find out if a fact or statement is correct or true. *Please verify that school will be closed tomorrow.*

vol•un•tar•y
(**vol**-uhn-*ter*-ee) *adjective*
Done willingly and not being forced or paid. *My dad coaches the football team on a voluntary basis.*

vul•ner•a•ble
(**vuhl**-nur-uh-buhl) *adjective*
Easily harmed or attacked. *The puppy looked vulnerable sitting on the busy street corner.*

yearn
(**yurn**) *verb*
To want something very much. *Vonda yearned for a cell phone for her birthday.*

vehicle

How to Use the Reading Handbook

This handbook includes the comprehension skills that you mastered in the **rBook**. You can use these directions and charts to review what you know. You can also use them in your other classes, like social studies and science. They can help you understand a new article or story.

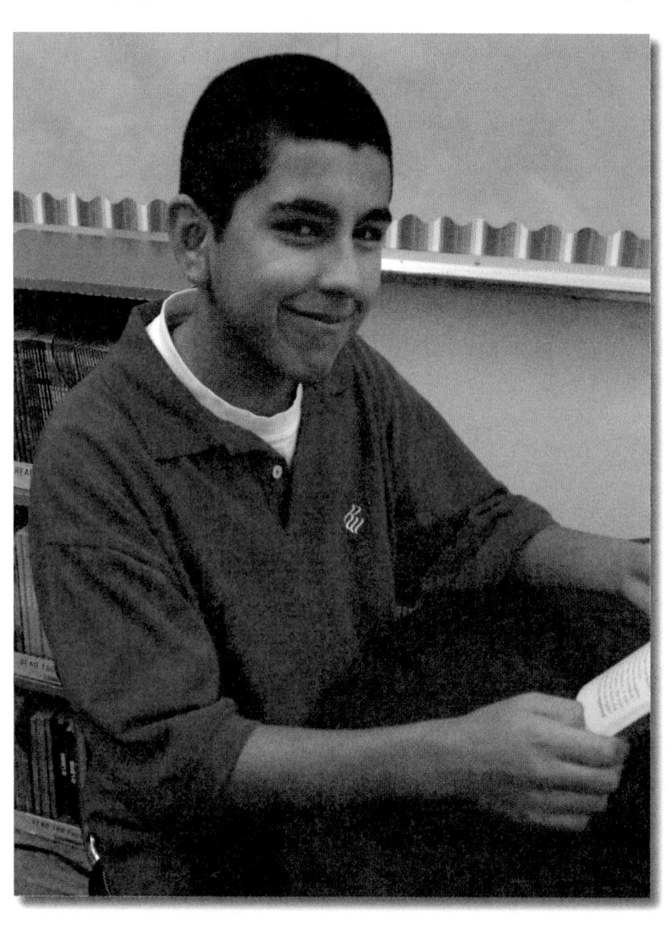

Main Idea and Details

The **main idea** is the most important point about a topic. **Details** are the facts that support the main idea. To find the main idea and details:

- **Decide what the topic is. Find the main idea about the topic.**
- **Look for the details that support the main idea.**

▶ **Use this chart to identify a main idea and supporting details.**

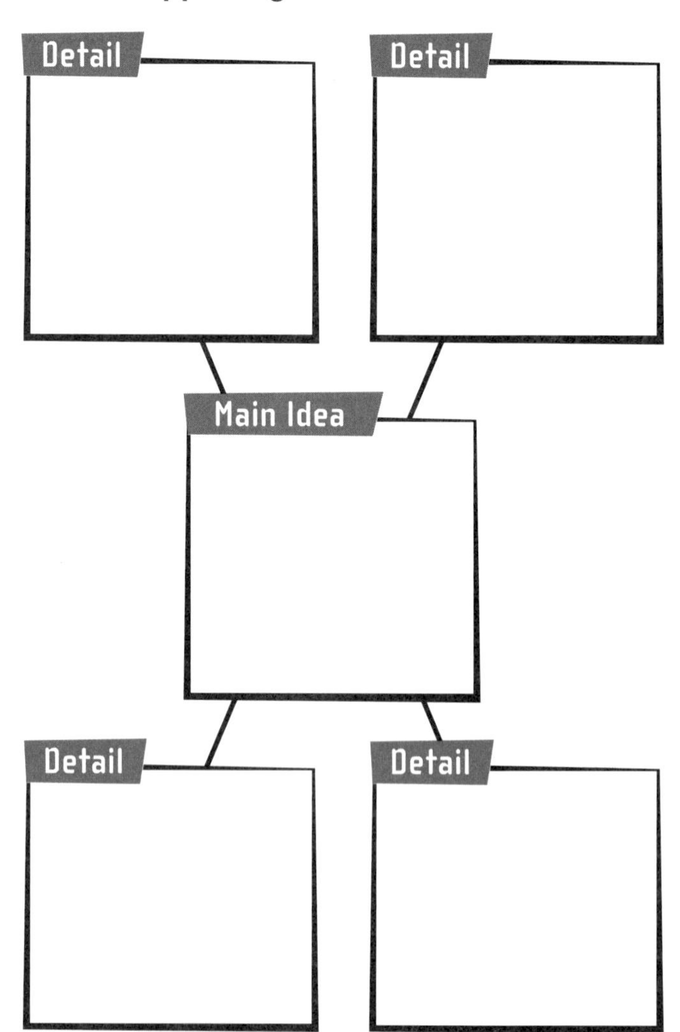

Sequence of Events

Sequence is the order in which events happen. To find the sequence of events:

- Try to remember the order in which events take place.
- Look for times, dates, and signal words, such as *first, then, next, soon, before, after,* and *later*.
- When you know the order, check it again. Make sure it makes sense.

▶ **Use this chart to identify a sequence of events.**

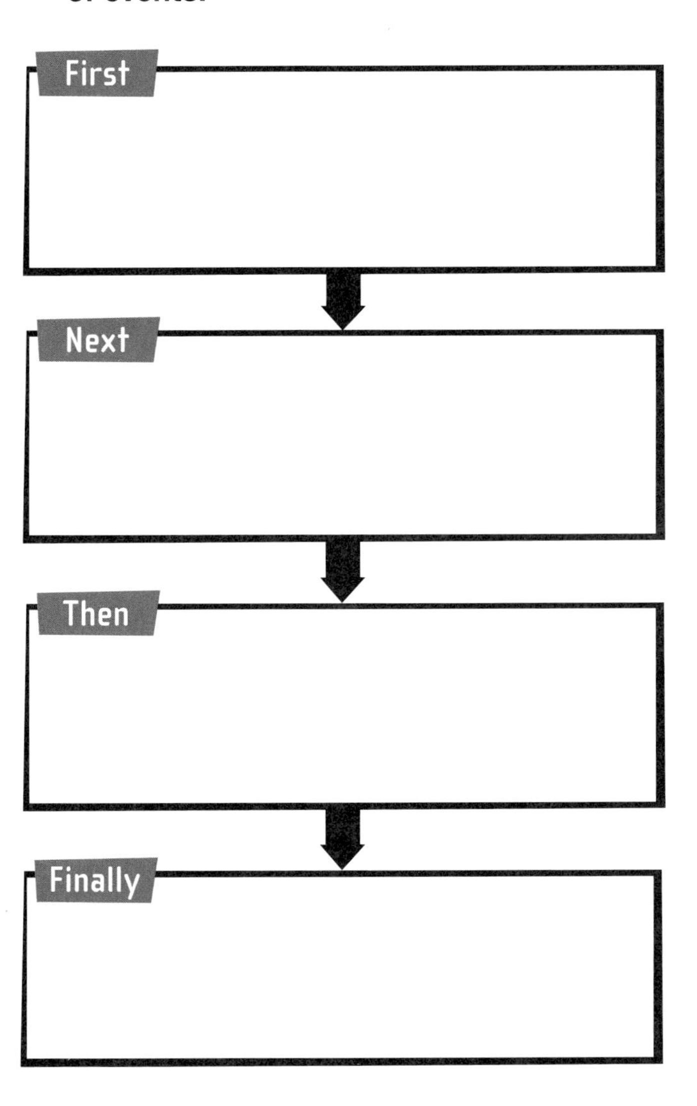

Summarize

A **summary** is a short statement of the most important ideas in a reading. To summarize:

- Find the topic of the text.
- Look for the most important details about the topic.
- Restate the topic and important details in a short summary. Use your own words.

▶ **Use this chart to identify the topic and important details in a summary.**

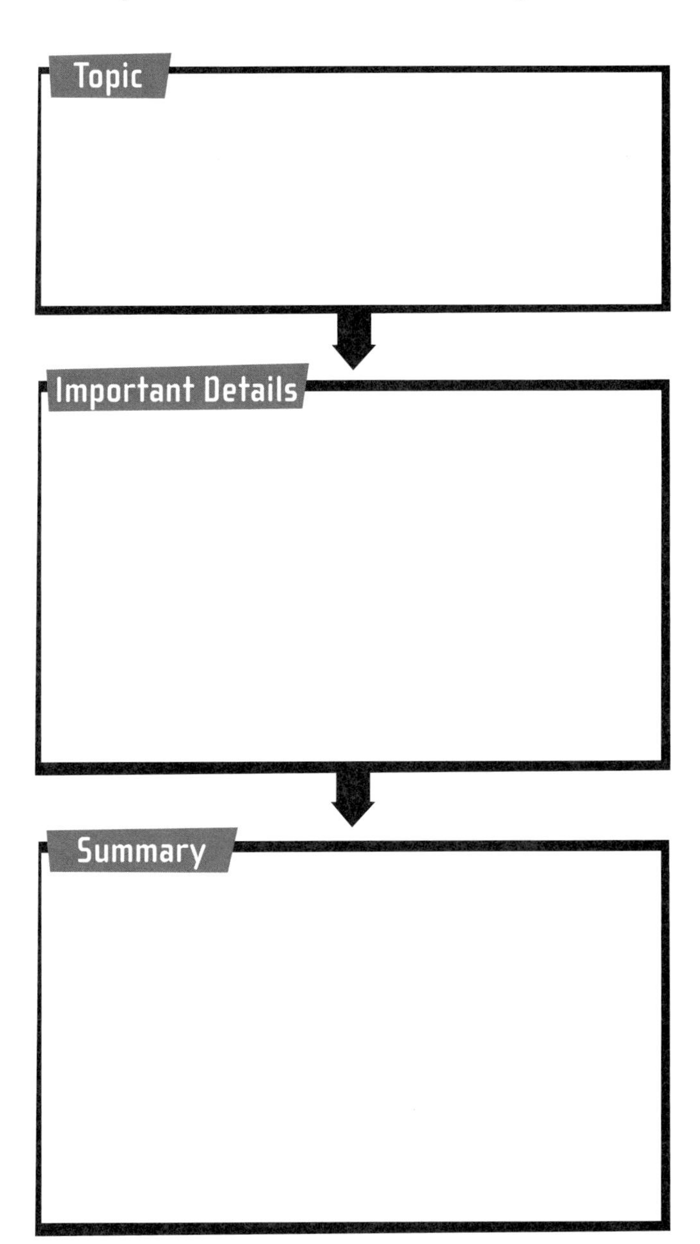

Fact and Opinion

A **fact** is a statement that can be proven true. An **opinion** is a statement that is someone's personal feeling or belief. An opinion can also be a judgment.

- **To identify a fact, ask: Can this statement be proven true? How or where could I check whether it is true?**
- **To identify an opinion, ask: Is this someone's feeling, belief, or judgment? To recognize opinions, look for signal words, such as *think, believe, best, worst, appropriate,* and *unfair.***

▶ **Use this chart to identify facts and opinions.**

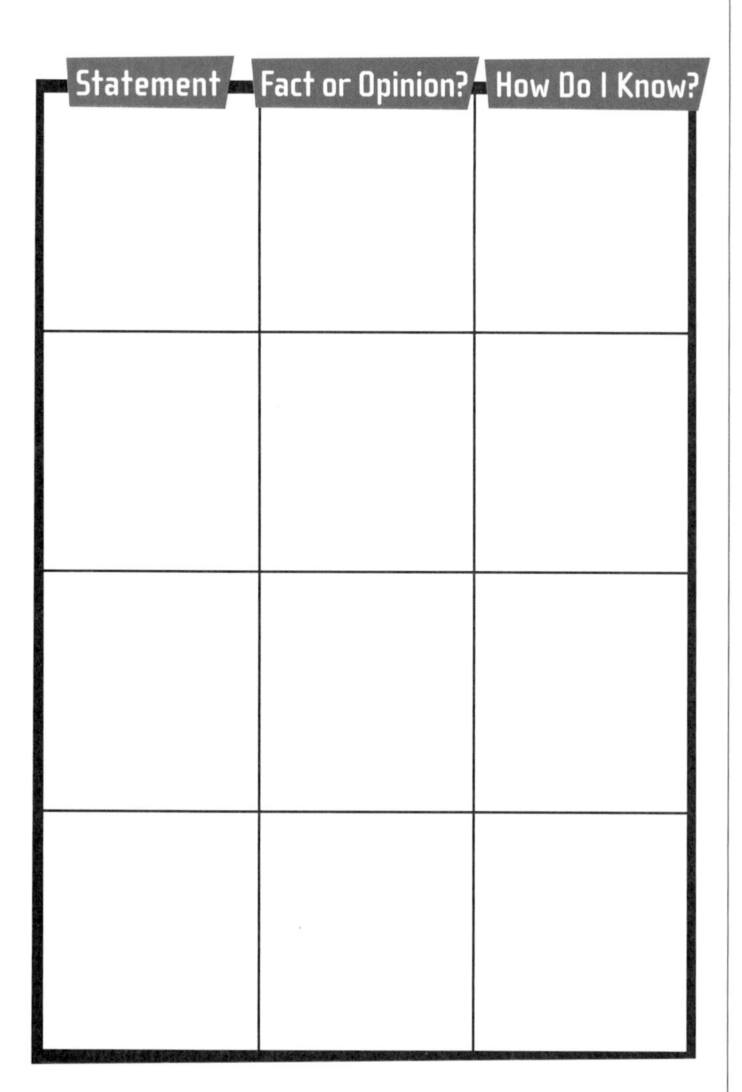

Cause and Effect

A **cause** is the reason something happens. An **effect** is the result of a cause. To find the cause and effect:

- **Ask yourself "Why did it happen?" to find the cause.**
- **Ask yourself "What happened?" to find the effect.**
- **Look for signal words or phrases such as *because, so, as a result, therefore, consequently,* and *for this reason.***

▶ **Use this chart to identify cause-and-effect relationships.**

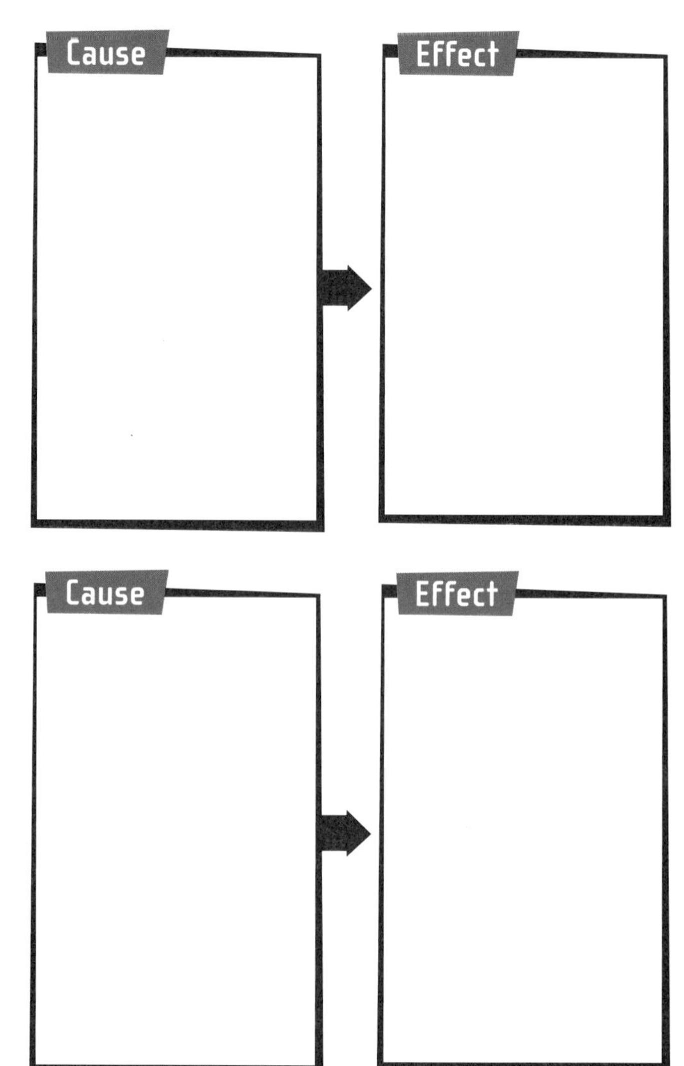

Compare and Contrast

When you **compare**, you tell how two things are the same. When you **contrast**, you tell how they are different. To compare and contrast:

- Ask yourself how two things are the same. Look for signal words such as *both, too, also,* and *in addition.*
- Ask yourself how two things are different. Look for signal words such as *but, rather than,* and *however.*

▶ **Fill in this chart to compare and contrast two elements in a reading.**

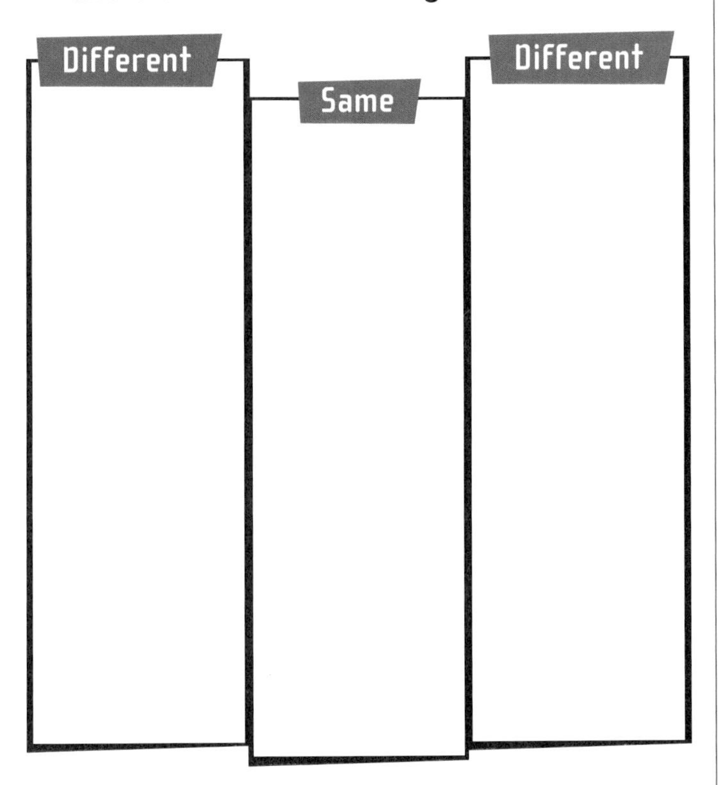

Make Inferences

When you **make inferences**, you form ideas about things that are not directly stated in the text. To make inferences:

- Look for a situation in the text in which the author gives clues but doesn't state exactly what is happening.
- Think about what you already know about the topic.
- Combine the text clues with your own experiences or knowledge to make an inference.

▶ **Fill in this chart to make an inference.**

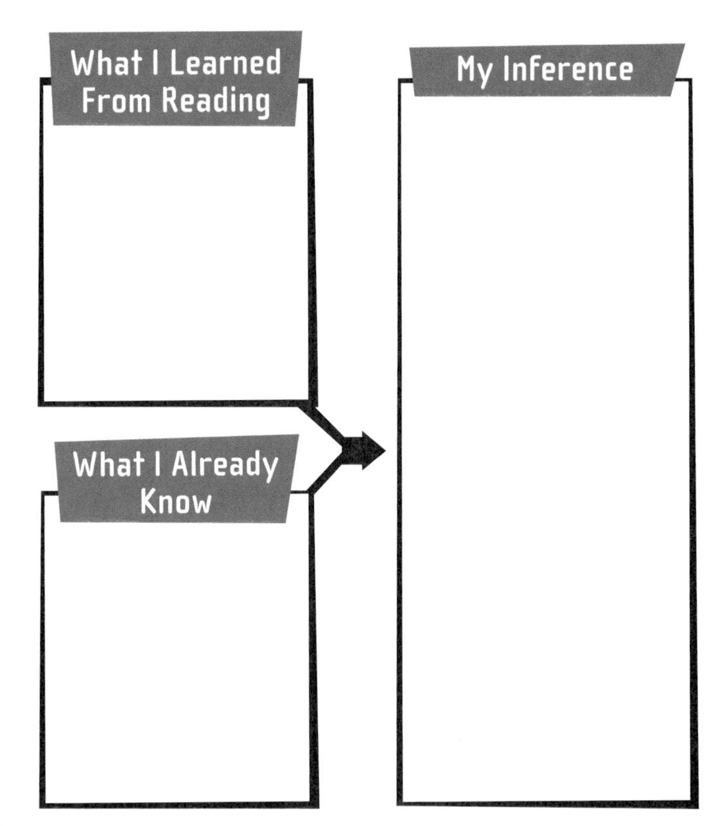

Story Elements

A short story is a brief piece of fiction. To understand a short story, look for four elements:

Setting

Setting refers to the place and time of a story. To analyze the setting:

- Look at the illustrations.
- Look for details that tell *where*. Ask yourself, "What words in the story help me imagine what the place looks like?"
- Look for story details that tell *when*. Ask yourself, "When does this story take place? Is it long ago, in the future, or the present?"
- Pay attention to any changes in the setting and how they affect the story.

Character

A **character** is a person or animal in a story. It's who the story is about. Often stories have several characters. We can identify the main characters because they are the ones the story is mostly about. Characters have special qualities, or traits, that make up their personalities. To analyze a character:

- Look for words the author uses to describe the character, especially adjectives.
- Pay attention to what the character thinks, says, and does.
- Be aware of what other characters say about the main character.
- Think about what you already know about people and their behavior.

Plot

Plot refers to what happens in a story, including the problem, the events that lead to solving the problem, and the solution. To analyze the plot:

- Find out what the character's problem is.
- Look at how the character tries to solve the problem.
- Pay attention to what happens to help solve the problem. Look at what happens that gets in the way of solving the problem.
- Think about how the story turns out. Does the character solve the problem? How?

Theme

The **theme** is the message that the author wants you to take away from the story. It often helps you understand the author's purpose, thoughts, and feelings. To analyze theme:

- Think about what the characters do and say.
- Think about what happens to the characters.
- Ask yourself: What does the author want you to know about?

▶ **Use this chart to keep track of the setting, character, plot, and theme of a story you are reading.**

Story Title: ____________________

	Part 1	Part 2	Part 3
Setting	Time and Place: ______ ______ Time and Place: ______ ______ ______	Time and Place: ______ ______ Time and Place: ______ ______ ______	Time and Place: ______ ______ Time and Place: ______ ______ ______
Character	Who is the main character? ______ Describe him/her: ______ ______ ______	How does the character change? ______ ______ ______ ______ ______	What is the character like now? ______ ______ ______ ______ ______
Plot Events	What happens at the beginning of the story? ______ ______ ______ ______ ______	What happens in the middle of the story? ______ ______ ______ ______ ______	How does the story end? ______ ______ ______ ______ ______
Theme	Author's message:		

Literary Terms

author a person who writes a short story, play, poem, novel, article, essay, or book

characters the people or animals in a story

concrete poetry poetry that has a shape that matches the meaning of the poem or a word in the poem

conflict an internal conflict takes place in the mind of a character who must resolve something. An external conflict takes place between two characters or between a character and a force of nature, society, or the unknown.

dialogue a conversation between characters

fiction an invented story

figurative language words used to say something other than their literal meaning, often to help the reader visualize what is happening. For example, "All the world's a stage."

flashback the return to an event that occurred before the present situation

foreshadowing hints of what is to come

free verse poetry that does not have regular patterns of rhyme and rhythm

historical fiction a story or novel whose setting is in some period in the past. Often real people from the past or important historical events are used in works of historical fiction.

imagery the use of vivid description to create pictures, or images, in the reader's mind

metaphor a comparison in which something is said to be something else. Metaphors use *is* or *was*. For example: He is a shining star.

mood the general feeling that an author creates. Mood is created largely through description and setting.

narrator the teller of a story. A first-person narrator tells a story using the word *I*.

nonfiction writing about real people and factual events

novel a book-length piece of fiction that usually has a plot and deals with human experience

onomatopoeia the use of a word that sounds like the thing it stands for, such as *buzz* and *sizzle*

personal narrative a true story about a person's life told in the first person

photo essay a collection of photos and words that tells a story

plot what happens in a story, including the problem, the events that lead to solving the problem, and the solution

plot twist a turn of events in the story, novel, or play that is unexpected

poetry literature that uses language chosen for its sound and for its ability to express and evoke emotion

point of view the point from which the story is told. In the **first-person point of view,** the narrator is usually a character in the story. This narrator tells the story by using the pronouns *I* or *we.* In the **third-person point of view,** the narrator may or may not be a character in the story. This narrator uses the pronouns *he, she,* or *they.* Sometimes the narrator in the third-person point of view seems to know what every character is thinking and feeling. This narrator is called *omniscient*, or *all-knowing*.

repetition words, phrases, or sentences that are used over and over again

rhyme two or more words that have ending syllables with the same sound

rhythm a regular, repeated pattern of sounds in music or poetry

setting the time and place of a story

short story a brief piece of fiction

simile a comparison of two unlike things, using the words *like* or *as.* For example: She was as sweet as candy.

stanza a group of two or more lines in a poem that are printed as a unit and held together by length, rhyme scheme, and meter

suspense a state of uncertainty that keeps a reader reading

symbol something that has meaning in itself, but also stands for something else. For example, in a story, a heart may also stand for love.

theme the message that the author wants you to take away from the story. The theme is conveyed by the whole story—by the title, the plot, the characters, the setting, and the mood.

How to Use the Writing Handbook

This handbook includes the writing skills that you mastered in the **rBook**. You can use these directions and charts to review what you know. You can also use them to help you with a new writing assignment.

Expository Paragraph

An **expository paragraph** provides information and explains it.

- State the **topic** in the first sentence.
- Use **details** to support or explain the topic.
- Arrange the details in a **logical order**.
- Use **linking words** to connect the ideas.
- **Sum up** or restate the topic in the last sentence.

▶ **Use this chart to plan an expository paragraph.**

Topic Sentence

Detail 1

Detail 2

Detail 3

Ending

Expository Summary

A **summary** gives the most important ideas and details from a reading.

- State the **topic of the reading** in the first sentence.
- Include only **important details.**
- Connect the details with **linking words.**
- **Use your own words** in the summary.
- Make sure your summary is **brief, yet complete.**

▶ **Use this chart to plan an expository summary.**

Topic

Detail 1

Detail 2

Detail 3

Last Detail

Persuasive Paragraph

A **persuasive paragraph** tries to convince the reader to share the writer's opinions.

- State your **opinion** clearly in the first sentence.
- Support your opinion with several **reasons.**
- Make sure that your reasons are **strong and convincing.**
- Use **linking words** to connect your reasons.
- **Restate** your opinion in a concluding sentence.

▶ **Use this chart to plan a persuasive paragraph.**

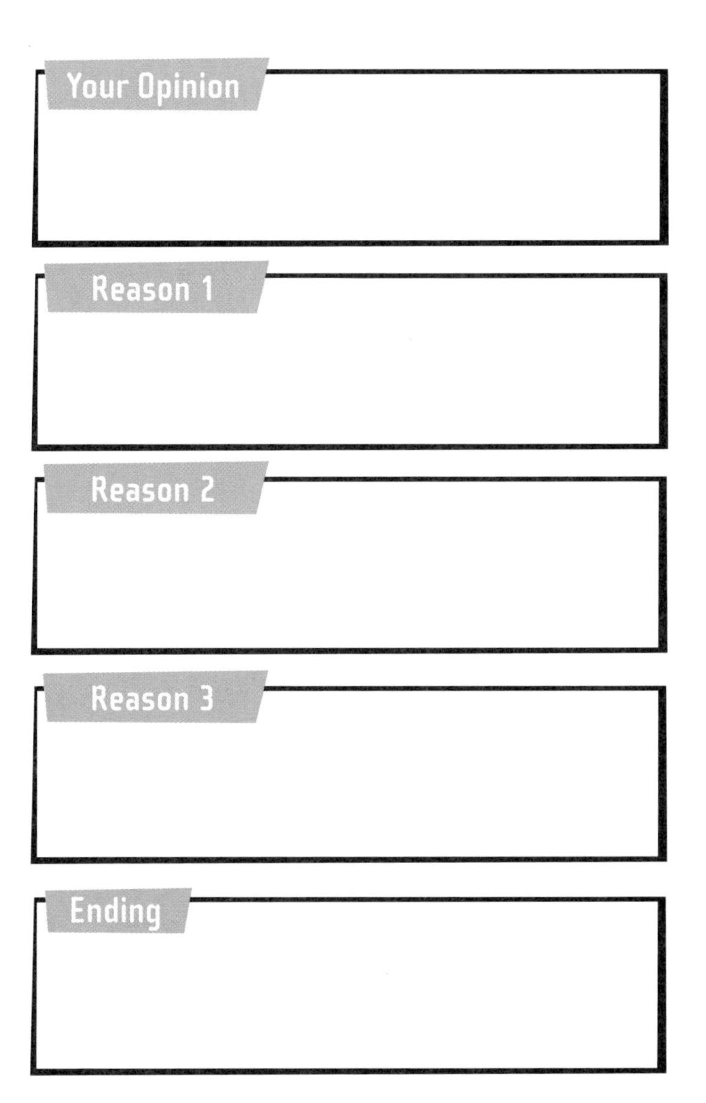

Narrative Paragraph

A **narrative paragraph** tells a story about an event.

- State the **event** in the beginning.
- Use **details** to tell about the event.
- Arrange the details in the **time order** that they happened.
- Use **linking words** to connect the details.
- **Sum up** the event and tell your feelings about it in the ending.

▶ **Use this chart to plan a narrative paragraph.**

Event

Detail 1

Detail 2

Detail 3

Ending

Descriptive Paragraph

A **descriptive paragraph** describes a person, place, thing, or event by using interesting and specific details.

- State **what is being described** in the beginning.
- Use **descriptive details** about the subject.
- Make the details as **interesting** as possible.
- Use **linking words** to connect the details.
- **Sum up** the description and your **feelings** about it in the ending.

▶ **Use this chart to plan a descriptive paragraph.**

Topic Sentence

Detail 1

Detail 2

Detail 3

Conclusion

Literature Response

In a **literature response**, a reader relates a piece of literature to his or her life.

- **Relate your experience** to the main character's experience in the beginning.
- Use **details** to describe that experience.
- Arrange the details in the **time order** they happened.
- Use **linking words** to connect the details.
- **Sum up** your ideas and feelings with the ending.

▶ **Use this chart to plan a literature response.**

Introduce the Topic

Detail 1

Detail 2

Detail 3

Conclusion

Literature Review

A **literature review** presents the reviewer's opinion of a story.

- State your **opinion** of the story in the beginning.
- Include specific **reasons** that support your opinion.
- Make sure that your reasons are **strong and convincing**.
- Use **linking words** to connect the ideas.
- **Sum up** your opinion with the ending.

▶ **Use this chart to plan a literature review.**

Statement About the Story

Example or Reason 1

Example or Reason 2

Example or Reason 3

Concluding Statement

Grammar

▶ Identifying Sentences and Fragments

A **sentence** is a group of words that tells a complete idea.

- The **subject** tells who or what the sentence is about.
- The **predicate** tells what someone or something does.

A **sentence fragment** is an incomplete sentence that can't stand by itself. Often, a fragment is missing either a subject or a predicate.

Example

Subject	Predicate
Tabitha	plans to pursue a law degree.
The doctors	work in their old neighborhood.

▶ Correcting Sentence Fragments

A **sentence fragment** is an incomplete sentence. Often, sentence fragments are missing a subject or a verb. To fix some fragments, add a subject or verb to make a **complete sentence**.

Example

Sentence Fragment	Complete Sentence
The tsunami of 2004. [missing verb]	The tsunami of 2004 killed many.
Destroyed so much. [missing subject]	The waves destroyed so much.

To correct some **sentence fragments**, you can connect the fragment to a complete sentence by adding a comma and any missing words.

Example

Sentence and Fragment	Complete Sentence
Many people lost their homes. Lost family members as well.	Many people lost their homes, and some lost family members as well.

▶ Correcting Run-On Sentences

A **run-on sentence** is made up of two complete thoughts that are incorrectly joined together.

- To fix a run-on sentence, separate the ideas into two **complete sentences**.
- Or, insert a comma and a connecting word between the thoughts.

Example

Run-on sentence:	Ayize needed money he went to the mines.
Complete sentences:	Ayize needed money. He went to the mines.
Complete sentence:	Ayize needed money, so he went to the mines.

▶ Using Correct Verb Tense

The **tense** of a verb shows when the action happens.

- A present-tense verb shows action that is happening now.
- The past-tense verb shows action that took place in the past. Most past-tense verbs end in *-ed*.

Example

Present-Tense Verb	Past-Tense Verb
The scientist examines the evidence.	The scientist examined the body.
A DNA sample is valuable.	The DNA sample was analyzed.

▶ Using Irregular Verbs

Most past-tense verbs end in *-ed*. **Irregular verbs** do not.

- You must remember the different spellings of irregular past-tense verbs.
- The verb *to be* is a common irregular verb. Its present-tense forms are *I am*, *you are*, *he/she is*. Its past-tense forms are *I/he/she was, you/we/they were*.

Example

Present-Tense Verb	Past-Tense Verb
I am online right now.	I was online yesterday.
Hector sends lots of emails.	He sent me a message today.
She knows his cell now.	She knew his old number.

▶ Subject-Verb Agreement

A **subject and verb** in a sentence must agree in number.

- A singular verb tells what one person, place, or thing is doing. It usually ends in *-s* or *-es*.
- A plural verb tells what more than one person, place, or thing is doing. It usually does not end in *-s* or *-es*.

Example

Singular Subject and Verb	Plural Subject and Verb
The dog follows the man.	The dogs follow the man.
The man drops the matches.	The men drop the matches.

▶ Using Subject and Object Pronouns

A **pronoun** is a word that takes the place of a noun in a sentence.

- Use a **subject pronoun** in the subject of a sentence.
- Use an **object pronoun** after a verb or after a word such as *for* or *to*.

Example

Subject Pronoun	Object Pronoun
I visited the ocean.	The waves crashed into me.
We went snorkeling.	Fish swam around us.
She studies marine biology.	Fish fascinate her.
They live in the midnight zone.	Dijanna studies them.

▶ Using Adjectives That Compare

A **adjective** is a word that tells about or describes a noun. Adjectives can help compare two or more people or things.

- To use an adjective to **compare two things**, add *-er* to the adjective or use the word *more*.
- To use an adjective to **compare three or more things**, add *-est* to the adjectives or use the word *most*.

Example

Adjective Comparing Two Things	Adjective Comparing Three or More Things
China is richer than it was 10 years ago.	He is the richest person in the country.
Outsourcing is more popular than before the 1990s.	She is the most popular actress in the world.

▶ Using Adverbs

An **adjective** describes a person, place, or thing. An **adverb** describes a verb, an adjective, or another adverb. Many adverbs end in *-ly*.

- Use an adverb to make your writing more precise.

Example

Adjective	Adverb
His teacher was a kind person.	His teacher kindly looked at him.
The family packed at a quick pace.	His family packed quickly.
Francisco was sad on the bus.	He looked sadly out the window.

Usage and Mechanics

▶ Using End Punctuation

Different kinds of sentences use different **end punctuation marks**.

- A **statement** always ends with a period.
- A **question** always ends with a question mark.

Example

Statement	Question
My sister wants to be a musician.	What career would you enjoy?
Tim's goal is to be a scientist.	How will you reach your goal?

▶ Using Capitals

Some words begin with a **capital letter**.

- The first word in a sentence begins with a capital letter.
- A proper noun begins with a capital letter.

Example

Correct	Incorrect
The waves were huge.	the waves were huge.
They hit Indonesia.	they hit indonesia.

▶ Using Correct Word Order

The **order of words** in a sentence must make sense.

- An adjective comes before the noun it describes.
- A helping verb comes just before the main verb in a statement.

Example

Correct	Incorrect
Zindzi gave Ayize white beads.	Zindzi gave Ayize beads white.
He realized why Nkosi was sewing.	He realized why was Nkosi sewing.

▶ Using Commas in a Series

Items in a series are separated by **commas**.

- A series is a list of the same kinds of words.
- Commas follow every item in the series except the last one.

Example

Correct	Incorrect
Blood, skin, and DNA are all studied in a crime lab.	Blood skin and DNA are all studied in a crime lab.

▶ Using Commas With Introductory Words

A **comma** follows an opening word or phrase at the beginning of a sentence.

- *Yes*, *No*, *Next*, and *Later* are examples of opening words.
- *In addition* and *After a while* are examples of opening phrases.

Example

Correct	Incorrect
Later, they emailed each other.	Later they emailed each other.
In addition, my phone broke.	In addition my phone broke.

▶ Using Possessives

A **possessive noun** shows ownership.

- Add an apostrophe (') and an *-s* to a singular noun.
- Add an apostrophe to a plural noun that ends in *-s*.

Example

Correct	Incorrect
London's story was suspenseful.	Londons story was suspenseful.
The friends' camp was set up.	The friends camp was set up.

▶ Avoiding Double Negatives

Negatives are words that express *no* or *not*.

- Use only one negative word to express a single negative idea.
- It is incorrect to use two negatives to express a negative idea.

Example

Correct	Incorrect
A diver should never swim alone.	A diver shouldn't never swim alone.
The scientists didn't find anything.	The scientists didn't find nothing.

▶ Using Quotation Marks

Quotation marks show the exact words of a speaker.

- The first word of a quotation is capitalized.
- Punctuation usually goes inside the ending quotation mark.

Example

Correct	Incorrect
Katie said, "Way to go!"	Katie said, "way to go!"
Alex yelled, "You did it!"	Alex yelled, "You did it"!

rBook Flex Workshop Log

▶ **Fill in the date that you start and complete each Workshop. Rate your effort on a Workshop using the Rating Guide. Then answer a final question.**

Rating Guide			
weak	okay	good	great
①	②	③	④

WORKSHOP 1 Eyes on the Graduation Prize

Date Started	Date Completed

Self-Assessment

Rate your effort during this Workshop.

① ② ③ ④

Who would you most like to meet?

- ❑ Tabitha
- ❑ Jorvorskie
- ❑ The doctors

Why? ______________________________

____

WORKSHOP 2 Tsunami: Disaster of the Century

Date Started	Date Completed

Self-Assessment

Rate your effort during this Workshop.

① ② ③ ④

If you worked for a relief organization, what would you want to do?

- ❑ Give out food and medicine
- ❑ Build homes
- ❑ Create a new tsunami warning system

Why? ______________________________

____

WORKSHOP 3 Long Journey to Justice

Date Started	Date Completed

Self-Assessment

Rate your effort during this Workshop.

① ② ③ ④

How do you feel about diamonds after reading this workshop? Why?

____

____

____

____

WORKSHOP 4 Crime Lab Science

Date Started	Date Completed

Self-Assessment

Rate your effort during this Workshop.

① ② ③ ④

Would you want to be a forensic scientist? Why or why not?

____

____

____

____

WORKSHOP 5 Wired for Trouble

Date Started	Date Completed

Self-Assessment

Rate your effort during this Workshop.

① ② ③ ④

Do you think you use too much technology? Why or why not?

____

____

____

WORKSHOP 6 Facing the Elements

Date Started	Date Completed

Self-Assessment

Rate your effort during this Workshop.

① ② ③ ④

What would you have done differently if you were the man in "To Build a Fire"? Why?

____

____

____

WORKSHOP 7 Creatures of the Deep

Date Started	Date Completed

Self-Assessment

Rate your effort during this Workshop.

① ② ③ ④

What would you like best about being a sea scientist?

- ❑ Going underwater in a submersible
- ❑ Examining sea animals in the lab
- ❑ Seeing unique sights like bioluminescent fish

WORKSHOP 8 Going Global

Date Started	Date Completed

Self-Assessment

Rate your effort during this Workshop.

① ② ③ ④

Do you think globalization is good or bad? Why?

____

____

____

WORKSHOP 9 The Art of the Memoir

Date Started	Date Completed

Self-Assessment

Rate your effort during this Workshop.

① ② ③ ④

What will you remember most about this Workshop? Why?

____

____

____

Stage B Topic Software Log

▶ **Use these pages to keep track of the Topic CDs you have completed. Check off each segment you finish. Then answer a final question about each CD.**

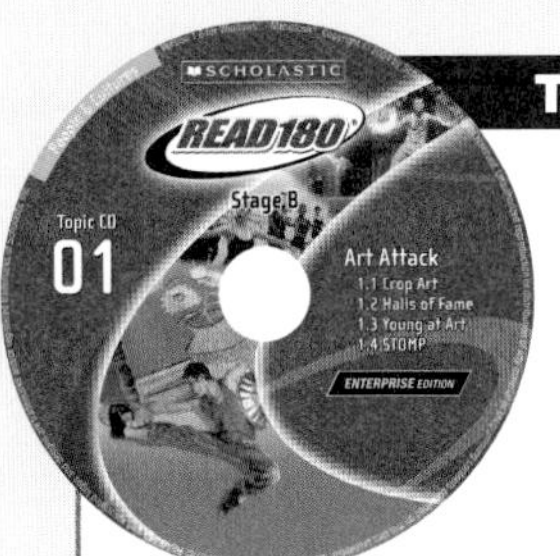

Topic CD 1

Art Attack

- ❑ 1.1 Crop Art
- ❑ 1.2 Halls of Fame
- ❑ 1.3 Young at Art
- ❑ 1.4 STOMP

One new thing I learned was ______________________

____

____

Topic CD 2

Disaster!

- ❑ 2.1 Flood!
- ❑ 2.2 Earthquake!
- ❑ 2.3 Avalanche!
- ❑ 2.4 Volcano!

The type of disaster that scares me the most is

____

____

Topic CD 3

Survive

- ❑ 3.1 Braving Alaska
- ❑ 3.2 Out of the Dust
- ❑ 3.3 In Search of Rain
- ❑ 3.4 Take a Dive

The people who had the toughest thing to

survive were ______________________________

____

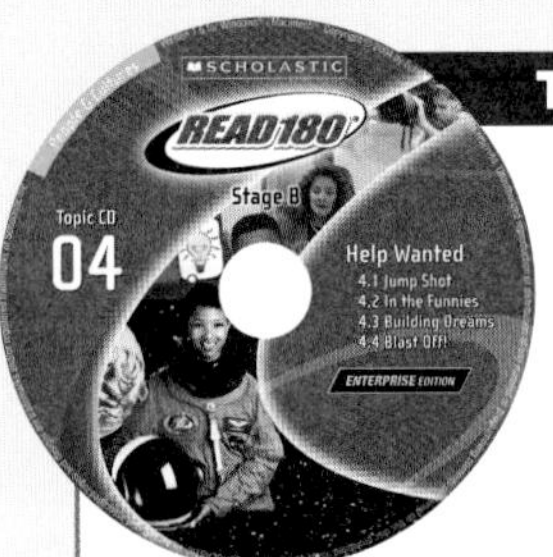

Topic CD 4

Help Wanted

- ❑ 4.1 Jump Shot
- ❑ 4.2 In the Funnies
- ❑ 4.3 Building Dreams
- ❑ 4.4 Blast Off!

The person in this Topic CD I'd most like to

meet is ______________________________

____

Topic CD 5

Show Me the Money!

- ❑ 5.1 Making Money
- ❑ 5.2 Bogus Bills
- ❑ 5.3 Fighting Forgery
- ❑ 5.4 Mangled Money

The most interesting thing I saw on this Topic

CD was ______________________________

Topic CD 6

You and the Law

- ❑ 6.1 Ban the Boards
- ❑ 6.2 What Curfew?
- ❑ 6.3 No Passing
- ❑ 6.4 Taking Mom to the Mall

One law that I agree with is ______________________

____

____

Topic CD 7

Beating the Odds

- ❑ 7.1 Feel the Beat
- ❑ 7.2 Second Chance
- ❑ 7.3 Little Rock Nine
- ❑ 7.4 Write Direction

The person in this Topic CD who had the hardest challenge was ____________________

____

Topic CD 8

Extreme Sports

- ❑ 8.1 Extreme Snowboarding
- ❑ 8.2 Extreme Biking
- ❑ 8.3 Extreme Kayaking
- ❑ 8.4 Extreme Surfing

The extreme sport that seems the hardest is

____

____

Topic CD 9

The Whole World Watched

- ❑ 9.1 A Dark Day in Dallas
- ❑ 9.2 One Giant Leap
- ❑ 9.3 Freedom in South Africa
- ❑ 9.4 The People's Princess

The segment I'd like to learn more about is

____

Topic CD 10

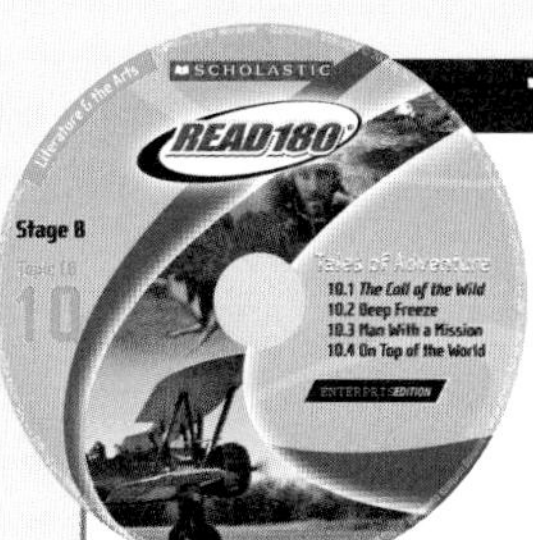

Tales of Adventure

- ❑ 10.1 *The Call of the Wild*
- ❑ 10.2 Deep Freeze
- ❑ 10.3 Man With a Mission
- ❑ 10.4 On Top of the World

I think a good movie could be made about

____

____

Topic CD 11

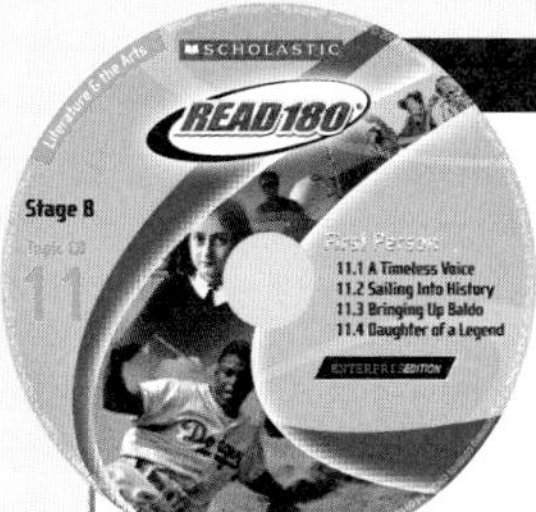

First Person

- ❑ 11.1 A Timeless Voice
- ❑ 11.2 Sailing into History
- ❑ 11.3 Bringing Up Baldo
- ❑ 11.4 Daughter of a Legend

I would recommend this Topic CD to __________

____

____

Topic CD 12

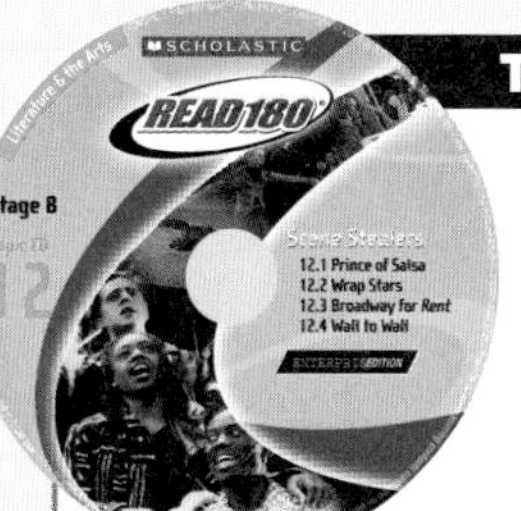

Scene Stealers

- ❑ 12.1 Prince of Salsa
- ❑ 12.2 Wrap Stars
- ❑ 12.3 Broadway for *Rent*
- ❑ 12.4 Wall to Wall

My favorite segment was ____________________

____

____

Stage C Topic Software Log

▶ **Use these pages to keep track of the Topic CDs you have completed. Check off each segment you finish. Then answer a final question about each CD.**

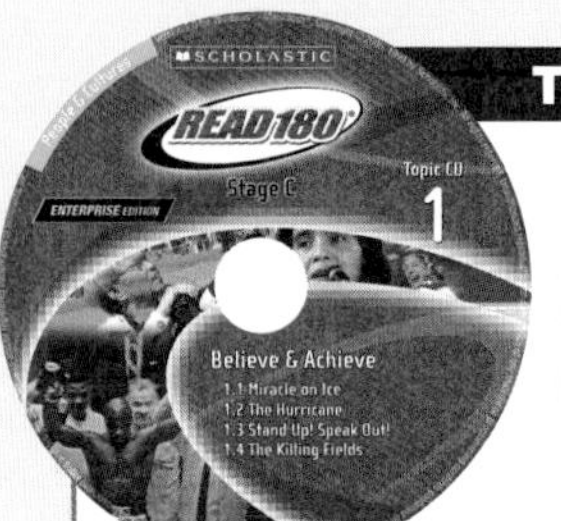

Topic CD 1

Believe & Achieve

- ❑ 1.1 Miracle on Ice
- ❑ 1.2 The Hurricane
- ❑ 1.3 Stand Up! Speak Out!
- ❑ 1.4 The Killing Fields

The person who had the toughest challenge

was ______________________________

____

Topic CD 2

Not Your Boring Science Job

- ❑ 2.1 Snake Stalker
- ❑ 2.2 Dr. Brain
- ❑ 2.3 Mummy Dearest
- ❑ 2.4 Cave Woman

The person in this Topic CD I'd most like to

meet is ______________________________

Topic CD 3

Made in the U.S.A.

- ❑ 3.1 Heart of Harlem
- ❑ 3.2 Going Hollywood
- ❑ 3.3 Road Trip
- ❑ 3.4 Surfin' U.S.A.

The segment I'd like to learn more about is

____

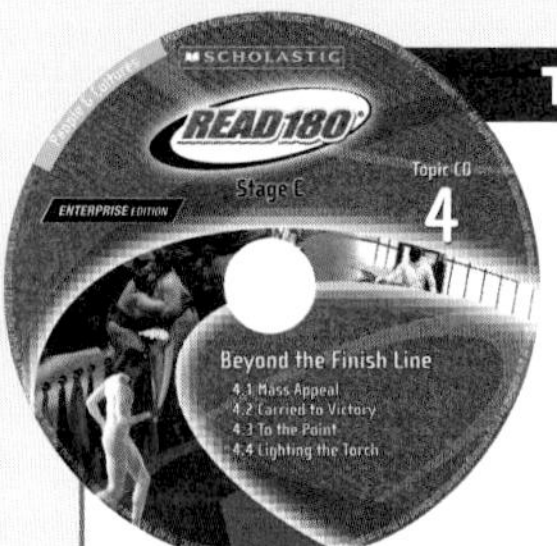

Topic CD 4

Beyond the Finish Line

- ❑ 4.1 Mass Appeal
- ❑ 4.2 Carried to Victory
- ❑ 4.3 To the Point
- ❑ 4.4 Lighting the Torch

The person I admire most from this Topic CD

is ______________________________

Topic CD 5

Big Money

- ❑ 5.1 Bright Lights of Vegas
- ❑ 5.2 Wall Street
- ❑ 5.3 Home is Where the Oil is
- ❑ 5.4 Diving for Treasure

The most interesting thing I learned was

____

____

Topic CD 6

Point/ Counterpoint

- ❑ 6.1 The Driving Dilemma
- ❑ 6.2 Coming to America
- ❑ 6.3 What's in a Name?
- ❑ 6.4 Should Animals Have Rights?

One issue that I feel strongly about is ________

____

Topic CD 7

Showstoppers

- ❑ 7.1 Blue Man Group
- ❑ 7.2 Slammin' Poets
- ❑ 7.3 More Than Hot Air
- ❑ 7.4 Selena!

The art I'd like to try to make is ____________

____

____

Topic CD 8

Body Shop

- ❑ 8.1 Bloodsuckers
- ❑ 8.2 Dying to Win
- ❑ 8.3 Replacement Parts
- ❑ 8.4 It Takes Nerves

My favorite segment was ____________

____

____

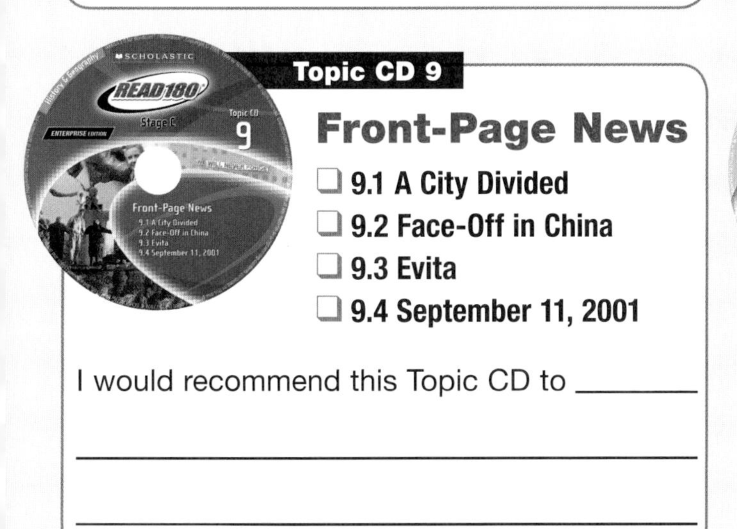

Topic CD 9

Front-Page News

- ❑ 9.1 A City Divided
- ❑ 9.2 Face-Off in China
- ❑ 9.3 Evita
- ❑ 9.4 September 11, 2001

I would recommend this Topic CD to ________

____

____

Topic CD 10

Shakespeare

- ❑ 10.1 A Day at the Globe
- ❑ 10.2 *Romeo and Juliet*
- ❑ 10.3 *Julius Caesar*
- ❑ 10.4 Acting the Part

If I could meet Shakespeare, I'd say ________

____

____

Topic CD 11

Writers Who Rock!

- ❑ 11.1 Breath of Fresh Air
- ❑ 11.2 Living Out Loud
- ❑ 11.3 Bringing Down the House
- ❑ 11.4 Tour de Lance

The writer I'd like to meet is ____________

____

Topic CD 12

Enduring Visions

- ❑ 12.1 Ring Masters
- ❑ 12.2 A Place to Remember
- ❑ 12.3 Step On It
- ❑ 12.4 Santana!

One new thing I learned is ____________

____

____

Book Log

▶ Use these pages to keep track of the books you read.

- Write the title in the blank box. Add a design if you like.
- Fill in the date that you started and completed each book.
- Mark what kind of book it was.
- Rate the book using the rating scale at right. Then write a statement about it.

Rating Scale

It was great!	★★★★
It was good.	★★★☆
It was O.K.	★★☆☆
I didn't like it.	★☆☆☆

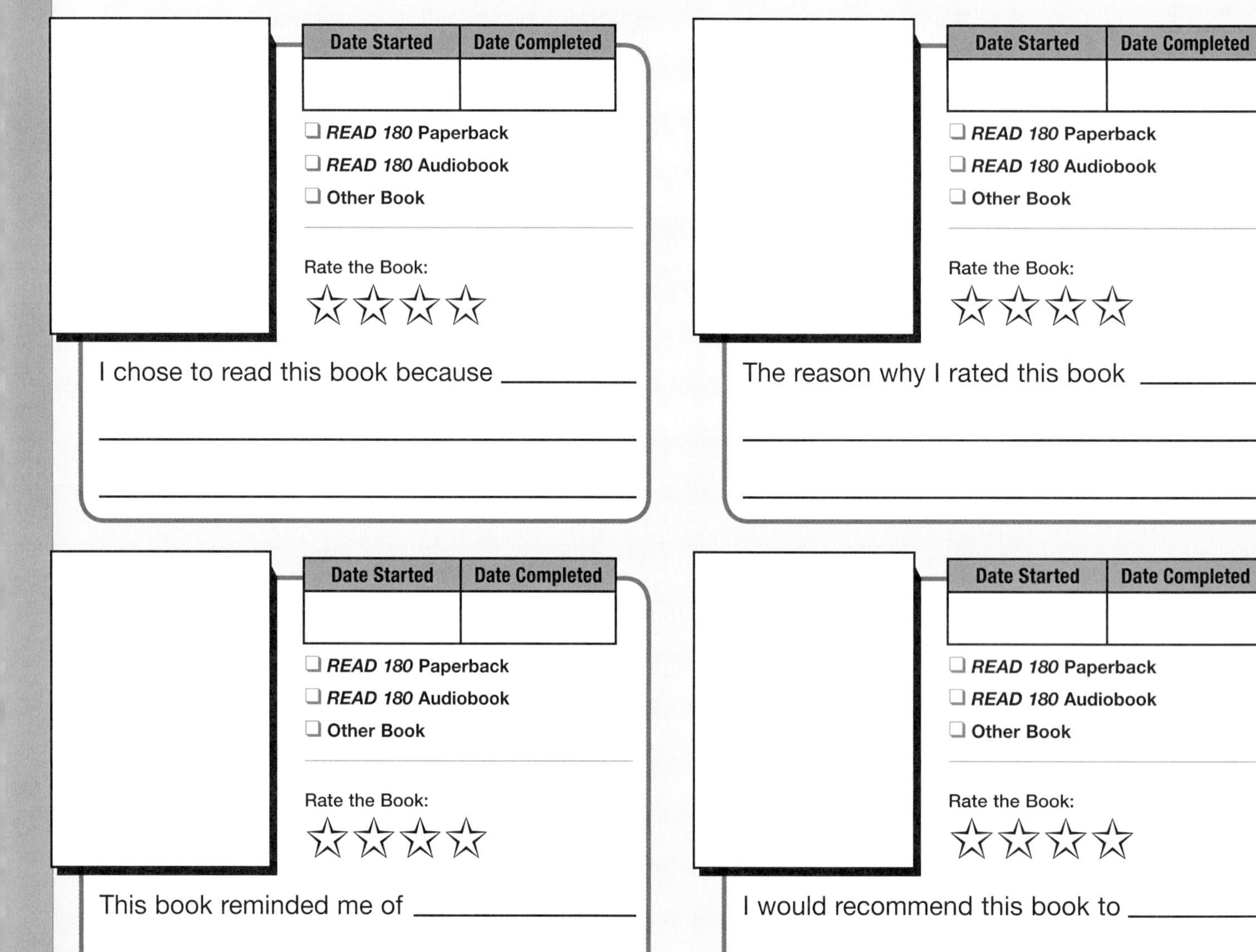

Date Started	Date Completed

❑ *READ 180* Paperback
❑ *READ 180* Audiobook
❑ Other Book

Rate the Book:
☆☆☆☆

I chose to read this book because ______

Date Started	Date Completed

❑ *READ 180* Paperback
❑ *READ 180* Audiobook
❑ Other Book

Rate the Book:
☆☆☆☆

The reason why I rated this book ______

Date Started	Date Completed

❑ *READ 180* Paperback
❑ *READ 180* Audiobook
❑ Other Book

Rate the Book:
☆☆☆☆

This book reminded me of ______

Date Started	Date Completed

❑ *READ 180* Paperback
❑ *READ 180* Audiobook
❑ Other Book

Rate the Book:
☆☆☆☆

I would recommend this book to ______

Date Started	Date Completed

❑ *READ 180* Paperback
❑ *READ 180* Audiobook
❑ Other Book

Rate the Book:
☆☆☆☆

One new thing I learned in this book was ____

____

____

Date Started	Date Completed

❑ *READ 180* Paperback
❑ *READ 180* Audiobook
❑ Other Book

Rate the Book:
☆☆☆☆

I think I will/won't remember this book

because ______________________________

____

Date Started	Date Completed

❑ *READ 180* Paperback
❑ *READ 180* Audiobook
❑ Other Book

Rate the Book:
☆☆☆☆

The best part of this book was ____________

____

____

Date Started	Date Completed

❑ *READ 180* Paperback
❑ *READ 180* Audiobook
❑ Other Book

Rate the Book:
☆☆☆☆

One question I have for the author is ________

____

____

Date Started	Date Completed

❑ *READ 180* Paperback
❑ *READ 180* Audiobook
❑ Other Book

Rate the Book:
☆☆☆☆

If I were making this book into a movie, it

would star ______________________________

____

Date Started	Date Completed

❑ *READ 180* Paperback
❑ *READ 180* Audiobook
❑ Other Book

Rate the Book:
☆☆☆☆

This book was easy/hard to finish because

____

____

Student Log

Date Started	Date Completed

❑ *READ 180* Paperback
❑ *READ 180* Audiobook
❑ Other Book

Rate the Book:
☆☆☆☆

If I were making this book into a movie, it would star ______________________________

____

Date Started	Date Completed

❑ *READ 180* Paperback
❑ *READ 180* Audiobook
❑ Other Book

Rate the Book:
☆☆☆☆

When I first saw this book, I thought it would be ______________________________

____

Date Started	Date Completed

❑ *READ 180* Paperback
❑ *READ 180* Audiobook
❑ Other Book

Rate the Book:
☆☆☆☆

One fact I learned in this book is ______________

____

____

Date Started	Date Completed

❑ *READ 180* Paperback
❑ *READ 180* Audiobook
❑ Other Book

Rate the Book:
☆☆☆☆

Reading this book made me feel ______________

____

____

Date Started	Date Completed

❑ *READ 180* Paperback
❑ *READ 180* Audiobook
❑ Other Book

Rate the Book:
☆☆☆☆

The most interesting thing about this book was ______________________________

____

Date Started	Date Completed

❑ *READ 180* Paperback
❑ *READ 180* Audiobook
❑ Other Book

Rate the Book:
☆☆☆☆

I'd recommend this book to ______________

____

____

Date Started	Date Completed

❑ *READ 180* Paperback
❑ *READ 180* Audiobook
❑ Other Book

Rate the Book:
☆☆☆☆

The best thing about this book is ______________

____

____

Date Started	Date Completed

❑ *READ 180* Paperback
❑ *READ 180* Audiobook
❑ Other Book

Rate the Book:
☆☆☆☆

Three words that describe this book are ______

____

____

Date Started	Date Completed

❑ *READ 180* Paperback
❑ *READ 180* Audiobook
❑ Other Book

Rate the Book:
☆☆☆☆

I would recommend this book to ______________

____

____

Date Started	Date Completed

❑ *READ 180* Paperback
❑ *READ 180* Audiobook
❑ Other Book

Rate the Book:
☆☆☆☆

If I were making this book into a movie, it would star ______________________

____

Date Started	Date Completed

❑ *READ 180* Paperback
❑ *READ 180* Audiobook
❑ Other Book

Rate the Book:
☆☆☆☆

This book should/should not have a sequel because ______________________

____

Date Started	Date Completed

❑ *READ 180* Paperback
❑ *READ 180* Audiobook
❑ Other Book

Rate the Book:
☆☆☆☆

One new thing I learned in this book is ______

____

____

Keep Track of Your Success!

▶ Create a bar graph showing your SRI Lexile® scores over the year.

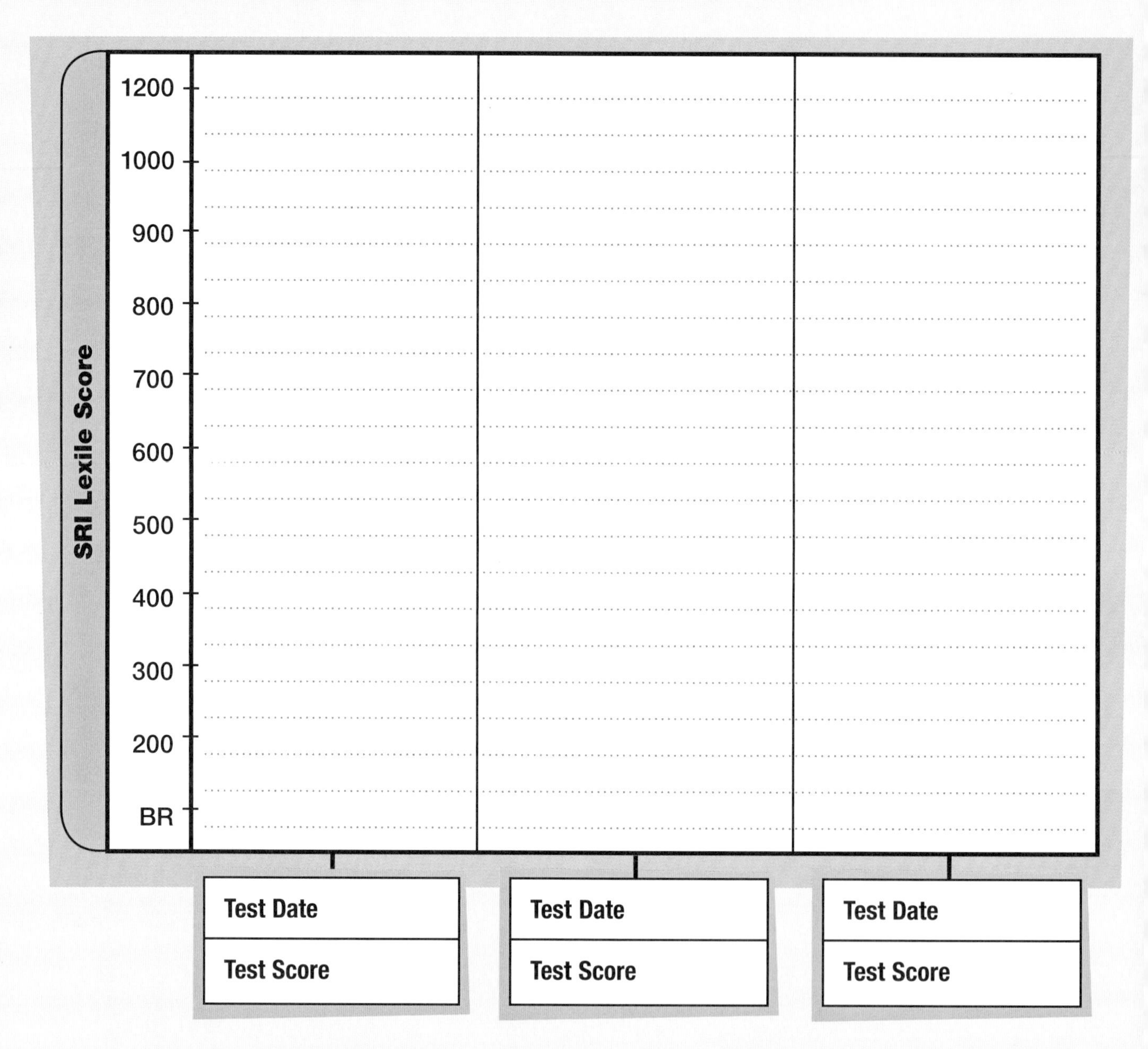

▶ Use this chart to keep track of your *READ 180* rSkills test scores.

	Test 1	Test 2	Test 3	Test 4	Test 5
Test Date					
Test Score					

Grateful acknowledgment is made to the following sources for permission to reprint from previously published material. The publisher has made diligent efforts to trace the ownership of all copyrighted material in this volume and believes that all necessary permissions have been secured. If any errors or omissions have inadvertently been made, proper corrections will gladly be made in future editions.

"The Pact" adapted from THE PACT by Drs. Sampson Davis, George Jenkins, and Rameck Hunt with Lisa Frazier Page. Copyright © 2002 by Three Doctors LLC. Reprinted by permission of Riverhead Books, an imprint of Penguin Group (USA) Inc.

Cover from THE PACT by Drs. Sampson Davis, George Jenkins, and Rameck Hunt with Lisa Frazier Page. Copyright © 2002 by Three Doctors LLC. Reprinted by permission of Riverhead Books, an imprint of Penguin Group (USA) Inc. Cover photo: © Anthony Barboza.

"Terror and Tragedy" adapted from "My Mother Died in the Tsunami" by Anuradha Raghunathan from *Seventeen* magazine, April 2005. Copyright © 2005 by Anuradha Raghunathan. Reprinted by permission of the author.

"Diamond Land" adapted from DIAMOND LAND by Rita Williams-Garcia. Copyright © 2003 by Rita Williams-Garcia. Reprinted by permission of Scholastic Inc.

"DNA Analysis" adapted from FORENSICS by Richard Platt. Copyright © 2005 by Kingfisher Publications. Reprinted by permission of Kingfisher Publications, a Houghton Mifflin Company imprint.

"Trouble at Your Fingertips" adapted from "Generation Speed" by Whitney Joiner from *Seventeen* magazine, November 2005. Copyright © 2005 by The Hearst Corporation. Reprinted by permission of The Hearst Corporation. All rights reserved.

"Staying Alive" adapted from TRAVELING LIGHT: COLLECTED AND NEW POEMS by David Wagoner. Copyright © 1999 by David Wagoner. Reprinted by permission of the author and the University of Illinois Press.

"From Breaking Through" and "Writing a Memoir" from BREAKING THROUGH by Francisco Jiménez. Copyright © 2001 by Francisco Jiménez. Reprinted by permission of Houghton Mifflin Co.

Cover from BREAKING THROUGH by Francisco Jiménez. Copyright © 2001 by Francisco Jiménez. Reprinted by permission of Houghton Mifflin Co. Cover photo courtesy of Francisco Jiménez.

"An Interview with Francisco Jiménez" from Scholastic.com Web site. Copyright © Scholastic Inc. All rights reserved.

Cover from THE CIRCUIT by Francisco Jiménez. Copyright © 1997 by Francisco Jiménez. Reprinted by permission of University of New Mexico Press.

Credits

Cover: clockwise from bottom right: Patrick Arrasmith © Scholastic Inc., © Burke-Triolo Productions/Brand X Pictures/Jupiter Images, © Scholastic Inc., © GSFC/NASA, © Mark Peterson/Corbis, © Martin French; p2tl: © Jeff Stead/AP/Wide World Photos, bl: © AID India; p. 3tl: © Martin French, lc: © Custom Medical Stock Photo, bl: © Burke-Triolo Productions/Brand X Pictures/Jupiter Images; p. 4tl: Patrick Arrasmith © Scholastic Inc., lc: © Norbert Wu/Minden Pictures, bl: © Steve Harris; p. 5tl: courtesy Francisco Jiménez; p. 6bl: © Anuradha Raghunathan, cl: courtesy Dr. Sampson Davis/The Three Doctors Foundation, rc: © H. Raguet/Eurelios/Phototake; p. 7bl: Patrick Arrasmith © Scholastic Inc., lb: © Bettmann/Corbis, tl: © Creatas/Jupiter Images, tr: © Disney Enterprises, Inc./Walden Media, LLC, courtesy Dijanna Figueroa, br: courtesy Francisco Jiménez; pp. 8–9: © Jeff Stead/AP/Wide World Photos; p. 9: © Tony Savino/The Image Works; p. 10tr: © Damian Dovarganes/AP/Wide World Photos; p. 12b: © Scholastic Inc.; p. 13t: © Rob DeLorenzo/Zuma Press, inset: © Texas A&M Athletics; p. 14b: © Scholastic Inc.; p. 15tr: © Photodisc via SODA; p. 16b: courtesy Dr. Sampson Davis/The Three Doctors Foundation; p. 20bl: © Jeff Greenberg/age fotostock, tr: © Lucianne Pashley/age fotostock; p. 21bl: © SuperStock, tr: © Photodisc via SODA; p. 22bl: © Kelly Tippett/AP/Wide World Photos; p. 23bl: © Mary Kate Denny/PhotoEdit Inc., tl: © Spencer Grant/PhotoEdit Inc., tr: © Purestock/age fotostock, br: © Doug Menuez/Getty Images; p. 28: Art Seitz © Scholastic Inc.; p. 28: courtesy Job Corps/MPF; p. 30br: courtesy Dr. Sampson Davis/The Three Doctors Foundation; p. 32: © Mark A. Johnson/Corbis, b: © Neil McAllister/Alamy, inset: Jim McMahon © Scholastic Inc.; p. 33: © Neil McAllister/Alamy, br: © Kim MacDonald/Habitat for Humanity; p. 36: © Anuradha Raghunathan; p. 38t: © Anuradha Raghunathan; p. 41t: © Eugene Hoshiko/AP/Wide World Photos; p. 42b: © Gemunu Amarasinghe/AP/Wide World Photos; p. 43: Jim McMahon © Scholastic Inc.; p. 44bl: © Richard Hutchings/PhotoEdit Inc., tr: © Masterfile; p. 45tl: © photolibrary.com pty.ltd/Index Open, r: © Photis/Jupiter Images; p. 47bl: © Bob Daemmrich/The Image Works, tl: © Bob Daemmrich/The Image Works, tr: © Michael Newman/PhotoEdit Inc., br: © Jeff Greenberg/PhotoEdit Inc.; p. 52: Kip Malone © Scholastic Inc.; p. 53b: © Kim MacDonald/Habitat for Humanity; p. 54br: © Anuradha Raghunathan; p. 56inset: Jim McMahon © Scholastic Inc.; p. 57br: © Hen von Horsten/Getty Images; p. 74: © Richard Kalvar/Magnum Photos; p. 76bl: © Gari Wyn Williams/Alamy, tr: © Michael Heinsen/Getty Images; p. 77tl: © Spencer Grant/PhotoEdit Inc., tr: © Michael Newman/PhotoEdit Inc., r: © Masterfile; p. 79bl: © Michael Newman/PhotoEdit Inc., tl: © Tom Carter/PhotoEdit Inc., tr: Sean Murphy/Getty Images, br: © Bob Daemmrich/PhotoEdit Inc.; pp. 84 and 85: courtesy Rita Williams-Garcia; p. 88bl: National Archives, insert: © photolibrary.com pty.ltd./Index Open p. 89tr: © photolibrary.com pty.ltd./Index Open p. 89r: © Dr. Jurgen Scriba/Photo Researchers, Inc.; p. 90tr: © Custom Medical Stock Photo; p. 92t: © Pascal Goetgheluck/Photo Researchers, Inc., bl: © Jerry McCrea/Star Ledger/Corbis, br: © Dennis Brack/IPN; p. 93bl: © Michael Donne/SPL/Photo Researchers, Inc., bc: © Matthew Neal McVay/Stock Boston/IPN; p. 94bc: © Michael Paul/StockFood Creative/Getty Images, br: © Owen Franken/Stock Boston/IPN; p. 97t: © Mark Peterson/Corbis; p. 98t: © H. Raguet/Eurelios/Phototake; p. 99l: © Teri McDermott; p. 100l: © JupiterMedia/Alamy, tr: © Scholastic Inc., rc: © Photodisc via SODA; p. 101l: © Markus Boesch/Allsport Concepts/Getty Images, tr: © Digital Vision/Getty Images, br: : © photolibrary.com pty.ltd./Index Open; p. 102bl: © Peres/Custom Medical Stock Photo; p. 103bl: © Michael Paul/StockFood Creative/Getty Images, tl: © Curtis Myers/Stock Connection/Jupiter Images, tr: © Photos.com, br: © Owen Franken/Stock Boston/IPN; p. 108: © Susan Goldman; p. 109: Images courtesy of National Institute of Standards and Technology; p. 110br: © Dr. Jurgen Scriba/Photo Researchers, Inc.; p. 112b: © Burke-Triolo Productions/Brand X Pictures/Jupiter Images; p. 113r: © Ron Chapple/Photis/Jupiter Images; p. 114t: © Scholastic Inc.; p. 116: © Royalty-Free/Corbis; p. 118t: © Daisuke Morita/Getty Images; p. 119b: © Kalle Singer/Bilderlounge/Punchstock; p. 120bl: © Topham/The Image Works, tl: © JLP/Jose Luis Pelaez/zefa/Corbis, tr: © Creatas/Jupiter Images, br: © David Young-Wolff/PhotoEdit Inc.; p. 124b: © Paul Barton/Corbis, tl: © Marc Vaughn/Masterfile; p. 125l: © Tim Boyd/AP/Wide World Photos, tr: © Lisa Peardon/Getty Images, b: © Holger Winkler/A.B./zefa/Corbis; p. 127bl: © David Young-Wolff/PhotoEdit Inc., tl: © Daisuke Morita/Getty Images, tr: © David Young-Wolff/PhotoEdit Inc., br: © Creatas/Jupiter Images; p. 132: Loren Santow © Scholastic Inc.; p. 134br: © Royalty-Free/Corbis; p. 136b: © Bettmann/Corbis; p. 137tr: © Paul Souders/Accent Alaska; p. 150: © Patrik Giardino/Corbis; pp. 152–153b: © Royalty-Free/Corbis; p. 154bl: © Tom Stewart/zefa/Corbis, tr: © Bill Aron/PhotoEdit Inc.; p. 155tl: © Denis Paquin/AP/Wide World Photos, tr: © Creatas/Jupiter Images, b: © Nancy Ney/Digital Vision/Getty Images; p. 162tl: © Bettmann/Corbis; p. 163l: IFA Bilderteam-Jupiter Images; pp. 166–167: © Stephen Frink/Corbis; p. 167rc: Ryan McVay/Getty Images; p. 168t: © Fred Bavendam/Minden Pictures; pp. 170–171: © Disney Enterprises, Inc./Walden Media, LLC, courtesy Dijanna Figueroa; p. 171br: © Disney Enterprises, Inc./Walden Media, LLC.; p. 172tr: Dr. Jim Childress,UCSB/Dijanna Figueroa; p. 174: © Norbert Wu/Minden Pictures; p176ct: Andrew J. Martinez/Photo Researchers, Inc., c: © Norbert Wu/Minden Pictures, b: © Norbert Wu/Minden Pictures; p. 178l: © image100/Alamy, tr: © Jonathan A. Nourok/PhotoEdit, Inc., br: p. 179tl: © Mike Macri/Masterfile, r: © Photodisc via SODA; p. 181bl: © Jeff Greenberg/PhotoEdit Inc., tl: © Walter Bibikow/Viesti Associates, tr: © Robert Fried/Alamy, br: © PIXTAL/age fotostock; p. 186: Tyson V. Rininger © Scholastic Inc.; p. 187tl: © Jim Schwabel/Index Open; p. 188br: © Andrew J. Martinez/Photo Researchers, Inc.; pp. 190–191: © Tom Van Sant/Corbis; p.190bl: Colin Gray/Photonica/Getty Images, lc: © China Daily/Reuters; tr: © Tony Karumba/AFP/Getty Images, rc: © Sajjad Hussain/AFP/Getty Images/Newscom, br: © Lakruwan Wanniarachchi/AFP/Getty Images; p. 191cr: © David Young-Wolff/PhotoEdit, Inc., b: © Supri/Reuters; p. 192: © Graphi-Ogre/Geoatlas; p. 194t: © David Young-Wolff/PhotoEdit Inc.; p. 195b: © Sherwin Crasto/Reuters/Newscom; p. 196t: © Alex Wong/Getty Images/Newscom; p. 197b: © Chris Maddaloni/Newscom; p. 198t: © Steve Harris, b: © Namas Bhojani/San Jose Mercury News/Newscom; p. 201: © 2005 Jeff Danziger/CartoonArts International/NY Times Syndicate; p. 202bl: © Bob Daemmrich/PhotoEdit Inc., tr: © David Kelly Crow/PhotoEdit Inc.; p. 203bl: © Michael Newman/PhotoEdit Inc., tr: © Michael Newman/PhotoEdit Inc.; p. 205bl: © Sherwin Crasto/Reuters/Newscom, tl: © Reinhard Krause/Reuters, tr: © Spencer Grant/PhotoEdit Inc., br: © Alex Wong/Getty Images/Newscom; p. 210: James Levin © Scholastic Inc.; p. 212br: © Lakruwan Wanniarachchi/AFP/Getty Images; pp. 214–215: © Bettmann/Corbis; p. 214r: courtesy Francisco Jiménez, br: © Hank Walker/Time Life Pictures/Getty Images; p. 215rc: © Jeff Greenberg/PhotoEdit Inc., br: Studio 10 via SODA; p. 218: © Susan Meiselas/Magnum Photos; p. 221br: Studio 10 via SODA; pp. 222–223b: National Archives; pp. 224–225b: © West Coast Art Company/Library of Congress; p. 227b: courtesy Francisco Jiménez; p. 228b: TH Foto-Werbung/Photo Researchers, Inc.; p. 231: Jim McMahon © Scholastic Inc.; p. 232: Charles Barry, Santa Clara University/courtesy Francisco Jiménez; p. 234bl: © Hans Neleman/Getty Images, tr: © Steve Skjold/PhotoEdit Inc.; p. 235l: © SW Productions/Getty Images, tr: © Ron Fehling/Masterfile, r: © David Young-Wolff/PhotoEdit Inc.; p. 237bl: © Peter Hvizdak/The Image Works, tl: © Royalty-Free/Corbis, tr: © First Light/Imagestate, br: © Chuck Savage/Corbis; p. 242tl: Charles Barry, Santa Clara University/courtesy Francisco Jiménez; p. 244br: courtesy Francisco Jiménez; p. 246b: © Richard Hutchings/PhotoEdit Inc.; p. 247bl: © Star/zefa/Corbis; p. 248b: © Jacque Denzer Parker/Index Open; p. 249r: © DesignPics/Index Open; p. 250r: © Jim Cummins/Getty Images; p. 251c: © Roger Ressmeyer/Corbis; p. 252br: © Steve Skjold/PhotoEdit Inc.; p. 253br: © Laureen Middley/Getty Images; p. 254bl: © Janine Wiedel Photolibrary/Alamy; p. 255br: © Bud Freund/Index Open; p. 256l: © Paul Harris; p. 264l: © Scholastic Inc.

"Long Journey to Justice": © Martin French

"Facing the Elements": Patrick Arrasmith © Scholastic Inc.